C000258922

HOME UK

HOME UK
HELEN KIRWAN-TAYLOR

HONOR RILEY CONTRIBUTING EDITOR

First published in 2005 by
Conran Octopus Limited
a part of Octopus Publishing Group
2–4 Heron Quays
London E14 4JP
www.conran-octopus.co.uk

Text copyright © 2005 Helen Kirwan-Taylor
Book and design layout copyright
© 2005 Conran Octopus Ltd

All rights reserved. No part of this book may be
reproduced, stored in a retrieval system or transmitted
in any form or by any means, electronic, electrostatic,
magnetic tape, mechanical photocopying, recording
or otherwise, without the prior permission in writing
of the Publisher.

The right of Helen Kirwan-Taylor to be identified as
the Author of the text of this Work has been asserted
by her in accordance with the Copyright, Designs and
Patents Act 1988.

British Library Cataloguing-in-Publication Data.
A catalogue record of this book is available from
the British Library.

ISBN: 1 84091 378 9

Publishing Director: Lorraine Dickey
Commissioning Editor: Katey Day
Editor: Sybella Marlow
Art Director: Jonathan Christie
Design: johnson banks
Production Manager: Angela Couchman

Printed in China

conran
OCTOPUS

CONTENTS

INTRODUCTION

A Servant's Heart or What Good Service Means

As I sit here writing, Kevin, a seasoned plumber from Essex is hard at work downstairs. He brought his 78-year-old father with him (also a plumber) and must have asked me 15 times to come down and look at his work. I could think of many things I would rather do than discuss the leak in my airing cupboard but the point is: he cares.

Britain is a service economy. Service is the UK's number one export, so why is bad service all we ever talk about? Why do we tear our hair out trying to get the smallest things done when the person who is being obstructive or indifferent is paid to serve us and wants *our money*? Why is it so difficult to find a decent plumber or get a repairman to quote a precise time? 'It's absolute nonsense this business of not being able to deliver at an allotted time,' says Willie Gething, Managing Director of Property Vision, the leading property search consultancy in Britain often singled out for its exemplary level of service . 'Imagine what would happen if I rang a client and said: I will be with you between 9am and 4pm. How long would I last?'

Gething and his team attended Harvard Business School's 'Achieving Breakthrough Service' course led by the formidable Professor Earl Sasser. Companies that achieve 'Breakthrough Service' – including Southwest Airlines and John Lewis – have one thing in common: A Servant's Heart. 'This means that you get a psychic kick from making people happy,' says Gething. The second principle behind successful companies is the concept of 'how we do things round here'. 'If a company has a culture of being helpful, working weekends and taking calls after 6pm, it's usually because that's what everyone in the company feels is important,' says Gething. We live in a highly competitive society where good enough is simply not good enough anymore. 'Unless you exceed a customer's expectations,' says Gething, 'they will be disappointed.' In other words, if you hate the idea of serving, do something else. Join the government.

Ford Motors published an interesting survey. If someone does a good job, a customer might tell two friends. If he does a rotten job, the customer will shout it over the mountain tops. 'It is five times harder to find a new customer than to hold onto an existing one,' says Sebastian de Groot, Managing Director of Ben Whistler Upholstery.

'The trick to good service,' says Sir Stuart Hampson, Chairman of John Lewis, 'is to look through the customer's eyes.' John Lewis did not get to where it is now (60,000 partners, £5 billion turnover) by accident. 'First and fundamentally we are a company owned by partners,' he says. 'We all have a single objective: to enjoy ourselves and make the customer happy. Culture is simply a question of wanting to do it. If, for example, a customer went to the trouble to find my name out and complain to me personally, I reply the same day. This sends a message down the line. If the chairman can interrupt the day because Mrs Smith in Portsmouth's new washing machine has a leak, then we can all find the time.' Hampson once received a letter from an irate customer. 'It said: "I bought a laptop to give to my wife as a birthday present. When she opened it, it was missing a part. It ruined her birthday".' What did Hampson do? Throw the letter in the bin, cc it to some obscure department in Halifax? 'I called the Managing Director of Peter Jones who instantly put a new computer into a taxi along with a letter of apology. A letter came back two days later with the words "I give up" written on it.'

So what's the trick? 'You have to win customers' loyalty it's as simple as that,' says Sampson. He also believes (give or take a few exceptions) 'that the customer is mostly right.' This is what Breakthrough Service means.

I spoke to one MD after another and the refrain was almost always the same. 'Good service means do what the customer wants, not what you want him to want or what suits you,' says Robert Hiscox, Chairman of Hiscox Insurance. 'It's as much about training staff as it is about service,' says Graham Doyle, managing director of Pilgrim Payne, whose carpet and curtain cleaning service is so far superior to anyone else's that it's a wonder competitors stay afloat. Doyle can get staff on the premises virtually the next day: other companies quote up to a week's wait. Most importantly, if a customer complains, Doyle handles it personally. 'The most demanding customers often end up being the most loyal in the end,' he says.

The culture in Britain is changing rapidly. The rise of personal services (see Service Plus chapter) is largely due to our collective frustration. Television watch-dog programmes and consumer magazines have all raised the bar. But it still needs raising. 'I would say service in Britain is evolutionary,' says organisational psychologist Jon Stokes who works with many of Britain's top companies, 'whereas in America it's revolutionary. Many Britons still take the view that things "aren't perfect". Get over it – as we say in my native country.'

Good service, whether you're an IT consultant, a builder, a washing machine repairman or a journalist for that matter, means being excited by the business. It means taking pride in both your work and your company. It means (when the client is in a huffy mood) being helpful and polite rather than hostile. It means taking the initiative rather than waiting to be reminded. It means never annoying the client to the point where he has to shout, write letters or engage a solicitor. 'It means having an understanding of the way the client is feeling,' says Gething, 'and, vitally, having a sense of urgency.'

For most of those included in this book, this goes without saying.

You're only as good as your client

I posed this question to virtually every architect and builder I spoke to. Who is *your* perfect client? Most replied 'bankers or businessmen' (one actually said anyone but American women – I don't think he was alluding to me).

This isn't because businessmen earn fat salaries (ok, it is a bit). It's because they understand what a Servant's Heart means and spend 12 hours a day grovelling to *their* clients. They know that being hostile or hysterical is unproductive. They also understand the principle of outsourcing (see Service Plus chapter) which is: why waste your valuable and expensive time doing something yourself badly (for example, gardening), when you can pay someone else (much less) to do it better? This is what business guru Stephen Covey calls a 'win/win' situation.

No one performs well when being micromanaged and second-guessed by an obsessive compulsive client with too much time on their hands. One client asked the architect Richard Paxton 'What's the best way to proceed?' 'Come back when it's finished,' he replied. 'I was only kidding, but they took me seriously. They didn't come on site once and appeared nine months later with their furniture. They were gloriously surprised.' Finally, a good customer pays his bills on time.

Chronology of a house refurbishment

Minus 6 months Viewing properties.

Minus 5 months Still viewing properties. If Madonna, bring Suzi Morris (020 7351 1788) to ward off evil spirits. If green, bring Andrew Ford of Fulcrum (020 7520 1313; www.fulcrum.first.com), the leading environmental engineers to advise on chilled ceilings, solar heating, coiled springs and using recycled cooking oil in car.

Minus 4 months Still viewing. Hire property finder: if banker, businessman, ting Property Vision (0207 823 8388) London, South East; if rock n' roller, call Pereds (020 7221 1404).

Minus 3 months Paid 30 per cent more for house than expected? Add £100K to refurbishment budget. Sacrifice wet room. Didn't have one? Sacrifice Dornbracht taps.

Minus 2 months Survey missed damp in basement. Add £10K from budget. Asbestos missed even though surveyor took pictures. Add £5K for cost of arbitration.

0 hours Pop open the Moet. You're now a proud first- or second-time homeowner! Deadline: Christmas.

0 plus 2 hours Decide your budget. Then add 30 per cent.

Week 4 If in country, book builder now (because he's busy until 2006). If in London, start interviewing architects or designers (see Architects and Designers) to tell the difference. Before calling: do a taste check. Deciding (true story) that you're a traditionalist six months after hiring John Pawson is expensive.

Week 5 Interview process begins. One architect is too few: 20 is too many. Have brief ready. A few tear sheets are helpful: a trunk full of seven-year-old copies of *House & Garden* is not.

Do not confuse architect with marriage counsellor. If pregnant, remember: 1) children grow; 2) hormones are the enemy of taste; 3) the nanny. Carve out a basement flat or large en-suite bedroom (with satellite tv of course). If big project, consider project manager. Check out architect/designer's previous work, call references, do police check. Suggest meeting on Saturday morning: if he/she goes silent on phone, review other architects.

Week 7 Architect appointed. Inform disappointed others. Negotiate fees (see Mike Hartley-Brewer, Builders). If designer unable to provide comprehensive fee structure and behaves like MI5 agent when asked how much she charges per hour, start worrying.

Confess now:
- That you have just inherited your mother's 68 piece Victorian sewing machine collection.
- That you want gold leaf and leopard print, everywhere.
- That you collect Jimmy Hendrix posters.
- That you don't have any art. Hire art consultant (Jonathan Green, 020 7499 5553 for traditional; Tim Taylor. 020 7409 3344 for modern).
- That you require some meditation space like Normandie Keith.

Week 8 Reality check: if thinking glass box, pod or something that looks like it belongs to a Teletubby, consider hiring a planning consultant: architect Tom Croft recommends Simon Avery (01256 766 673).

Week 9 Weekly design meetings begin. If architect is late and yawns throughout, go back to week 4.

Week 10 If thinking Italian kitchen, order now – 12 week delivery means 36. Ditto with one-man joinery band in north Cornwall. Ditto with handmade rugs from India. Want to be like Blur's Alex James and have an amazing bespoke staircase? (See Made to Order chapter). Then better order now.

Week 11 Start thinking gardens (see Gardeners chapter). Think access. Think views. Think floor levels. Think muddy labourer's shoe marks across priceless stone floor if no access. Put in irrigation system: if not, add £5K to budget for the cost of buying new plants in September. Mud room a must in country.

Thinking of a home disco/cinema? Planning to work from home? Consider hiring IT/AV consultant (see Consultants chapter). CAT 5 wiring advisable in these fast times. Think telephone, computer, security systems and where you want to put the kettle. Remember triangle in kitchen between fridge/tap/cooker. If half a mile apart on plan, go back to week 5.

Week 12 15 Question Time. Want open-plan living? Think. Are you noise sensitive? Do you entertain? Who's going to wash up at dinner parties: you or the help? Playroom upstairs? Impractical unless you want to keep fit.

Think storage for suitcases, bicycles, books. Pretend you're Jeremy Paxman and keep asking the architect: where you gonna put them?

Warning. Laundry room: take size architect suggests and double it. No ventilation? Add £500 for price of agency fee for new cleaner or a new ad in *The Lady*.

Remind architect about nanny (and her en suite). If planning to build Versailles in your dressing room, consider a joinery company (see Made to Order chapter). Want lights that know your mood before you do? Consider hiring a lighting consultant (see Consultants chapter).

Week 16 Wife discovers she's pregnant. Allow £50K for daily changes of mind.

Week 18 Honeymoon stage. Drawings completed, planning permissions submitted. Sign off (or don't, depending on self-knowledge).

Week 19 Wife's had a change of heart. Hates glass extensions. Hates architect. Wants cosy designer. Add £10K to budget and start again.

Week 20 Decorating time. Start thinking curtains, carpets and colours for walls. Better now than when in cold unpainted house with builders' finish and draughts.

Week 21 Discover architect never filed planning application (true story). Go back to Week 7. Add £20K for next set of fees.

Week 22 Appoint builders (after meeting them all), having tendered, negotiated or begged depending which firm you choose (see Builders chapter). Ask them: do you use Tyvec (new breathable membranes that do something useful in a roof). If never heard of it, worry.

Week 24 Builders on site. Allow £20K for pleasure of arriving and setting up. Set house rules. No bricks down the loo. Meet with Lithuanian foreman to discuss. Consider video surveillance or paying the next-door neighbour to spy.

Week 25 Worst rains in British history. Builders say: 'Don't have raincoats.' Two weeks delay. Add £5K to budget waiting for sun. Hire project manager to take over or start eliminating costs. Kill home cinema, order Dixon's special.

Week 26 First fix begins (structural work; excavation, electrical). Speak up if you want:
- a two-ton antique French fireplace in the master bedroom (requires steel joists so floor doesn't cave in);
- a 500lb crystal chandelier by Patrice Butler or Tord Boontje (see Made to Order chapter);
- Claudio Silvestrin's £16,000 900kg 'Po' for Boffi limestone bath (Robbie Williams has one) that requires 25 workmen and a crane to be installed.

Appliance checklist. Inform builder now if thinking American Maytag, Traulsen refrigerator and Viking cookers? All require special circuits or all fuses will blow. Forgot to? Add £10K for electricians and builders fee later.

Roof goes down. If 'Po' not airlifted in now, it is too late.

It's now too late to:
- have a swimming pool built in the basement
- order an Italian Kitchen
- install CP Hart's Waterblade Taps that you spotted in a magazine (they require super-duper fancy pump).

Forgot the garden? Don't worry, Practicality Brown will supply instant mature hedge. (see Gardeners chapter).

Week 36 Second fix begins. This is close up the walls time: plastering, decorating, joinery. It's too late to:
- put in Lutron lighting
- wire in AV/IT points
- design open-plan kitchen after wife changed mind (again).
- underfloor heating, chilled ceilings or heating within walls
- go Green
- decide you're a maximalist.

Week 37 Builders go on holiday. Two week delay.

Week 38 Issue AI (architect instruction) because wife suddenly decides she wants the laundry room upstairs. Of course having ordered two industrial Maytags, you now have to strengthen the ceiling, insulate the walls and put in ventilation and cupbaords (add £20 for Ikea shelves and £100 for Screwdrivers to put them together. See Service Plus chapter).

Week 37 Symptoms of AFS (architect fatigue syndrome) appear: tremors, nightmares, panic attacks, dizziness plus uncontrollable urge to hit architect in face, as project now running one month late and he hasn't been seen on site once, your spies tell you. All of Europe on holiday. Add four weeks delay to existing delays.

Week 38 Symptoms persist, this time when builder shows up. Call Wendy Denning for weekly vitamin injections (0207 224 5111).

Week 39 Builder's wife leaves him for Lithuanian foreman. Three-week delay. Marriage already under strain because of AFS and BFS. Add £1K for the price of weekend at Babington House (where wife decides she should have used their architect Simon Morray-Jones instead of her own).

Week 45 Budget 30 per cent over. No money left for bespoke home office. Refer to Viking and Ikea Catalogues. Start spending PS (provisional sums) now. Consider putting children into state school. Consider wife returning to work.

Week 46 Decorator arrives. Subtract two weeks because handpainted Venetian wallpaper stuck in customs. Curtains delivered four inches too long (true story), add £200 for seamstress fees or yell at designer.

Week 47 Chakras need replenishing. Call Debbie Donovan of Liteworks, an agency that sends energy healers into the home (www.liteworkers.com; 07958 955 055)

Week 48 Architect not told of new oversized B&B Italia six-seater sofa bought in sales. Pay £200 for chippie to remove door and put back afterwards.
    'Po' causes major cracks in limestone floor. Add £3K to replace screed (can't collect on insurance because structural engineer failed to do the maths).

Week 50 Christmas. Rental coming to end.

Checklist:
- Has the wood dried out? Has builder done moisture reading?
- Is marble sealed?
- Do toilets flush?
- Do lights turn on?
- Does heating work?
- Has Italian kitchen been installed? If not consider takeaways (see Service Plus chapter).

Week 55 Security/lighting system goes bonkers and won't let movers in (true story). Builder says: don't know much about this technology stuff. Supplier closed for holidays. Architect ignoring mobile. Book into local hotel with nanny. Add £1,000 to budget. Add £100 for present for pissed-off nanny.

Week 60 Movers arrive. Better yet, ask your architect to help arrange furniture. Snagging period begins.

Week 61 Put carpets down now (and not week 45). If already down, budget for a long visit from Pilgrim Payne (see Domestic Diva chapter).

Week 61 Ajax spoils priceless 'Po' bathtub. Nanny not happy with wing, wants self-enclosed flat, resigns. TV heard five flights up. B&B sofa never made it past front gate. Call Unlisted for massage, reflexology, better yet, counselling (0870 2255 007).
    Join concierge service (see Service Plus chapter) for immediate assistance.

Week 70 Happily installed. Print two hundred change-of-address cards.

Week 90 Pay final deposit (5 per cent) to builder. Say thank you.

Week 96 Italian kitchen finally arrives. Add £2K to get builders back in to install. They agree because on week 90 you said thank you.

Week 97 Wife says: 'Honey, I'm expecting again.'

How your marriage can survive the building process

We haven't even appointed an architect for our recently purchased house in Gloucestershire and already my husband and I are fighting. The budget hasn't been determined, but we're both awake at night worrying about money. I want a new build, he wants to respect the house's history. I want a meadow garden planted by Tom Stuart Smith (as if): he wants me to do the garden myself. As you can tell, we're off to a bad start.

Why *do* marriages take such a battering over the building process? 'I think it's about money and expectations,' says architect Guy Stansfeld. 'So much is invested into our homes, both financially and emotionally.' 'You're dealing with people's aspirations and dreams, and often they wake up in the morning with a hangover,' says Somerset-based architect Martin Llewellyn. 'We all like to relive our happy times, but there are moments when copying the holiday house in the velvet heat of the Caribbean seems a rotten idea, especially when it is rebuilt in rain sodden Somerset, with February gales blowing birthday cards off the driftwood mantelpiece, and a steady stream of cold water dripping on to the starched linen sheets through the terracotta roof tiles.'

Paul Hellier, Managing Director of D&T Electronics is a regular observer of the marital battleground. 'Typically a couple makes a deal,' he says. 'She gets thirty grand for the kitchen. He gets the same amount for the hi-fi system.' Barter can work, though most of the time it's just posturing. 'Really she doesn't want anything to do with the home cinema. Should anything go wrong, *she will let him know it* for the rest of his life.' 'Sometimes it is made clear that one of them is the main driver and typically we are told things like: "My wife is the one with taste, aesthetics are not really my thing",' says architect Simon Morray Jones. 'This is often conditional on things like "I do not really care so long as I get this plasma screen and that central music system".'

Another favourite trick clients do is to feign agreement with the wife in front of the architect (this is known as the 'yes dear phenomenon' in marital guidance circles). As soon as her back is turned, he calls the architect and says: 'You know when I said I liked the pink marble idea – well I don't. Can't stand it. Tell her there was no marble at the quarry.' Twenty minutes later she rings the architect. 'I overheard that conversation.' Or one party really thinks 'the limestone bath is just so cool' but the other (always the bread-winner) freaks at the numbers, says Morray-Jones. Now we are into the serious negotiations: emotional blackmailing. 'Don't you think I'm worth it?' or the more subtle added-value tactic such as 'but it

would be so sexy, can't you just imagine?' The hope is, and often results in, 'Oh, alright then.'

'The absolutely worst thing you can do at this point is start taking sides,' says Hellier. 'That's a recipe for disaster.' Architects are often seen as dream killers because they have the unenviable job of saying: 'You can't afford it.' Having said that, couples often have more than they admit to spend and architects can smell it. 'Whenever I say you can't afford it to a client,' says an architect, who wishes to remain anonymous, 'they suddenly find more money.'

I have friends who couldn't agree on anything, so they split their house down the middle. She got the top two floors (in chintz and floral swags); he got the kitchen and basement, which he proceeded to turn into a futuristic discotheque-like space. Sadly, the architect still had to design the staircase, which then became another battleground. Many a wife also plays 'the husband will never know game' (women are shrewd money launderers). Architects have long since learned the ropes. 'We once designed a bedroom with a bed in the middle that a couple could run around chasing each other with the bed pan or what ever comes to hand,' says architect Jonathan Stickland. 'A counselling service is deemed to be included in the architect's fee, although that in itself can result in an argument. For our part, we keep our heads down and think of quiet whites and other calming colours.'

How to avoid divorce

- Do be upfront about money. This is not the time to show off in front of anyone, least of all the wife. Be realistic about what you can afford. Remember it's going to cost 30 per cent more than you thought.

- You can save money in lots of places – you just have to agree which places.

- Don't expect to build anything overnight.

- Begin with the end in mind, as the executive gurus say.

- Bartering can work. If he insists on a home office, insist on a boudoir. If you (man) can't be bothered to discuss wallpapers, fabrics and colours, then don't criticise her choices. Ditto with conversations about water tanks for her.

- Listen carefully to your spouse during meetings. Often the mere act of nodding profusely is enough. 'What a great idea!' works miracles for improving the general mood.

- If it's a productive meeting, celebrate.

- Don't hide the fact that you bought a chandelier spontaneously or enlisted the help of a colour consultant. This makes men worry about what else you're not admitting to. Ditto for the man who went out and spent £2,000 on a fridge (true story) even though they had no house to put it in.

- Practise bridge-building exercises. If he's stonewalling (i.e., 'absolutely no way are we having this'), don't vent ('you never let me have anything I waaaant'). It always helps to start a sentence with: 'This is important to me.'

- Don't conduct meetings when you're exhausted and children are unattended. Who wouldn't fight?

- Disengage when necessary. If you really can't deal with a situation then and there, file it away. Live in 'Now Time'.

- No point pointing fingers ('you hired him... it was your stupid idea). The cheques have been cashed, so get on with it.

- Practise cognitive behavioural therapy. For example: 'It would be preferable if the project was running on time' as opposed to 'I can't believe that this &*%@*&* builder has done this to me. How dare he!'

- Moving in is hell. Accept this, prepare for it. Be Zen-like. Things will get better. Hire someone to help prepare it. Call mum. Have a massage, or several (see Service Plus chapter).

- Do not move in three days after giving birth. If anything, think about the poor child.

- Better to be wrong than divorced. Remember what made you choose your partner. Can you remember?

- Do say: 'This will be great' 10 times a day. Saying so really will convince you.

- Remember that it's the builders' site until you move in. Don't choose site visits as the time to mount an arsenal attack.

DE MATOS STOREY RYAN LO
ADAMS + COLLINGWOOD A
OBJECT ARCHITECTURE RI
MICHAELIS BOYD ASSOCIA
HARRISON SUTTON PARTN
JOHN FALCONER ASSOCIAT
WILSON KERR BOB HARDW
KATHRYN FINDLAY STICKLA
RICHARD ASHBY ASSOCIATE
MANALO AND WHITE POWE
GEBLER TOOTH ARCHITECTS
STUDIO KAP QUINLAN POW
RABIH HAGE TREVOR LAHI

SE CROSSMAN ARCHITECTS
HITECTS ROGER DONGRAY
ARD MURPHY **ARCHITECTS**
S LLEWELLYN HARKER LTD
RSHIP FOUND ASSOCIATES
S ABBERLEY DESIGN MAKE
HUF HAUS URBAN SALON
D COOMBE ALP ARIKOGLU
TD SNELL DAVID ARCHITECTS
GEARY AND BLACK LIMITED
RAIG HAMILTON ARCHITECTS
LL TUCK ASSOCIATES MAKE
ARCHITECTS STUDIO KAP

ARCHITECTS

'Architects are like estate agents,' says my friend Suzie. 'They always make you feel as if you don't have enough money. The next time one makes you feel poor, say: "Show me a picture of *your* house"!'

Architects often get a bad rap. I think it's because there is a general confusion in the minds of clients as to what it is they do. Are they like solicitors or are they too often, as David Adjaye recently complained to me, 'confused with butlers'? 'I like to think of architects as pilots of a yacht,' says George Ferguson, President of RIBA (Royal Institute of British Architects). 'It is an important role that takes initiative, skill and leadership. It's not just a question of reacting to a brief.'

Architects are the butt of many jokes. When a client called Frank Lloyd Wright to complain that the ceiling was leaking on her precious dining table, he replied: 'Then move the table.' A client of Edwin Lutyens requested a wooden staircase. 'I don't think it's a good idea,' Lutyens replied. When the client visited the house a few months later, the staircase was made of black granite. 'But I specifically told you I wanted wood!' the client exclaimed. I *told* you it wasn't a good idea,' Lutyens replied. I have heard at least six versions of this story but the point is: architects don't always listen. Our first architect came back to us with an amazing design proposal. 'Can we afford all this on our budget?' my husband asked. 'You're a banker,' he replied, 'can't you find more money?'

Ferguson admits that architects can be arrogant: 'Some certainly have an attitude or a style – that's why it's so important to choose the right one.' Architects (of whom there are 30,000 in the UK) have seven years of schooling under their belt; this makes them more educated than doctors. Note: You can only call yourself an architect if: 1) you are registered with the ARB, the Architectural Registration Board or 2) are a chartered member of RIBA or 3) have special dispensation given by Ferguson himself. 'Architectural services' and other variations do not mean the same thing. Architects have protection of title. 'Anyone who calls themselves an architect who is not an architect is liable to prosecution,' says Ferguson.

When you need an architect

You need an architect if you want to rework, extend, expand, refurbish or build a house. Getting more space and light where there is none, is what they're trained to do.

According to Ferguson: 'An architect should take the project from concept to completion. He should be fully aware of builders, practical regulations, contractual situation, and perform routine site inspections.' On a domestic job 'there has to be room for flexibility'. You heard the man. This means you have a right to call him at home at night. Ferguson also says you should not have to chase them. 'Architects should obey the same principles as the business world and return calls by the end of the business day.'

Costs and so on

As for payment, RIBA has just been attacked by the Office of Fair Trading, which means that the advisory fee scales no longer apply. Most are still charging between 10 and 15 per cent of contract size anyway. Architects in reality make very little money.

Clients complain that the process isn't always clear: Some architects bill upfront, others send invoices, some on a monthly basis calculated on a percentage of the contract costs (which, of course, can change or not go ahead at all). 'I wish it was clearer what you were paying for,' says a frustrated client.

Finding an architect is largely a word of mouth process (though RIBA's advisory service is excellent). Youth works harder; experience speaks for itself but can get bored, lax and repeat what was done on the last ten houses. And just because an architect builds museums, skyscrapers or schools (Eric Parry, Ken Shuttleworth), doesn't mean he or she doesn't want your job. 'No one ever asks me,' says Kathryn Findlay who struck gold the first time she tried (with a RIBA award).

Architects all design in different ways. Many like Alp Arikoglu and Wilson Kerr still draw plans by hands. Others (Urban Salon, 6a, and anyone under 45) are CADed (Computer Aided Design) to death. Some will build you models. Craig Hamilton is as talented an artist as he is an architect (you can see why Prince Charles loves him).

I have purposely not included big name architects such as Norman Foster and John Pawson because you already know them and, besides, they're very busy building monasteries and skyscrapers. Some well-known residential British architects think they're grander than their clients. Even if they are, they shouldn't behave that way.

If you go for a large firm, chances are you won't see much of the architect. On the other hand, they will have many resources to throw at you. Always ask: who is going to make site visits, you or one of your staff? Decide what kind of service you want/expect. Finally, apart from coming up with solutions, a good architect should stretch you. Let him.

Every architect likes a challenge. That's why so many say the same thing: 'We will consider anything… if it's interesting.' See Stickland Coombe (page 45), who won an RIBA award for a window.

Success

Personally, I think the sign of success is not whether an architect was nominated for an award but whether you invite him to dinner afterwards. I met Rodney Black of Geary and Black (our chosen pin-up, see page 20–21) at his client's house. Mind you, she invited him for dinner on purpose but the point is: they're still friends.

Dos and Don'ts:

1. Do define your brief. Ilse Crawford asked Tom Emerson of 6a for a flat that looks like a 'well-worn white shirt'. Be realistic: £50K won't get you Blenheim.

2. Do your homework. The architect is only as good as his last job. References are essential. Insist on seeing other houses and talking to recent clients.

3. Always sign a contract. People who live in the country sometimes don't even ask the/costs. Unless the architect is family (all the more reason, then), use the RIBA contract.

4. Absolutely do appoint a quantity surveyor or clerk of works. Architects are not accountants and sometimes live in never-never land. It's a false economy not to.

5. Do stay local: it's an advantage (though not always necessary). Their relationship with the planners is what really matters. Speaking of which, ask how successful they've been in the past. If they're glib, worry.

6. Be disciplined. Every time you change your mind means the architect needs to revise drawings.

7. Don't turn the architect into a therapist. Save it for the therapist.

8. Do make sure your architect is on your wavelength and timetable. If you work 18-hour days, he will have to meet you at weekends. Make that clear from the start.

9. Do tell your architect if you plan to use a designer (they hate each other's guts).

10. Don't expect an architect to be a decorator. Though they fancy themselves as designers, many architects' idea of décor is a cement floor.

11. Do complain if you think they're doing a rotten job. The earlier you clear the air, the better.

12. Don't let your builder convince you he can do a better job. He can't.

13. Do stay on top of the building situation. Architects wear white shirts and holiday in the south of France, just like you do. They're not builders, so ask questions.

14. Litigation is a lose/lose situation. Though most architects carry hefty indemnity insurance, it's hard to prove that he was responsible for putting in the wrong floor (that buckled overnight like ours).

15. Do thank him if he's done a good job and pass his name on. Architects have to be published in journals to survive.

16. Never work with a friend (who happens to be an architect). It is unprofessional and always ends in tears/fallings out. Also be wary of references given for the architect by his friends. This is how we got into the mess we did – they could hardly be objective, now could they?

GEARY AND BLACK

Geary and Black Limited
Gun Hill House
Ipswich Road,
Dedham, Colchester
Essex CO7 6HR
T: 01206 322800 F: 01206 322088
design.studios@gearyandblack.co.uk
www.gearyandblack.co.uk

Costs Reasonable. Profit is not what motivates Black. Having said that, he favours expensive materials, which adds to the budget. Charges based on RIBA rates.
Travel Has worked in Italy and pretty much all around East Anglia.
Size of job From £250K upwards.
Attitude Friendly psychiatrist.

New Zealand-born Rodney Black embodies what an architect should be. Deeply intelligent, he brings many years of knowledge to the table. Shy and thoughtful, he ponders decisions carefully. He is quietly winning awards but shows no signs of an ego. He also has a sense of humour, a must for any residential architect.

Black worked for Quinlan Terry for four years before joining the practice that he took over in 1999. He can do the whole stately home thing but prefers to be a bit more of our time. He calls himself a classical modernist, which means he can go either way and doesn't mind either. This can be a small extension or a large refurbishment. He admits to being somewhat scholarly, but that doesn't prevent him from getting the most from his repeat clients. What he does try to bring into a house is light, something he thinks about a lot. Clients come first, though. 'I really try to achieve something joyful to live in,' he says. He is famous for his sketches and the collaborative manner in which he works. 'Residential projects are very intense. It's important to have the maximum involvement.' The firm has won two RIBA Spirit of Ingenuity Awards, the Home Award and the Heritage Conservation Award. He employs four people full time, though it's clearly Black you're dealing with.

What the clients say
'Rodney is phenomenal. He is quite simply a fantastic architect. Incredible attention to detail and is so adorably nice. He takes all the time and trouble over the smallest things. He has amazing relationships with his clients: after he finished a project for some friends, they wanted to build something else just to keep working with him.' Suzie Dolbey, client
'Rodney came in very sympathetically to what could have been an awkward situation. We were helping my in-laws renovate a home they had lived in for 60 years. He was sensitive to the emotional needs, the Georgian structure and listened to us. He immediately saw the importance of linking the garden with the house, leading the inside into the out harmoniously. He is brilliant in efficiency, diplomacy and seeing the job through. Absolutely beautiful drawings and such a stickler for keeping up the standards.' Victoria Pilkington, founder Brora Cashmere

The Perfect Client According to Rodney Black
The perfect client wants to get on and build, enjoys throwing around ideas together, the frenzy of sketching and rubbing graphite-y sheets of detail paper with finger or pencil with endless 'what if we…', and doesn't mind doing part of the work on the ironmongery and sanitaryware schedules themselves. The perfect client is someone who loves the thought of introducing the garden and interior of the house into the brief so we can really set about bringing a fully rounded and essentially magical world into existence; who stands shoulder to shoulder if battle must be joined to win with the Local Authority (Planning Permission, Listed Building Consent); who realizes there are reasons for decisions we have taken and holds by them (even if the builder's foreman says he can do it another way). The perfect client pays our bills and basically reciprocates what is actually a friendly relationship even after the whole glorious process is all over…. And in my experience that doesn't seem to happen often; not because the projects never get finished but because there is usually another project or phase in the pipeline.

Rodney Black is principal of Geary and Black, Architects, Interior and Landscape Designers.

6a Architects
6a Orde Hall Street
London WC1N 3JW
T: 020 7242 5422
F: 020 7242 3646
post@6a.co.uk
steph@6a.co.uk
www.6a.co.uk

Abberley Design
4 Silver Street
Cirencester
Gloucestershire GL7 2BL
T: 01285 644 460
F: 01285 658 577
abberley@tiscali.co.uk

Costs Still reasonable, though they're now doing a £2 million conversion for a developer in Scotland.
Travel Most projects are in London, but they have worked in other areas of the UK and in Europe.
Size of job From £100K.
Attitude Book early.

Costs Every client has an individual fee proposal; it works on the scale of the project.
Travel Countrywide.
Size of job Reasonable. From extensions to huge barn conversions.
Attitude One man and his rain mac.

When I asked Ilse Crawford whom she would recommend as an architect, she instantly mentioned 6a (they did her flat). Graduates Tom Emerson and Stephanie Macdonald met at the RCA. They created 6a in 2001 after winning a competition to design oki-ni on Savile Row. 'We pretended we were a firm. We didn't have an office,' says Tom, age 33.

It's this kind of chutzpah that has made 6a one of the hottest new architectural practices in Britain. This is out-of-the-box architecture. As oki-ni is an on-line clothing company, Tom and Stephanie chose to go in the opposite direction. 'We took a low-tech approach. We wanted the store to be tactile, so we chose felt, and wood because it's heavy and physical,' says Emerson. Not only did they beat off more established firms like Wells Mackereth, but they also won four architectural awards, including the D&AD. This got them noticed by big companies such as Motorola for whom they mounted a 'mobile exhibition'.

Residential clients can expect an upside down view of the world; by this, I mean expect to be stretched. They're not David Adjaye (no brown boxes here) but what they produce for clients, like record producer Tony Crean, is a hybrid between art and architecture. They design everything themselves, including the door handles and the light fittings.

Julian Phillips is a bit of an anomaly in this part of the world. 'All the other architects we interviewed showed up in nice German cars,' says a client, 'but he came in a beat-up old Toyota.' He also looks like a hell's angel, but everyone swears by him, including William Yeoward, who knows a thing or two about design. His ideas can be adventurous but he still draws everything by hand the old fashioned way, which can mean waiting, and waiting a bit more, for that detailed drawing of the fireplace. Patience is needed if you hire Phillips. Traditional country houses and agricultural conversions are his thing. If it's possible to get planning permission, he will get it.

What the clients say
'Phillips has such an enthusiastic, creative and can-do approach – quite a world apart from the rod up the bottom architects we interviewed at the same time to convert our cowshed and barn. Cotswold stone houses and conversion of agricultural buildings are his thing helped along by his strong relationship with the planners.'
Honor Riley, contributing editor
'If you saw Julian Philips walking towards you on a dark night in Cirencester you might decided to cross the road. Don't. Give him a drawing pen and his architect's tools and you will quickly discover his superb vision, and wonderful drawings for transforming redundant Cotswold farm buildings!'
Oliver Preston, cartoonist and illustrator

What the clients say
'I think they are lovely. Very bright, friendly people with lots of ideas, as well as practical. They're good at marrying form and function.' Ilse Crawford, design consultant
'I originally had problems persuading the others that I thought 6a was right for the job. Finally, they agreed. Well, we've now won four design awards and if I can afford them now that they're famous, I'll ask them to do my house. They're pure and cerebral but also wacky.' Paddy Meehan, founder oki-ni

Adams + Collingwood Architects Ltd
1 Dalling Road
Hammersmith
London W6 0JD
T: 020 8563 7191
F: 020 8563 7133
info@adamscollingwood.com
www.adamscollingwood.com

Alp Arikoglu
Kimpton Mill
Codicote
Herts SG4 8ST
T: 01438 832 020
F: 01438 832 606
alparikoglu@arikoglu.co.uk

Costs Fees tailored to suit each project, but typically 12 per cent for a £1 million house. Base hourly rate £70.
Travel Pretty much global.
Size of job Budget is unlimited up and down, from a new school with a budget of £25 million to a planning application for a barn with a budget of £50K.
Attitude We do the worrying for you.

Robert L Adams of Adams + Collingwood is what I would call a family architect: he is solid, hard-working and able to handle some of the most demanding clients. He gets passed around within a select circle of friends, designing their first (London) house, then their second (country) house, then their sister's house, then their best friend's house… most clients don't bother interviewing anyone else. Adams also does commercial and educational projects, such as the Rhodes House at Oxford University, Betty Jackson's Clothing Factory and the Bute House Prep School in Hammersmith.

His style is classical modern – sure he'd love to use large expanses of glass and stainless steel but mostly his clients want something traditional. 'We don't really think architects should just flog one style regardless of the context or their clients' interests and tastes,' he says. 'Most of the people we work for are pretty discriminating – they have their position, we have ours, the site or the place gives another lead, and really it's about listening to all of that and coming up with something appropriate, interesting, elegant.' What clients like about him is that he thinks practically. He know about kids, their toys when they're small and their new toys (plasma screens) when they start staying up to 2 am. He knows how a normal mother wants to use a kitchen; how a normal man wants to dress in the morning. He's down-to-earth and prepared to collaborate wholeheartedly.

He has a partner, Robert Collingwood, and employs five architects.

What the clients say
'Robert is a good solid reliable architect who has the bedside manner of an obstetrician.' Victoria Sharp, client
'Robert is very prepared to listen to you and work it out your way. He takes on board everything you say.'
Sarah Chappatte, client

Costs Reasonable. Working from home and no overheads means clients get a really good deal. 'I charge a standard 10 per cent rate,' he says. 'I don't have to row. It's the same for everybody. I don't count the hours.'
Travel Essex, Hertfordshire, Newmarket, Oxfordshire and abroad.
Size of job From £100K–£1 million.
Attitude Ottoman Empire doing stand-up.

The phone may ring off the hook in Alp's office. 'I'm a one-man band.' he says, 'I can't be on the phone and answering it at the same time.' He then knocks back a great laugh and you are in for a jolly time. Originally from Turkey, the 62-year-old architect has nabbed most of Hertfordshire as well as all the surrounding counties. He is old-fashioned: 'I'm way too old to be designing white boxes,' he says, but, like the local doctor, he is always at the end of the telephone.

He does entirely residential work for clients such as the Sangsters, the Uptons and the Wentworth-Stanleys. He is now designing a 12,000 square foot house in 100 acres at Newmarket for Simon Crisford, the horse racing manager for Godolphin. He is not one of those grand architects who seek out only the rich: 'Definitely not. I have cycles of farmers, barristers, bankers and back again. I never turn down work,' he says.

His attitude towards architecture is: 'I look at a house and think to myself what would I want from this house. My refurbishments are a complete replanning of a house, unless you're in a Grade 1 strait-jacket. I look at it more like a new build.' In 35 years this is the first time he has spoken to a member of the press. He's 62 and 'will retire when people stop coming to me.'

What the clients say
'What is interesting about Alp is that he has the capability to project manage as well as being creative – unusual in an architect!' Will Hobhouse, entrepreneur
'Alp has worked for many of our friends. He is wonderful, civilized, gentle, unflashy, unassuming. His bathrooms and kitchens are superb. He is really practical about space. He always acts as though you were the only client, even though he's very busy.' Selina Franklin, client

Richard Ashby Associates Ltd
Kemps Place
Greatham, Liss
Hampshire GU33 6HG
T: 01420 538 316
F: 01420 538 544
admin@architectraa.com
www.architectraa.com

Costs RIBA fees of between 12 and 15 per cent.
Travel Fairly local – will go to Kent and Cornwall.
Size of job Doesn't often handles projects less than £50K
and not often over £1 million.
Attitude Professor with things on his mind (your house probably).

Those who can't afford Robert Adam or simply don't want Robert Adam, turn to Richard Ashby. The utterly charming Ashby is known to be a worrier. He takes his client's concerns to heart and is often working late into the night to make sure that everything is just so. He does exclusively domestic work, much of it on listed houses. He is traditional with a modern interpretation, and fond of arts and crafts. He is presently building a new house in Winchester having beaten his aforementioned competitor.

Clients (such as Tim and Jinny Hoare) are mostly local. He gets the odd celebrity like the Eurythmics' Dave Stewart, and almost got involved with Jody Schechter, but mostly it's families with practical considerations, which includes the sordid business of budgets. It's a smallish practice (nine people) with a reputation of putting the client first. One gets the sense that he never stops working (his secretary had to drag him away from drawing to speak to me).

What the clients say
'I have a huge admiration for Richard. He's versatile, good at changing tack if you want to do something different. He's down to earth, very efficient and good at details. He knows the history of all the houses in the area and has all the right contacts. Most important he puts himself out: he called me from a garden centre to ask whether he should go ahead and order a barbecue. This saved me time and money. I have since recommended him to all of my friends.' Kate Barton, client
'Richard is very nice and very competent. My impression has been uniformly good. We've done a lot of work on our farm, renovated the inside of the house. He's also very patient. He has very good taste. He has very good craftsmen – hard to find in these parts. He did a full service and paid all the bills.' Eric Wilkinson, client

Jonathan Clark Architects
Second Floor
34–35 Great Sutton Street
London EC1V 0DX
T: 020 7608 1111
F: 020 7490 8530
jonathan@jonathanclarkarchitects.co.uk
www.jonathanclarkarchitects.co.uk

Costs Charges RIBA rates.
Travel Anywhere, happily.
Size of job Won't go below £180K . 'Projects below that squeeze you,' he says.
Attitude Diligent.

Jonathan Clark is a young architect (42) who set up on his own in 2001, having previously been part of established firms such as Munkenbeck and Marshall, and Wells Mackereth, the team behind Smiths of Smithfield. This means he has all the same contacts but doesn't charge the same fees.

Fresh-faced and enthusiastic, Clark will do what the older architects won't: that is, fairly small refurbishment jobs for people (in Acton, Hampstead, Brooke Green) with big plans but, as of yet, limited wallets. His is a clean but practical style – he calls it 'warmed-up modernism'. His own flat in Maida Vale received a lot of press attention because of the clever use of space (doors that slide and turn into a guest room from a dining room, floating ceilings that hide storage), as well as the original use of lighting and joinery. Since leaving Wells Mackereth, Clark has clinched some pretty good jobs: a couple of flats in the new Westbourne Grove Church Development (by Harry Handelsman), the Essenza restaurant on Kensington Park Road and a hotel/gastropub in Tetbury in the Cotswolds (for the founder of Smiths of Smithfields). A new build is already in the pipeline.

He has a small child, so is likely to understand the needs of a young family. Trained at Kingston, he speaks a normal language: he won't try to convince you to live in a solar-powered tree house, like some of his contemporaries.

What the clients say
'Just fantastic! We wanted a modern bathroom in a 1800s home. He did it so beautifully. It sounds corny but it has changed our lives. People just go, "Wow!"' Suzie Dennis, client
'They're great – a young, fresh company. We bought an empty shell of an old church: they took our ideas on board and interpreted them. They are very accommodating. I've changed my ideas quite a few times, and they are still smiling.' Susanna Constable, client

Thomas Croft Architect
9 Ivebury Court
325 Latimer Road
London W10 6RA
T: 020 8962 0066
F: 020 8962 0088
email@thomascroft.com
www.thomascroft.com

Costs **Mid to high end. Charges RIBA rates, but likes to use the best materials and builders. Fee is negotiable.**
Travel **Works across the country – Oxfordshire, Wiltshire, Kent and the Isle of Wight – but is willing to go anywhere for the right job.**
Size of job **Budget – any size.**
Attitude **Dot the i's, cross the t's.**

Tom Croft is a rising star: the careful, somewhat academic, 44-year-old already has A-list clients like screenwriter Richard Curtis. Having said that, his Royal Yacht Squadron pavilion on the Isle of Wight brought in many new clients as well. Croft has the benefit of having worked for many of the great architects: Richard Meier in New York; Rick Mather, John Pawson and John Stefanidis in London. He is as interested in the past as he is in the future. What you get with Croft is studied intelligence: he likes things done properly, which can make him expensive. He listens more than most architects and shows a quiet determination but you never feel that you are part of his agenda. He does mostly residential work across the country (though W11 is his patch). He sits on several planning committees and works closely with a planning consultant.

What the clients say
'Tom took what was an historical building and turned it into a modern gallery. He did it economically. I was very impressed.'
Tim Taylor, Tim Taylor Gallery
'Thank heavens for Tom. He was fantastic from the beginning with the neighbours, the planner and the builders. He's incredibly organized, focused and calm. The most important part is that he doesn't carry an ego on his shoulders. He doesn't need to push his view on you. He is completely professional.'
Caroline Pereira, client
'Tom's strength is that he had a great apprenticeship working for people who were obsessed with details. He asks questions that others find irrelevant, such as where do you want your taps. He helps clients work through the whole process.'
Philip Hooper, interior designer
'He's serious, efficient, creative. He crosses the t's and dots the i's. We didn't fall out during my pregnancy which is saying something.' Nicola Reed, client

Louise Crossman Architects
The Potato Store
Court Place, Withycombe
Somerset TA24 6QB
T: 01984 640 988
F: 01984 641 146
design@louisecrossmanarchitects.co.uk
www.louisecrossmanarchitects.co.uk

Costs **'We're completely transparent. We will set a budget and do not exceed it.' RIBA rates.**
Travel **Devon, Somerset area – one hour from base.**
Size of job **Projects from £10K to £1.5 million.**
Attitude **Polished.**

It's unusual to find a modernist in the depths of Somerset, let alone a female modernist. Level-headed Crossman calls her style 'sensitive contemporary', though she operates in an area full of listed historical houses (which make up the bulk of her work). Many of her clients are relocating from London but that doesn't mean they suddenly want to give up all the latest mod cons. 'My clients are generally people who are good at what they do,' she says; 'they want a quieter life, but they still want the TVs and the electronic equipment to work.' The 44-year-old architect employs a further five architects: there are 12 people working in an office that is almost entirely focused on residential work. The firm is well known for getting planning permission (they won the Standsel Award for a restoration scheme) and for their interest in green issues. They consider their approach 'bespoke' and they collaborate with other designers and joiners in the area. They offer a high level of service to clients such as bankers and professionals who are used to it. 'We aim to please,' says Crossman.

What the clients say
'Louise worked on our very old, listed property, which we completely refurbished, including conversion of a period barn and adding on a new section of building. We are very pleased indeed; we now have a beautiful family home.'
Mr and Mrs M G C Harris, client
'Louise is a remarkably consultive architect. Unlike other architects she will bring in other experts when appropriate. Her general approach had everyone working cooperatively.'
Dr Prideaux, client

D–F

d-squared
1 Hatfield House
Baltic Street West
London EC1Y 0ST
T: 020 7253 2240
F: 020 7253 2241
info@d2-design.co.uk
www.d2-design.co.uk

De Matos Storey Ryan
99–100 Turnmill Street
London EC1M 5QP
T: 020 7336 0100
F: 020 7336 0111
mail@dmsr.co.uk
www.dmsr.co.uk

Costs **Reasonable but eco-friendly, which often means imported from Europe so can be more expensive.**
Travel **Prepared to go abroad for bigger projects – prefer French- and Spanish-speaking countries where they can communicate.**
Size of job **£200K–£3m**
Attitude **Worthy.**

Mark Hewitt and Clare Gerrard are 'worthy' architects. They care deeply about the environment. In fact, they would resign before agreeing to use chemicals or machines that emit more pollution than already exists. Having said that, they don't expect you to live in a bubble either. 'Eco-friendly design can be exciting and beautiful. It can also be simple, reusing existing bricks or staying local rather than buying wood shipped from Jakarta,' says Cambridge-educated Hewitt, who already lectures on the subject. Gerrard (who also trained as a filmmaker) turns some of their philosophies into videos. In fact, they have just finished a video installation at the British Council HQ.

d-squared's approach is academic: they will fuss almost as long over a laundry room as they will the overall design. Clients admire them for their commitment and their causes. They also design furniture (their aluminium Swing Chair sells through major stores including The Conran Shop). Only 10 per cent of their work is residential; the rest is projects, installations, videos, educational books and products. This has to do with the fact that to engage these two is to be engaged yourself. 'Clients don't realize how much hard work it is going to be for them,' says the sometimes blunt Hewitt, who maintains that getting on with the client is 'essential', and 'we prefer clients with a sense of direction'. This is code for undisciplined planet killers will be sent packing.

What the clients say
'Their work is very intelligently resolved and manages to combine practicality and function in a stylish way.'
Janice Blackburn, craft curator
'We have collaborated together on many projects. Mark is very clear and challenging. He forces you to think things through. He never says anything that doesn't make sense.'
Andrew Ford, engineer, Fulcrum Consulting

Costs **Flexible but essentially based on RIBA sliding fee scale.**
Travel **Have worked in Spain, Brussels, south-east and north-east England.**
Size of job **From £100K upwards.**
Attitude **Accelerating.**

Angus Morrogh-Ryan and Jose Esteves De Matos are hot-shot architects. They're hardly out of nappies (in their 30s) and already they have a large number of awards, including one from RIBA for the hotel and spa they built at Cowley Manor in Oxfordshire (which brought them many new clients). They have almost as many degrees (Cambridge, Harvard) as awards, which makes them very much the new kids on the block. They are slick modernists when it comes to style – you will get a radical rehaul of your existing space (in either the city or the country) with lots of glass. In fact, older clients are now coming to them saying: 'We want to go modern.'

They specialize in bringing old and new together (they are presently converting Led Zeppelin's old barn). They cut their teeth on Cowley but now they know what they're doing.

What the clients say
'They were at Cambridge with us. We never looked widely but they were fabulous. They have an academic approach and can deal with planners. They are great with clients and really do their homework'. Jessica Sainsbury and Peter Frankopan, directors, Cowley Manor in Oxfordshire
'They've done a great job for us. Their efficiency was considerable, which for an architect is quite a thing. Whenever we'd have a meeting, the minutes of it would be on the Internet by that evening. Their design is faultless, too. Everyone who has visited our house since they finished has complimented us on what a wonderful job we've done.' Martin Langdon, client

Roger Dongray
Town Arms Stables
Guildhall Lane
Lostwithiel
Cornwall PL22 0BW
T: 01208 873 648
rdongray@aol.com

John Falconer Associates
101 Promenade
Cheltenham
Gloucestershire GL50 1NW
T: 01242 58 23 62
F: 01242 2228 55
tobyfalconer@btconnect.com

Costs **Works mostly by the hour (charges £60 per hour).**
Travel **Stays local.**
Size of job **From £150 upwards**
Attitude **A hero who doesn't want to be sung.**

Roger was reluctant to be interviewed. He is so in demand that already there is a two-year back log. But that's because the architectural technician is also a consummate boat designer. In fact it's such a big part of his life, that he hardly has time for his second business. Based in Lostwithiel, Cornwall, Dongray was trained as an architectural technician and then branched out to general design. He works (with his wife) mostly on houses and barns in the area. Commissions are entirely word of mouth. He is known for his attention to detail and absolute discipline: 'I won't take on more than I can handle,' he says. He worked on the St Enodoc hotel with Emily Todhunter, and now has repeat clients in the area. The fact that he designs boats means he understands sea air and the effects of erosion. 'That's something to be taken very seriously,' says one client.

What the clients say
'I had a very precise brief in mind. I handed Roger a piece of driftwood and said this is what I want. They were a great husband and wife team who thought ahead and saved us a lot of money.' Helen Notley, client

Costs **Charges a fee based on a percentage of the building costs, broadly in line with RIBA guidelines. It's the materials more than the man that add up.**
Travel **Gloucestershire and the surrounding counties, but doesn't like to spend too long in the car.**
Size of job **£5,000–£2 million**
Attitude **Professor of medieval architecture.**

Toby Falconer is an old-world architect who went to Cambridge and doesn't even own a mobile. The practice was established in 1976 by his father John Falconer and focuses mostly on grand country houses, ecclesiastical work (of all kinds including repairs) and what the very proper Toby calls 'Appropriate interventions'. Art and Crafts, though, is really his thing. The client relationship is key but you can tell that Toby won't put up with nonsense, that's for sure. Clients include Sir Anthony Bamford and Martin and Elise Smith. Architectural writers such as Giles Worsley are fans but complain: 'We can never get any pictures.'

What the clients say
'I was always impressed with how closely he worked with not just me but everybody involved with the project. The builders had great respect for him due to this mutual respect.'
Viscount Sandon at Burnt Norton
'He is very good on design and concept, and one of the great things about the practice is that there is usually someone available to tend to a project at fairly short notice, compared to all these one-man bands who are booked up for ever.'
Jonny Rigg of J Rigg Construction

F–G

Featherstone Associates
74 Clerkenwell Road
London EC1M 5QA
T: 020 7490 1212
F: 020 7490 1313
enquiries@featherstone-associates.co.uk
www.featherstone-associates.co.uk

Costs **RIBA sliding rate.**
Travel **Has worked in Japan – loves to travel.**
Size of job **From £250K upwards but smaller projects slip through the net.**
Attitude **Never gives away how much she knows.**

Sarah Featherstone, former partner of Anthony Hudson (they built Gavin Davies' two houses together) is rapidly moving up the ranks. Though the 37-year-old comes from a modernist background (Kingston, the AA and Bartlett), her architecture is sensual and full of surprises. She loves the colour pink for example. She puts 'rice-crispie' floors into projects (pebbles inset into resin) and cement imprinted with timber blanks for a bit of novelty. She is increasingly being asked to do social housing and cultural centres but it's really her unusual conversion of a Bethnal Green house (her own) that got her noticed. Now most of Bethnal Green and her former neighbourhood, Shoreditch, wouldn't dream of using anyone else. She's cool, she's attractive and she's already teaching at Central St Martins. The practice is still small (it was set up two years ago and consists of her and four directors). The website suggests that it's all one big party.

What the clients say
'Sarah worked on our flat. We needed to get planning permission regarding one particular wall and Sarah was very determined and positive about the whole experience. She is intelligent, inspirational, has original ideas and is fun and lively to work with'. Dominic Ash and Kate Mellor, clients
'I have known Sarah for a number of years and she worked on our redevelopment in Shoreditch. The warehouse was gutted, two stories added and a side of the building made out of glass. I couldn't recommend her more highly. It was a tricky project, there were no right angles in the building, and she used the space well. It is a liveable space with a bold design. Good attention to detail and practical elements. She didn't view it as "just a job" and was personally involved, putting her sensibility and style into the project.' Misha Manson-Smith, filmmaker

Found Associates
21 Pall Mall Deposit
124 Barby Road
London W10 6BL
T: 020 8964 3667
info@foundassociates.com
www.foundassociates.com

Costs **From £200 to £1.5 million.**
Travel **Europe, including Stockholm and Paris. He recently bought a farm in Gloucestershire so will soon be local there as well.**
Size of job **Will consider anything. Still hungry.**
Attitude **What, me, worry?**

He's not much of a golfer, Ian Stanley (of Tears for Fears) tells me, but he does everything else brilliantly. Think of Richard Found as a soft minimalist (who although is a designer himself, employs two architects in his firm). The spaces he creates are slick, but the surfaces are tactile and sexy, shiny even. Trained at North London Polytechnic, the unassuming and modest Richard has won some pretty cool contracts such as the new clothing shop, Bamford & Sons (which belongs to Sir Anthony Bamford), seven Jigsaw stores, a nice slice of the Selfridges pie (he did the hi-fi and women's department in Manchester, the men's shoe department in London) and the Hobbs shoes stores (20 so far). He is currently planning the new Bulthaup showroom on Wigmore Street. Clients include DJ Jeremy Healy, for whom he did an apartment in Kings Cross. About 30 per cent of the work is residential, though personally I could easily live in Bamford & Sons (snuggled up in one of those sheepskin coats).

He calls himself a modernist, but he doesn't want to overshadow the brief. 'I just get as much information as possible, then I try and make sense of the brief. Rather than just going away and working in isolation, I want to understand exactly what it is that the client wants.'

At 37, he isn't very well known, but says Ian Stanley: 'He will be. He should be.' He has a PR firm already, which tells you he's ambitious.

What the clients say
'He's as high as you can get as a person and as a designer. He did our house in Notting Hill. He's incredibly thoughtful and very sympathetic to the clients' needs. His vision really helps. He makes you see things very clearly. Never gets stressed. Can't praise him enough.' Ian Stanley, keyboard player and songwriter, Tears for Fears
'I think Richard and his team are fantastic. They take your comments on board. They are very conscientious and deliver what you expect.' Mike Spearing, managing director, Hobbs

Craig Hamilton Architects Ltd
Coed Mawr Farm
Hundred House
Llandrindod Wells
Powys LD1 5RP
T: 01982 570 491
F: 01982 570 492

Costs Is RIBA registered and charges RIBA percentages
Travel Absolutely. Does a bit of work in Italy already.
Size of job Will consider anything…
Attitude Harbours a secret desire to go wild (architecturally speaking that is).

South African-born Craig Hamilton is one of the few architects that Prince Charles admires and, more importantly, frequently employs. He doesn't use computer-assisted design, preferring to draw by hand (and he's a talented artist, so drawings are framed and kept). This is a small practice (three architects and a student) that hardly ever gets a mention in the press. The idea even is anathema, 'We're completely word of mouth,' Hamilton says. He calls himself a 'progressive classicist': the (huge country) houses he restores are most often listed and of great historical value. Though he gives those with classical and old-fashioned tastes a meticulous service, he longs for a bit of edge. 'It's time we moved forward,' Hamilton says. He won a RIBA award in 2001 for a new-build scheme but still couldn't get planning permission. This frustrates him, enough to long for some foreign commissions. His patch is rural England: from Cumbria to the Duchy of Cornwall. There's no other word for him but impeccable.

What the clients say
'Craig is an exceptional, nice and extremely talented architect. He is easy to work with and is well respected.'
Lucy Manners, designer
'Craig is really committed to what he does in every last sense of the word. He will pull out all the stops to get the client what he wants. He's understated and modern yet inspirational.'
Serena Williams Ellis, designer

Gebler Tooth Architects
62 Glentham Road, Barnes
London SW13 9JJ
T: 020 8600 2800
F: 020 8600 2849
M: 07966 205 499
www.geblertooth.co.uk
info@geblertooth.co.uk

Costs Fixed price, lump sum, for each aspect of project.
Travel Very urban but will work abroad. Gebler built his mother's house in Northern Ireland.
Size of job The firm employs ten people and can accommodate anything. Gebler has designed staircases and £10K glass extensions. No minimum.
Attitude He says it himself. 'I don't want to be too clever.'

This is a mixed practice, meaning that partners David Tooth and Sasha Gebler do both commercial and residential work. British Airways and BAA are clients, for example, so are Heathrow Express and Theo Fennell (they did his new store on the Fulham Road as well as his house) and San Lorenzo, the famous restaurant, but this doesn't stop them from being the architects of choice to many South and West London residents, including Nick Jones of Soho House. Sasha Gebler was responsible for the Electric Cinema development commissioned originally by Peter Simmons. Nick Jones took over the lease and the two continued working together.

Gebler's original interest was the Arts and Crafts movement but he got a bit distracted with modernism. A dogmatic approach to the finer nuances of property history and law means that he can sometimes produce planning consent where all others have failed. The Irish well-spoken Cambridge-educated Gebler takes on jobs only if they are enjoyable. 'Many of my clients have expectations beyond reality,' he says. He diplomatically steers them in new directions. 'A lot of architects aren't interested in the details. I think if you say this will cost you £170,000, that means £170,000 – not £370,000.' For one client, Gebler took on the job of main contractor to get the costs down. He loves these kinds of challenges.

What the clients say
'Sasha is fantastic. He involves you in every aspect of the design. He does the legwork thoroughly and gets the planning permissions.' Jonathan Green, Richard Green Gallery
'We've done two properties together. What's great about Sasha is that he thinks out of the box. He comes up with solutions that no one else has thought of. He's artistic and highly efficient.'
Elisabeth Hoff, photographer

James Gorst Architects Ltd
The House of Detention
Clerkenwell Close
London EC1R 0AS
T: 020 7336 7140
F: 020 7336 7150
info@jamesgorstarchitects.com
www.jamesgorstarchitects.com

Costs Have to have the right budget. Gorst charges 12.5 per cent of the contract value.
Travel Gorst has just taken on a hotel/resort in Portugal, which will mean five years of commuting. There probably isn't any place in the country that Gorst hasn't worked in.
Size of job He's not interested in projects valued at less than £250K. Like most architects he thinks the project is more important than the price.
Attitude Tough on the outside, soft on the inside.

James Gorst has the slightly wary look of a man who has built a great many great houses since he set up shop in 1981. Around 80 per cent of his work is residential, which perhaps explains the exhausted look on his face. With only five architects in his practice, you can rest assured that it's Gorst who is going to spend the time slaving over your drawings and all the details, which in his case extends to colours of paints, furniture, panelling and even the knobs on the door. His clients – bankers, entrepreneurs, adventurous lovers of contemporary architecture – have a pretty big commitment to his modernist but sensual aesthetic, but that doesn't mean he won't follow a brief. 'If people are charming, I'm happy to work with them,' he says. His most famous project is the award-winning Whithurst Park Cottage, a new-build barn in Sussex commissioned by the entrepreneur Richard Taylor and his partner Rick Englert. The soft-spoken Gorst prefers to work with clients who know their minds (first-timers could irritate him).

What the clients say
'James designed our back extension. His greatest gift is the way he manipulates space. He has a very strong aesthetic, which may not be for everyone. He has a total view of what can be achieved. But you need to trust his instinct. He is immensely patient and easy to work with.'
Giles Worsley, architectural critic, *Daily Telegraph*
'Gorst has (a) a powerful visual imagination and (b) relentless attention to detail. The former might seem obvious in an architect, but I suggest it is actually fairly unusual. The result is that he is able to see how rooms and spaces should relate in ways that I certainly cannot. His designs are not routine. The focus on detail is expensive but worthwhile: it means, for example, that not even the door handles are routine.' Richard Morris, banker

Greenway & Lee Architects
Branch Hill Mews
London NW3 7LT
T: 020 7435 6091
F: 020 7435 6081
nick@greenwayandlee.com
www.greenwayandlee.com

Costs 'We'll look at anything,' says Lee, 'if it's of architectural interest.'
Travel: Open to suggestions. Presently North London and Oxford/Gloucestershire area. Have also worked in Spain, France and Taiwan.
Size of job 'We prefer contracts of £250K upwards because it means we can do something.'
Attitude You'll hear about us soon.

Given that they've worked for Stella McCartney (on her design studio), Neisha Crosland and Jimmy Nail, it's surprising that the Hampstead-based architects aren't better known. Nick Lee of Chinese parentage is your archetypal modernist. He first earned his stripes working for Norman Foster and set up shop three years ago. Partner Alex Greenway trained at the London College of Furniture and therefore really does know a thing or two about design. Theirs is a slick modernist style (light, spacious, clean) with great attention paid to detail. So far this has gotten them much word-of-mouth work in Hampstead, Gloucestershire and Oxfordshire. 'Nightmare clients are those who go to see six projects and come armed with 300 cuttings. Then we know we're in trouble,' says Lee. What they do is offer a full service that includes project management.

What the clients say
'I worked with Greenway & Lee on the design of my new studio in London. They were able to interpret my brief from which they generated an excellent concept design, resulting in a building that is a delight to work in and has become a wonderful home for our company. They are professional, committed and stylish and I would highly recommend them.'
Stella McCartney, fashion designer
'I'm a great fan of Nick's. This house had a limited amount of space and Lee managed to make it all flow beautifully. He's efficient and has a great understanding of where you're coming from. He has an amazing sense of space.'
Karen Paul, private client

Rabih Hage
69–71 Sloane Avenue
London SW3 3DH
T: 020 7823 8288
F: 020 7823 8258
info@rabih-hage.com
www.rabih-hage.com

Costs **Charges £110 per hour.**
Travel **London/Europe.**
Size of job **From £20K to £500K.**
Attitude **Cuddly but ambitious.**

Hage is a softer version of the über-French designer Christian Liaigre. He brings that haute Parisian glamour to a job but without the haute Parisian snobbism (and thank God for that). He graduated from the Ecole Nationale Superieure des Beaux-Arts in Paris in 1991 and now does a combination of interior and exterior architecture (though more of the former than the latter) for clients like Manolo Blahnik and the Queen of Jordan. He calls his style 'functional aesthetic' though it's also quite decadent. Luxury plays a big part (the French would just call it chic): only the best quality wool and linens (Dominique Kieffer, Bruno Triplet) are used. It's Kelly bag design without the Kelly bag price tag (because Hage is still relatively unknown). He stands out from the crowd because he doesn't do white walls and stone floors: it's more likely to be leather, metal, wenge wood and crocodile skin. His design store on Sloane Avenue sells modern French furniture, lighting and accessories, and also fabrics.

What the clients say
'I found Rabih to be very talented and amiable to work with. I didn't use a decorator and did it myself and he was very helpful. His designs are beautiful, contemporary and he uses high-quality materials. He absolutely, totally delivers. I recommend him unreservedly.' Odile Griffith, client
'I would most certainly recommend Rabih; he has become a friend. He won't be walked over, so we compromised. We had a good working relationship. He did the job well. Opened up new doors that we didn't know about.' Justine Naviede, client

Harrison Sutton Partnership
Little Priory Court
Fore Street, Totnes
Devon TQ9 5NJ
T: 01803 865084
F: 01803 865114
design@harrisonsutton.com
www.harrisonsutton.com

Costs **From £300K upwards.**
Travel **All over the West Country, from Cornwall to Dorset.**
Size of job **Will do small jobs for locals.**
Attitude **Enjoy.**

What strikes you immediately about Mike Inness, one of the three partners, is that he really enjoys his job. 'People dream of moving down here,' he says 'so we've got a niche market.' The practice is fairly large. It was started by Anthony Harrison and Peter Sutton in 1980 and now employs 18 people. Theirs is a mixed style: some jobs are contemporary, others are sensitive restorations of old piles. The practice has won its share of awards too, such as the National Pool of the Year Award and Civic Trust Award. Clients include Peter Richardson (from the Young Ones), David Dimbleby, Lord Somerset, as well as the local MP. This is one of English Heritage's preferred firms.

What the clients say
'Mike was described to me by the foreman on site as the best architect he had ever worked with. Mike is soft spoken but still insistent. He did a very good job'. Professor Collin Platt, client
'We asked around and every road led to Mike. He really understood the brief. He was very efficient and got things through the planners.' client

H J

Huf Haus
Tanglewood
Oxshott Road, Leatherhead
Surrey KT22 OER
T: 0870 200 0035
F: 0870 200 0036
www.huf-haus.com
london@huf-haus.com

Ad Maiorem Dei Gloriam
Thomas Faire Chartered Architects
Ulpa Place
Burnham Market
Norfolk TE31 8EL
T/F: 01328 738 276

Costs Prices start at £250K (one of their house is 11,000 sq ft so that's a few more zeros there).
Travel All over Europe and UK. (Booming market at the moment.)
Size of job Anything from 2,000 sq ft upwards.
Attitude: German know-how.

Prefab once had a bad rap but now it's positively trendy. Nature friendly, quick and modern, what more could you ask for? And it's made in Germany! Huf Haus produces environmentally friendly, energy-saving timber and glass houses using 1,000-year-old construction methods. There is only one catch: everything is made in a factory in about three months. The client's first contact (in the UK) is the architect Peter Huf who visits the site and advises the client on the many design options. Once agreed and costed, the company puts in for planning permission, measures up, sends the specifications to Germany and the rest is as smooth as a ride in the new Audi. Once completed, the house is trucked over, craned onto the site and installed almost overnight by Huf Haus' very tidy group of German builders. So far 64 houses have been built in the UK (8,000 in the continent) and another 50 are waiting for planning permission. St George's Hill, a private estate in Surrey, already has six. They were recently featured on Channel 4's *Grand Designs*, which opened the floodgates.

What the clients say:
The Iredales agreed to build their house in front of Channel 4's *Grand Designs* cameras. The neighbours were envious watching the German builders at work. The results speak for themselves.

Cost Reasonable.
Travel All over East Anglia.
Size of job Project size averages £400K–£500K but he will consider smaller projects as well. 'I'm not going to turn work away,' he says.
Attitude Proper but could go wild.

Tom graduated from Cambridge and set up his practice shortly after that. What he really likes is to build new houses that rely on the local materials and aren't pastiches of what was there 200 years ago. But he's no modernist and has done his fair share of listed houses and renovations as well. His speciality is straddling old and new. 'We're half CAD and half old-fashioned draughtsmanship,' he says. His clients are barristers, city people, a sprinkling of Shakespearean producers and film directors. Clients find out about him either through dinner parties or because they ended up at his famous Sunday night movie night and were impressed with the house. He looks the part of the Cambridge professor and comes off as a complete gentleman.

What the clients say
'Tom designed our house in Brancaster. He is a real gentleman and takes real care to get things right. This includes the details like the flint work. I look at other people's houses and think: why didn't they take care. They should have used Tom.'
Mr & Mrs Macfarlane, clients
'My wife and I bought the Old Railway Station in 1996. We are so pleased with what he's done there that we've employed Tom to do all our houses, hotels, etc. He's even looked at our house in South Africa.' **Mr Paul Whittome, client**

Bob Hardwick
Aycote Lodge
Rendcomb
Cirencester
Gloucestershire GL7 7EP
T: 01285 831 559
sallyann@hardwick66.freeserve.co.uk

Roderick James Architects LLP
The Framing Yard
East Cornworthy, Totnes
Devon TQ9 7HF
T: 01803 732 900
F: 01803 732 901
enquiries@carpenteroak.com
www.carpenteroak.com

Costs Some clients don't even ask, he says. Charges £90 an hour.
Travel Not too keen to leave the area (Gloucestershire).
Size of job He has no lower limit. The largest jobs are in the £1.5 million region. He is used to tackling any kind of building in the area.
Attitude Teacher – not desperately interested in ten-hour conversations about where the microwave goes.

Bob Hardwick is one of Gloucestershire's best-kept secrets. He operates on his own with the help of his garden-designer wife and seeks no personal publicity at all. His name is passed from neighbour to neighbour, which keeps him happily occupied. Although not a qualified architect, he is straight talking, to the point and very concerned with details. He still draws by hand and only emails reluctantly. Stylewise, most of his clients want classical houses and help getting local planning consent, something he's brilliant at. He started his own firm almost as soon as he left university (he is now 57) and believes in doing one thing well. 'If you want to be an architect, be an architect,' he says (referring to the new trend for multi-tasking). Clients are bankers like Michael Dobson and many local residents.

What the clients say
'We were very pleased with our house. Bob has a very good eye, can be a bit pernickety, but is very down to earth.' John Bays, client
'Bob is an extremely talented architect and has a real understanding of Cotswold architecture. Also, he has a good sense of space inside the home. He understands how to create a space that feels good to live in. He's a real talent and designs beautiful classical detail.' Charles Fisher, client
'Very talented and very good.' Patridges, builders

Costs £100 per square foot. From approx £150,000 to supply and build a single timber house. £240K for a four-bedroom barn (this is variable because of all the other factors). For bespoke design, he follows RIBA standards and bills per hour from £20–£70, depending on which architect is assigned.
Travel UK.
Size of job This is a 12-man firm, large for country standards. They are used to budgets from £100K–£1 million-plus. 'A lot of our work is in the £250K range,' James says.
Attitude Upbeat Marlon Brando.

Roderick James is a highly amusing, occasionally temperamental, bit of a wheeler-dealer architect, who probably has more new builds under his belt than any other architect in Britain. His thing is timber houses, which he designs then has made in his carpentry shop called Carpenter Oak Limited. Both businesses are based in Devon and the 56-year-old runs a small empire. He had (when I spoke to him) 175 jobs on the go, all of which he does from his own new-build barn at the edge of a river. He is specialized enough for Windsor Castle restoration project to ask Carpenter Oak to restore the medieval kitchen, and artistic enough to have designed Bedales School Theatre.

Clients don't come to him for the ordinary. One client asked for a Seaside House in Florida in the middle of Oxfordshire. Light and space are his thing, and takers are some pretty swanky people such as Euan Baird, the chairman of Rolls Royce, and Sir George Russell, the former chairman of Camelot. James works his way. 'I don't go to tender. I just look the builder in the eye,' he says. He also runs a financial services business on the side – altogether a bit of a character. Clients love him but warned me that 'hands on' is not his approach. He won't be running on site every five minutes, that's for sure, but with 175 projects, how could he?

What the clients say
'He is a man of the most astonishing energy. It is really good working with his team.' Charlie Nairn, client
'His ideas are creative and clearly presented. He is outrageous and outspoken. So working with him is a challenge and, for me, has resulted in us becoming good friends and having a wonderful house.' Tim Holley, client

Wilson Kerr
15 Chepstow Place
London W2 4TT
T: 020 7229 1140
Wilson@wilsonkerr.co.uk

Trevor Lahiff Architects
Geneva House
99 Knatchbull Road
London SE5 9QU
T: 020 7737 6181
F: 020 7326 0349
design@tlastudio.co.uk
www.tlastudio.co.uk

Costs Charges RIBA rates 11–15 per cent, or £100 per hour if acting as consultant.
Travel Has designed houses in Gloucestershire (two in the same village), Ireland, Switzerland, the Middle East.
Size of job Up to 750K.
Attitude Servant's heart (see Introduction).

Wilson Kerr looks a bit like Prince Charles and is just as polite. Needless to say he's also discreet. In former times, architects were a hybrid between a personal assistant and an artist. Clients consulted them on everything. Glasgow-born Wilson Kerr is of the old school. 'I was looking for a particular kind of tissue box for my client, the other day, ' he says. 'An interior decorator friend said to me, "You're mad," but that is the sort of attention I pay to details. I see my job as pleasing the client.' It's this kind of attitude that has landed him pretty high-octane clients (several countesses and relatives of King Khalid). Most clients, though, are City types who want only Wilson, which is why he works by himself.

There is no house style: 'I respond to a brief and place.' He has done modern, classical, grand and quite simple buildings. Clients are given working sketches, room layouts, and elevations painstakingly drawn by hand – Kerr does not use CAD.

Up to 90 per cent of his work is residential. Clients come to him to design a house, then they ask him to design their office, then he does their country house. Then he repeats the process for their best friend. He remains close friends with most of his clients.

What the clients say
'Nothing is too much trouble for Wilson. He is a joy to work with and has become a real friend.' Mrs A, client
'We were on holiday with the children the week before we were due to move in to our new house: Wilson discovered there was no soap in any of the bathrooms, provided it and took away the new bathtowels for a cycle in his own washing machine. A gorgeous bouquet of flowers and card greeted us on arrival.' Private client
'Wilson is wonderful. He is very thorough and will see to everything from the building works to hanging paintings. If there's a problem, he's there immediately.' Pilar Everington, architect

Costs Charge 12–15 per cent RIBA fees.
Travel Have already been to Bahrain and Shanghai, though they seem to spend a lot of time in Kensington and Chelsea.
Size of job Won't go below £150K.
Attitude So relaxed it's hard to know how they got this far.

You won't find many architects who will draw light switches for you. But Carolyn Trevor and Pat Lahiff, partners in work and in life, have a few feathers in their caps. They've worked for Stefanidis (where they met) and Rick Mather, which means they're real insiders. Carolyn's the creative one; Pat is rock solid technical Australian. They have five children but still put in 12-hour days.

They cite such influences as Jean Michel Frank and Andre Putman on their website. They can do nice neo-classical detailing as well as state-of-the-art glass and steel back extensions. 'We can do anything,' says the off-the-wall Trevor, who roomed with Tino Zervudachi of David Mlinaric. This is bespoke architecture: clients such as Damien Aspinal, Rupert Murdoch and Paul Cook of the Sex Pistols get 'the full treatment', says Trevor. Some choose them just because they're fun.

The 20-man firm employs quite a few specialists: this means that you don't have to hire both a designer and an architect should you want clean lines, great light, state-of-the-art technology and the creature comforts such as fluffy cushions, wood panelling, maybe even some wallpaper. They won't make you feel embarrassed that you don't hanker to live in a white cube. They have collaborated with many other designers, such as Veere Greeney and Jacques Grange in Paris: this adds up to a lot of good suppliers and ideas at the fraction of the cost of some of their better-known contemporaries. The firm also offers a designer service that few know about.

What the clients say
'Carolyn helped us with our London house. She is phenomenal. I think she's one of the best architects in London. Both she and Pat are honourable and creative. They're not prima donnas.' Gerald and Simone Davidson, clients
'We love their work. They did our whole flat. They were fun and understood, to the letter, what we were looking for throughout the entire project.' G D, client

Llewellyn Harker Ltd
Home Farm
East Pennard
Shepton Mallet
Somerset BA4 6TT
T: 01749 860022
F: 01749 86 00 33
martin@llewellynharker.com

Costs They charge an hourly rate of £85.
Travel Scilly Isles and the West Country.
Size of job Projects cost from £200K.
Attitude After-dinner speaker.

The reason why Martin Llewellyn gets the plum jobs in Somerset is because, aside from being infinitely patient and artistic (he went to art school), he is also great company.

'Everyone comes to us and says: "It was a disaster last time." This time, with a new architect, designer and builder, it will be perfect,' he says, with the comic timing of an actor. 'Three weeks later, they're in tears,' he continues. Ditto with stories on budgets. 'Everyone says, "This time, we've got a lot to spend."'

The firm was founded by Llewellyn and Jonathan Harker in 2000. They specialize in farms and old rectories, though they also do the occasional hotel and school. They are particularly good at drawing ('we can deal with CAD if pushed, but we prefer to use pencil'). At 54, Lewellyn has seen it all and done it all before. He admits his is a hand-holding job. 'It's important that the client is still cheerful after two years,' he says. He failed to mention (until we called back), that they've won a few competitions: The Ebbw Vale Garden Festival Urban Village scheme, a Welsh housing award, the RIBA Wessex Region Countryside Design Award in 2000, and the Country Living and Council for the Protection of Rural England New Buildings in the Countryside Award.

What the clients say
'Very pleased with Martin; he has very good taste and a real "feel" and sympathy for old buildings.'
Alexander Russell, CEO Imo Car Wash
'He's known as a man with great ideas. He has worked on three projects for us and we are delighted with the results.'
Mrs Michael Carter, client

Lloyd-Thomas Architects
Pytchley Stables
Main Street, Watford Village
Northamptonshire NN6 7UY
T: 01327 844 986 / F: 01327 843 894
M: 07803 080 224
mail@lloyd-thomas.co.uk
www.lloyd-thomas.co.uk

Costs Reasonable. They don't use the RIBA scales, preferring to work on a fixed fee.
Travel Leicestershire, Bedfordshire, Northamptonshire. Further, if necessary,
Size of job 'You don't have to be rich to use us,' says Roland Lloyd-Thomas.
Attitude Double dip.

Youth has its advantages: enthusiasm, for one, the willingness to work hard for another and, most of all, the willingness to do the smaller jobs such as back extensions. Husband and wife architectural team Roland and Sevil Lloyd-Thomas, graduates of Birmingham School of Architecture and Oxford Brookes, set up two years ago in their converted barn in Watford and now service the Leicestershire, Bedfordshire, Northamptonshire area (all work comes via word of mouth). They offer a complete design service – they like contemporary, but will do what the client asks and planners will tolerate – and are very much part of the community they live in. 'In London you can escape into a hole if you screw up: here everyone knows everyone,' says Roland, aged 36 and father of two young children. The couple work with many listed and historic houses in conservation areas and are no strangers to the planning office. Their clients are 'normal people' with big plans but limited wallets. It's their ability to do a lot for a little that is getting them noticed. They've done six or seven barn conversions already.

What the clients say
'Sevil and Roland were very good at understanding the deeper brief and not just focusing on our likes and dislikes. They explored this far more than any other architect we have worked with in the past. They have a lot of integrity and put in the hours. They also have a great combination of skills – both on the conceptual and the project-management side of things. By charging an hourly fee, they made us much more willing to explore and change our minds.' Jenny Jones, client
'Roland and Sevil designed our barn. They were very personable and gave us great advice. They're happy to take the time to chat through things. Also, very good with materials.'
Clive Nichols, garden photographer

Patrick McInerney Architect
75 Wigmore Street
London W1U 1QD
T: 020 7224 6626
F: 07224 662 720
patrick@pmalondon.com
www.pmalondon.com

Costs Charges RIBA rates, though not the long hours.
Travel 'Sure.'
Size of job From £120K.
Attitude California breeziness meets North American grit.

The 34-year-old California-born McInerney graduated from the AA then went straight to work for David Chipperfield, where he became the senior architect (meaning he managed dozens of other architects) and site manager for many of the most demanding jobs, including the private residence of Neville and Carol Conrad (he subsequently did both daughters' houses). He had barely started up on his own in 2000 when former client and friend Chris Martin of Coldplay, who is married to Gwyneth Paltrow, said: 'Do you fancy designing our house?' Talk about baptism by fire.

He's done 35 projects already, a mixture of commercial and residential (Julien Silver is also a client) and was asked to do four schemes on the Blenheim estate.

You get the sense that Patrick is only years away from becoming a star himself. He says things like 'I work like a doctor. I'm always on call. I never turn the phone off.' He was in the office at 8pm when I rang. His style will have been influenced by Chipperfield. It's all about light and flow and space, and will rely on the latest technology and materials, though not in a faddish way. 'Our design development is adjusted on an individual basis so as to convey the ideas to the client in the clearest way. This may include models, images, collages, sketches, material samples, etc.,' he says. This is very hands-on modernism. Because he's only 34, you can expect focus, time and the benefit of five years of hard work at DCA.

What the clients say
'Patrick is extremely hard-working, dedicated and determined. He's very good with builders. Behind the easygoing exterior is a steely interior. He's also very talented and really knows how to manipulate space. He designs everything down to the beds. He won't leave anything half-finished.' Carol Conrad, client
'Patrick was fantastic. He has great attention to detail. I was away for eight weeks and came back to an amazing extension.' Charlotte Warshaw, client

McLean Quinlan Architects
1 Milliners
Riverside Quarter
Point Pleasant
London SW18 1LP
T: 020 8870 8600
info@mcleanquinlan.com
www.mcleanquinlan.com

Cost Charges sliding RIBA rates.
Travel All over the country: has worked in Devon, Cornwall, Gloucestershire and London. Will enlist the help of a local architect when outside London.
Size of job Budgets from £500K upwards.
Attitude Will get things done, no half measures

Fiona McLean is a woman operating in a man's world. This makes her unusual. The Scottish-born and trained architect is a true modernist, but years of working with families has made her sensitive to the realities of life. Her strength is for designing beautiful spaces that work and filling them with unusual details: she'll design a storage unit rather than simply bang in a wall of doors. She'll use colour. For one client she designed a cantilevered table in the front hall for the telephone with tiny compartments for keys, files, post-it notes and any other useful items. She designed an entire home office around box files. She spends as much time thinking about the laundry chute in the basement as she does the use of space. Fiercely organized, she won't do anything in half measures. Clients wouldn't dream of using anyone else. She's a big name without being a big name, if you know what I mean. Her husband, an architect with Denton Corker Marshall, works closely with John Pawson.

What the clients say
'We have done two projects together, one in London and one in Devon. We wouldn't have thought of using anyone else. Fiona is very good at being on top of planners and builders. She operates brilliantly in a man's world. She's clean and minimal but also sympathetic to the architecture. She recommended we use a lighting consultant in Devon because, though she is very good at lighting, she felt the technology was moving very fast. She has a very diplomatic way of steering you in the right direction if she disagrees with you.' Rosemary Yallop, client
'Fiona was recommended to us by a friend and we clicked with her right away. She understood us, that we were building a "home" and not a "project". She can read what you want to do and lead you in a very intelligent way. She is very persuasive, in a good way. Extremely empathetic, creative, professional and easygoing, a special person and has become a friend to us.' Macarena Wheldon, client

Make
Asta House
55–65 Whitfield Street
London W1T 4HE
T: 020 7636 5151
F: 020 7636 5252
info@makearchitects.com
www.makearchitects.com

Costs **Charges RIBA rates.**
Travel **Anywhere and happily.**
Size of job **Says he will consider most things but the smallest project at the moment is £350K.**
Attitude **Zen master with PhD.**

The best time to nab an architect is when he's just left a big practice to start on his own. He will be humble, hungry and most likely to want your business. Ken Shuttleworth, a former partner at Norman Foster and Partners, may have wanted to build you a dream house in his former incarnation but most likely you would have been pawned off on some junior so that he could concentrate on the skyscrapers. He's only been in practice for a short while and already he's been commissioned to do two major residential conversions, not to mention a few office blocks. Clients have trailed his work ever since he designed and built his moon-shaped glass-fronted Crescent House in Wiltshire.

The soft-spoken, 50-something, professorial Shuttleworth is a thinking man's architect. He's also very kind by the sound of it. Many of his staff left Foster and Partners to follow him and he has thanked them by making them full partners. His Power-Point presentation is full of words like 'listen, new, flexible'. The atmosphere in Shuttleworth's office is so mellow, you could confuse it for a yoga studio. If you're the shouting type, this is not for you.

What the clients say

'We're doing 255 apartments together in Chelsea. Ken has a fierce intellect. He's incisive and sees a solution to every problem. He's quietly spoken but forceful in character. He also employs first-rate people. His team is absolutely first class.'
Alaister Mellons, St James Homes
'We have worked with Ken 'the pen' Shuttleworth on a number of schemes, first at Forster's and more recently at Make. I love his freehand sketches – it's uncanny how the first sketch often stays so close to the final building – and he's that rare breed of architect who, as well as being passionate and driven about design, can present superbly well. He is also a charming, gregarious and very social individual – all that talent in one person, doesn't it make you sick! Well done, Ken.'
Tom Bloxham MBE, Chairman of Urban Splash

Makstutis Architecture and Design
Unit 1A, North Clapham Arts Centre
26–32 Voltaire Road
London SW4 6DH
T: 020 7498 6060
F: 020 7498 4466
www.maad.info
query@maad.info

Costs **Reasonable because young and hungry.**
Travel **Will go anywhere (tube, bus, plane and foot).**
Size of job **Average budget about £250K upwards.**
Attitude **Midwestern American.**

I met 39-year-old American Geoffrey Makstutis for an interview for the *Financial Times* on up-and-coming architects. He left quite an impression – of being a thoroughly nice guy, willing to listen, hard-working – and two years later, I called him and asked him whether he would help me reorganize our house. Geoffrey is a deliberate, cautious architect, who is still hungry enough to take on a small project such as my own. He's not trendy, does not wear Commes, but he's prepared to work hard. He's just been made a course director for the Arts, Design, Environment BA course at Central St Martins College of Art & Design, so other people are catching on, too.

Trained at the AA, he worked for Branson Coates (and therefore worked on the Jigsaw shops and parts of Liberty) and 51% before starting up on his own in 2002. Stylewise, he's an all-out modernist (lots of glass, wood – not too much stainless steel), though he will always argue in favour of the practical as opposed to the esoteric. He arrives early for meetings and follows up instantly. Clients are urban professionals with kids, mortgages and stress in their lives.

What the clients say

'He designed our house in Chiswick. We expected three solutions to every problem: Geoffrey gave us six. He's very professional and sensitive to the client's needs. He's not one of those arrogant architects you hear about. Creative but not mad.'
Jane Pryce, painter
'He's somebody that when you call and ask to perform, does perform. His designs are innovative. Generally, a very nice man, pleasant to work with, easygoing, but still driven. Gets the stuff done.' Marco Pangherz, developer

Manalo and White
Westfield
Common Road
Bressingham, Diss
Norfolk IP22 2BB
T: 01379 688 371
F. 01379 688390
brian@manaloandwhite.co.uk

Costs Reasonable. Does a fixed-fee percentage based on the project size. Tries to economize on behalf of the client.
Travel Will travel anywhere within about 100 miles – East Anglia, and the home counties. London. Plus Broxburn.
Size of job Current range from £30 to 250K. Will gladly go up to £500K.
Attitude Knows he's going places without being a prat.

If you don't get the name of the firm, you might not get the architect. Brian Greathead used to DJ under this name (as in Barry Manalo and Barry White), and it amuses him to see whether clients get it or not. The Bartlett-educated, 35-year-old architect used to work for Hudson Featherstone (the architects behind Gavin Davies's Baggy House in Cornwall) and now lives in Norfolk, where he designs bungalows, log cabins and – talk about contrasts – a very large luxury flat for a very rich overseas client. Brian chose to design bungalows because 'I like them and live in one'. The log cabins came about because he was working on the dining-room table and decided he needed an office. 'I ordered a cabin from Finland, which was really a sauna, then stripped away the insides.' The importer was so pleased with the results that he asked him to design more and now he's making 20 of them for a caravan park in King's Lynn.

He has clients like Antony Gormley, but is too young to be smug. Clients are taken much further than they expect, thanks to Brian's low-key manner (he's quite wry). Definitely a-watch-this-space architect.

What the clients say
'We thought Brian was fantastic. One of the great things is that he is practical when it comes to children, kitchens, things like that. He also has a good eye and did a brilliant job with the planners. We have maximized the space more than anyone on the street. He's also very good at using inexpensive materials in a creative way and saved us a lot of money.' Victoria Penny, barrister
'We asked Brian to design a modern back extension for us. This is a 1930s house in a conservation area. Needless to say, he gave us a better place than we expected. He's extremely efficient with site management (he takes minutes and never does anything twice), but he's also very up to date with design and technology. We have since recommended him to many of our friends.'
Robin Gardner, musician and property developer

Maxwell Pierce Architects
30 Paget Lane
Enniskillen BT74 7HT
Northern Ireland
T: 028 6632 6630/3099
F: 028 6632 5186
mail@maxwellpierce.com

Costs He charges 8 per cent of project costs, plus expenses.
Travel All over the world. Presently Russia.
Size of job Size is not as important as opportunity for creativity.
Attitude Could have been an actor.

The bearded, jolly Richard Pierce has very strict criteria: 'I need three things from a client,' he says: 'Financial reward, interesting people and artistic satisfaction.' After 35 years of working in the business for big clients (the Duchess of Abercorn, Lord Belmore), he is now semi-retired and, in his words, 'I just do the fun stuff.' He's very pleased to say that his own house, Dresternan, built into the countryside, has appeared in 41 magazines, probably a record for an Irish architect. He works on grand restorations and church projects, such as the restoration of an early 20th-century cathedral in Hyderabad. He just completed a project for Lord Erne of Crom Castle (the wing, by the way, is now open to holiday-makers) and is presently working for a Russian oligarch, whom he has never met – though he was quite impressed by the former SAS bodyguards.

What the clients say
'One of the outstanding heritage architectural firms in Ireland. I am familiar with a lot of their projects and they are personally doing something for me right now. They are extremely good at the conservation side of converting heritage buildings.'
Viscount Dunluce, Glenarm Castle
'I can't speak highly enough of Richard. As far as personalities are concerned, I think he's witty and clever. Architecturally speaking, he is very well known for his innovative work, though for us he did a restoration of an 1840 castle. Whatever he did design was wonderful.'
Lord Erne, Crom Castle

Michaelis Boyd Associates
90A Notting Hill Gate
London W11 3HP
T: 020 7221 1237
F: 020 7221 0130
info@michaelisboyd.com
www.michaelisboyd.com

Simon Morray-Jones
21 Milsom Street
Bath BA1 1DE
T: 01225 787900
F: 01225 787901
sm-j@sm-j.com

Costs Charge RIBA scales. Negotiable.
Travel Anywhere, depending on the project. Have worked in Italy, France, Switzerland and South Africa.
Size of job From £250 upwards
Attitude Could have been pop stars.

Tim Boyd and Alex Michaelis are almost too good-looking to be architects. They ride around on bicycles, hang out with interesting people, have beautiful children. They also have an amazing clientele: everyone from Eric Felner, Paul Whalen and Annabel Heseltine to the writer Sebastian Faulks. Their style is cutting edge but comfortable, adapted to families and real life. Clients typically get them to design a modernist shell with their famous bathrooms (wet rooms) and then fill it with their own choice of furnishings. Michaelis Boyd were also involved in the design of both Babington House and the Electric Cinema, as well as Moro and Sophie's Steakhouse. This is a particularly creative firm so, if on very tight deadline, best to use a project manager. You know a practice is popular when the clients hunt you down to give you a reference. The word of mouth has now gone beyond Notting Hill so expect to see their names popping up in a neighbourhood near you.

What the clients say
'Alex Michaelis's vision of how we should open up our kitchen via a staircase leading from the entrance hall to french doors into the garden was an inspired start to our building work. He, Tim Boyd and practice architect Caroline Spencer saw the project through with tact, efficiency and humour, and their charm seemed to work its magic on the various planning authorities, too.' Veronica Faulks, client
'Put it this way: Alex Michaelis is the only architect I've never fallen out with. Alex is very talented and keeps things simple.' Paul Whalen, film director

Costs Reasonable. 'I don't have fancy offices full of exotic flowers.' He charges in one of three ways: a lump sum, an hourly fee and the RIBA sliding scale fees. 'I'm open to discussion.'
Travel Most of his work is not in Bath. Instead it is based in Norfolk, Gloucestershire, Cornwall, London and Barcelona.
Size of job From £400K upwards
Attitude 'Should have a Stirling Prize for what I do' – which he probably should.

Morray-Jones was first recommended to me as a 'bathroom architect' because he designed the wet rooms in Babington House (as well as everything else). He gives couples such novelties as his and her baths with his and her plasma screens. 'There's more to a bathroom than a limestone sink and stainless steel taps,' he says. He also does his fair share of Grade I listed houses, which means he spends a lot of time negotiating with English Heritage. He's not a stick in the mud, though. 'We're totally CADed out,' he says. 'We have a drawing board but no one ever uses it.' He has a contemporary flair but understands that his job is to service the client. 'I work Sundays, I work all the time in fact,' he says. His practice also focuses on interior design. 'You need to take in the whole picture.'

Clients include Jane Seymour, Mick Jagger, Nick Jones and Kirsty Young, David Ross and Charles Dunstone, though the majority are just nice normal people who heard of him through friends. He is very much part of the Bath scene.

What the clients say
'Simon took our not-so-beautiful house and turned into something very attractive. When the Bath Building inspection team came to see it, they said it was one of the finest buildings they have seen and suggested it be put up for a prize. Simon doesn't want to radically change your house. If you say I want open living, he gives you open living. But he's very now. He's just got it.' Mrs Susanne Giggins, client
'Simon is refurbishing an Edwardian House for us. It is not beautiful but he has been sympathetic to the challenge it posed. He is modern but without being faddish. He is creative and pays a great deal of attention to detail. It really has been a joy working with him and his excellent team.' The Honourable Bobby Yerburgh, client

M–P

Richard Murphy Architects
15 Old Fishmarket Close
Edinburgh EH1 1RW
T: 0131 2206125
F: 0131 220 6781
mail@richardmurphyarchitects.com
www.richardmurphyarchitects.com

Costs RIBA based. Minimum budget for residential is around £400K total construction cost, although this is negotiable if the proposed site and proposed requirements in design sound interesting.
Travel All over the country and abroad, depending on the job.
Size of job Big projects. Definitely would not do anything under a total construction cost of £250K.
Attitude Watch out, Norman Foster.

He flies a Microlight, but he is no Norman Foster, not yet. The affable but steely and determined Richard Murphy has risen very rapidly up the ranks and is now competing in the big boy league. He was one of eight British architects chosen for the British Pavilion at the Venice Biennale this year. He has scores of buildings coming up all over Edinburgh; he's written and published a number of books, the most recent on Carlo Scarpa, yet he still manages to do private houses, albeit for pretty serious clients. 'We'll do it if we think it's going to be fun and, most of all, if we like the client.'

Murphy started his firm and now employs 25 people. He has been called a 'maximalist', meaning he gets the most from the least (promising site). This is state-of-the-art architecture for people who want modernism, better yet, cutting edge modernism. Having said that, Prince Charles wrote Murphy a letter telling him how much he admired his House at Killeenaran in Ireland.

What the clients say
'What can I say? In the Pacific sphere he is a fast rising star. He designed our house in Ireland (which has since won a slew of awards). He is delightful, intelligent and has a clear artistic vision. His feet are still on the ground now, though, like most talented people, he has strong views. He once said if you're too timid (for a tin roof), I'll give you something else. We agreed in the end and it was absolutely the right decision.' Rod Stoneman, film and television producer, owner of House at Killeenaran
'Absolutely brilliant! Richard is an architect who knows how to cook, so he knows how to design a kitchen. He was fun to work with and very creative.' Carol Hogel, client

Duncan O'Kelly Partnership
Garden House Studio
Eartham
Chichester
West Sussex PO18 0LS
T: 01243 814 673
F: 01243 814 532
architects@duncanokelly-partnership.com

Costs Charges standard RIBA rates, varies from 10 to 12 per cent.
Travel West Sussex.
Size of job No minimum for former clients. From £200K otherwise.
Attitude Paul Newman.

The dashing 53-year-old, Irish-born O'Kelly is the architect of choice to the smart West Sussex set who want a bit of edge. He does everything from small residential projects for the likes of Bryan Ferry to grand undertakings like Didling Manor. His strength is relationships. 'It's important to understand what the client wants,' he says. Though he designs a lot of conventional houses, he is at heart a modernist. 'I think you have to be sympathetic to the existing building but you also have to take into account the times we live in.'

He is known for his charm, which gets him invited to all the smart dinner parties. 'In the country you can't really afford to fall out,' he says. He runs a very small office (three people) and services the local community. He recently won an award from the Sussex Heritage Trust for restoration of a medieval farmhouse. Plans are underway for a Carluccio restaurant in Notting Hill.

What the clients say
'Duncan had the task of turning my childhood home into a modern 21st-century house. We got along very well, fun but professional. Pleased with the end results. Professional with contractors. Would highly recommend him.'
Jo and Rupert Clevely, clients
'Duncan is extremely competent, produces high-quality detail and is very fair and helpful in the handling of contracts. He has a very good flair for design, having a flexible vision that always captures the mood of the setting perfectly.'
David Hobson of J C Lillywhite, builder

Object Architecture
19 Montana Rd
London SW17 8SN
T: 020 8682 9300
M: 0795 781 4633
box@objectarchitecture.co.uk
www.objectarchitecture.co.uk

Eric Parry Architects
87–89 Saffron Hill
London EC1N 8QU
T: 020 7831 4464
F: 020 7831 4074
eric.p@ericparryarchitects.co.uk
www.ericparryarchitects.co.uk

**Costs Affordable. Charges a lump sum again each section
of work.**
Travel London, Suffolk, Norfolk.
Size of job No minimum.
Attitude Street cred.

Nigel Buckie was recommended to me by the girls in
the RIBA Press Office. They offered me dozens of
names until I said: 'Who would you use?' 'Oh, Nigel,'
they replied. The 40-year-old Buckie, a keen
weightlifter who rides around on a scooter, graduated
from the Bartlett School of Architecture. He's part of the
new-wave school of multi-tasking architects: he can
design houses, furniture, gardens, mosaics, websites,
light installations, even rod-iron gates; he will also build
them himself. And he's green to boot. Helen Standring
came to him for a simple flat extension in
Wandsworth. Instead, she's getting 'a slot house', an
infill between two buildings: it's low impact, uses
water-harvesting techniques, has solar panels, heated
walls and sedum mats on the roof, which double as a
garden. What's more, it's being built as a pod by Atelier
One. And it's on a very tight budget.
    While all the other kids were hanging in pubs at
the Bartlett, Nigel was working full-time for a builder.
He collaborates with Craig Driver, a former school chum
based in Suffolk. Together they can cover a lot of land.
    Buckie wants to 'change people's perceptions of
what they can and can't have'. He aims to give his
clients something that is 'better than what they asked
for'. He prefers to take a holistic approach, doing
everything from the front gate to the back of the garden.

What the clients say
'He's been fantastic to work with. I met him during Architecture
Week and somehow we got to where we are now (which is
building a pod), thanks to his vision. He is incredibly patient and
has become a friend.' Helen Standring, client
'Nigel was great. Immensely cordial and very good at listening,
which is good starting point in any relationship. He interpreted
the brief very well and things came out just as he'd described
they would. He put his suggestions in a very understandable and
considerate way and I'm happy I went along with the ones I did.
I would happily recommend him to anyone.' Jane Wilson, client

Costs He charges straight RIBA fees.
**Travel He and interior designer Chester Jones have just been
asked to build a house in Greece. He has also worked in the
Far East.**
Size of job From £1 million.
Attitude Half-asleep genius.

'I don't have a style, I'm not a member of the taste
brigade,' says Eric Parry, who nonetheless produces
world-class modern architecture. He wouldn't thank me
for calling him a teddy bear but there is simply no other
way to describe this highly talented architect, who
does everything from lecturing at Cambridge, to judging
the RIBA awards, to designing public spaces, office
blocks, a couple of chateaux and the Mandarin Oriental
Hotel Spa. He has also designed Antony Gormley's
studio and the homes (and gallery) of Tim Taylor and
Sir Stuart Lipton. But he has never been asked to build
a country house, so a first may be welcome. Parry is
the reflective sort: he gives the impression of being
half asleep which really means he's thinking. 'What
fascinates me about houses is the vertical organization,'
he says. When he discusses home offices it's 'clutter
and clarity' that he mentions. He takes on only one
domestic project at a time ('they're consuming and
compelling'), which he enjoys at a professional distance.
'I don't want to be going to dinner parties with clients,
that's for sure.'
    Art is his passion, having worked as a night guard
at the Serpentine for four years ('I lived Henry Moore,'
he says). He has also been a member of the Architecture
Advisory Panel and the Visual Arts Advisory Panel.

What the clients say
'I was so happy with the house he built us that I asked him to
build me another one and then a gallery. Eric is very clever and
really relates to the client. He is also very economical in his
approach.' Tim Taylor, gallery owner
'Eric Parry has the twin skills of an academic's knowledge of
architecture and a searching vision of leading-edge design.
Eric's use of materials is skilful, and his feeling for exterior
and interior spaces and interesting materials makes him an
architect who will continue to the top of his profession.'
Sir Stuart Lipton, chairman, Stanhope plc

Richard Paxton Architects
15 St Georges Mews
London NW1 8XZ
T: 020 7586 6161
F: 020 7586 7171
mail@rparch.com
www.rparch.com

Powell Tuck Associates
6 Stamford Brook Road
London W6 0XH
T: 020 8749 7700
F: 020 8749 8737
mail@powelltuck.co.uk
www.powelltuck.co.uk

Costs Expensive, above RIBA scales.
Travel Caribbean, Antigua, anywhere.
Size of job Average budget £1 million, though would never say no to something really interesting.
Attitude Charming nutty professor.

Costs Charges percentage of costs.
Travel Has built a house in South Africa but never in the British countryside.
Size of job From £200K upwards.
Attitude Grown-up.

Though he has designed theatres and even buildings, Richard Paxton has a reputation for building houses (including his own) around indoor pools. These aren't normal pools: they often run through the centre of the house and use the most advanced technology available. Clients are as excited as he is about innovating and developing intelligent light and heating exchange systems, retractable roofs, suspended swimming pools and other ingenious things still to be invented. He comes over like a nutty professor but has clients who let him lead and wouldn't dream of using anyone else.

'We work with interesting people on interesting projects to expand our knowledge,' says Paxton, who takes on only jobs that appeal to him. One client trusted him enough to give him a brief and a budget then disappear for nine months.

Pioneering technologies are what makes Paxton tick. Walking through his own new build in Primrose Hill like a boy with a very exciting new toy, he demonstrates how this extraordinary development in a land-locked site will work around his family: soundproof doors that use fridge-sealing technology; the glass box swimming pool in his main living area beneath a fully retractable roof. Even the furniture and sinks do not escape a rethink. Clients get the same level of detail. 'We design everything, including taps,' he says. When I spoke to him he was planning an underwater office in Antigua.

What the clients say

'We're doing our third project together now. Richard is an inspirational architect, who really looks after his clients. He's very responsive. He's very good at responding to a brief. He takes in the whole concept.' Sir Peter Middleton, former chairman, Barclays Bank

'Richard is charismatic, original. He has lots of ideas. He is always trying to figure out ways to do things. If a wall doesn't quite fit, he will go and have it made by some new manufacturer.' Robert Taussig, client

Julian Powell Tuck is a name that comes up frequently at dinner parties. This may be because his practice in Chiswick has won more than its fair share of awards but mostly it's because Powell Tuck is rigorous and artistic in his approach to design – an unusual combination in an architectural practice. Powell Tuck is adamant that clients should do their research before coming to him (this includes checking references, which he is happy to supply). Up to 50 per cent of the work is residential: the rest is mostly offices (not just any office) such as the Bloomberg European headquarters.

Stylewise, this firm is haute modernism. Expect large expanses of glass and wood, dramatic lines designed entirely around a landscape and entirely tailor-made. 'We're very good at space,' says Powell Tuck 'but we won't destroy a house to do a conversion. So many London houses look like heaps as a result.' They (the ten-man practice with two long-standing directors) are known for their attention to detail, their creativity and their no-nonsense attitude. His own award-winning house in Chiswick is a good indication of what can be done artistically and on a budget.

What the clients say

'Julian is an outstanding and mature architect of international stature. I have worked with several architects in several countries, but none who can match the quality and depth of his work. His team reacts to the different demands of each individual client, site and environment, and has the confidence to create subtle, unique and individual solutions to each project, rather than imposing a preconceived design style. The result is beautiful and sublime architecture.' Mr Carey Taylor, client

'I have run an interior design business for many years. I can definitely say they compare with the best I have worked with. Not only fantastic design but excellent administration. Most architects cannot keep track of their own paperwork. I would DEFINITELY DEFINITELY use them again' Mrs Rosie Fox Andrews, interior designer

MRJ Rundell & Associates Ltd
Unit 2a
The Courtyard
44 Gloucester Avenue
London NW1 8JD
T: 020 7483 8360
office@rundellassociates.com
www.rundellassociates.com

Costs Anything is welcome. No minimum budget.
Travel He spends half of his time in St Petersburg (where he is designing an apartment). He was off to Morocco the day I met him.
Size of job He's presently doing a house for £100K. 'This is my hobby and I'm lucky that people ask me to do it,' he says.
Attitude I can see every point of view.

Mike Rundell could be smug. He does, after all, have clients such as Stella McCartney, Jay Jopling, Earl Spencer and Damien Hirst. He has designed both the White Cube Gallery and the original Pharmacy Restaurant. What's more he lives in the famous house with the blue door immortalized in *Notting Hill*. He knows everyone (Sam Taylor Wood, Richard Curtis) and hangs out with them, but in reality he's Mr England: attentive, polite, enthusiastic and, most of all, a gentleman. Clients adore him.

Rundell is a sculptor by training: he studied at Oxford University and Camberwell, where he met Hirst. He's not a qualified architect but has eight of them working in his practice. He designs everything (including cars). He's really an artist working in the home milieu. Rundell is not your average Mr Architect, so a certain amount of flexibility of mind is necessary. What he gives (just to judge from how helpful he was with us), he gives in spades.

What the clients say
'It was great to work with Mike because it was such a collaboration; he never tried to impose his own "style", but rather we developed ideas together… He refused to give up on any problem, large or small, and would happily turn up to meetings at any time of the day or night. But, most importantly, he gave me exactly what I wanted: exciting buildings that really work. No frills. Minimum fuss. A complete pleasure from start to finish.' Jay Jopling, White Cube Gallery
'Mike has really great ideas but is happy to change them if they just would not work for me. In the end everything is a collaboration – you just need to find a great collaborator who is a creative and positive influence, rather than a machine or a Prima donna… So for as far into the future as I dare to look, we are still working together, and as people of his calibre are hard to find, I would still expect to be beyond the grave.'
Damien Hirst, artist

Snell David Architects
12 Princeton Court
53–55 Felsham Road, Putney
London SW15 1AZ
T: 020 8780 5161
F: 020 8780 5171
sda@snell-david.co.uk
www.snell-david.co.uk

22 High Street
Little Abington
Cambridge
CB1 6BG
T/F: 01223 890659

Costs Are sticking by the old RIBA scale.
Travel Putney, Wimbledon and North London and then the home counties, Dorking, Basingstoke and East Anglia.
Size of job From £350 upwards
Attitude Theatrics are for other people.

Based both in Putney and Cambridge, James Snell (Cambridge) and Richard David (London) are one of the few architectural firms that seem content doing residential schemes. 'We enjoy people,' says Snell, 'we like to give clients what they want. We've had no nasty fall outs.' This is a practical, service-driven firm of only four years standing. 'We're still hungry,' says Snell. Not for long. An extension (in Snell's own house) in Little Abington was shortlisted in the AJ Small Projects Award. It has also been awarded runner-up in the RIBA East 'Spirit of Ingenuity' Award (there is one winner and one runner-up) and shortlisted for the Homebuilding and Renovation Award run by the *Daily Telegraph*. They have also had a project featured in Channel 4's *Room for Improvement*. Clients include Charles Dunstone (they're doing his moated manor house in Norfolk), Samantha Bond and Jocelyn Dimbleby.

What the clients say
'James is an easy architect to work with and great at designing strikingly modern (but very liveable) extensions, which are sympathetic to the history and style of a property and always respectful of the surrounding space.' client
'We had Snell David redesign our house. Throughout the project they were efficient, professional, supportive, fair and made things happen. We are especially appreciative that they made our project on time and on budget and generally made the process a lot easier than it could have been. We would strongly recommend them as a very high-quality architect practice.'
Ian and Sheena West, clients

Guy Stansfeld Architects
318 Kensal Road
London W10 5BZ
T: 020 8962 8666
F: 020 8962 8777
M: 07711 254 253
guy@stansfeld.com
www.3xarc.com

Costs 'Depends on the job,' he says.
Travel Has built houses in Wyoming, California and Ireland. Also a huge house in Buckinghamshire.
Size of job Will consider anything interesting but would rather avoid small extensions. Average budget: £500K–£1.5 million.
Attitude Never a problem.

No one has a bad word to say about soft-spoken 40-year-old architect Guy Stansfeld. This includes his former employer Piers Gough, who still works with him on a regular basis. Stansfeld's clients (David Macmillan and Bella Pollen, William Sieghart) have high expectations and he never seems to let them down. He builds house after house for friends and friends of friends. 'It's a self perpetuating circle,' he says, adding that he wouldn't mind some commercial work now and then. Stylewise, University College Dublin-educated Stansfeld is clearly a modernist, who loves to emphasize space and light, but he does his research the old-fashioned way. To get a detail right for the library in David Macmillan's house, for example, he spent hours in the Sir John Soane Museum. He shares his London practice with another firm called 23 Architecture, which means he has a pool of 19 architects to choose from should things get really busy. Stansfeld is interested in everything from furniture, which he designs, to the garden, which he does as a team with designer Helen Tindale. Colour is allowed: in fact, real life is welcome.

What the clients say
'Guy is a very nice, honourable architect, who will tell you when you're completely wrong. He has lots of wonderful ideas but respects the age of the house. He knows what normal family life is about. He always remembers that it's your place. He has a great team of equally nice people. He designs real houses not showplaces.' David Macmillan, publisher
'We gutted our house – it was a total inside rebuild. I chose Stansfeld because he was wide open to ideas. My first meeting with him was to talk about a fireplace design that everyone had told me wouldn't work. Guy not only liked the idea – he made it work – it looks great. Guy has no ego, and is incredibly CALM at all times. He translated our style and wish list, and we got the house we wanted.' Honor Riley, contributing editor

Seth Stein Architects
15 Grand Union Centre
West Row, Ladbroke Grove
London W10 5AS
T: 020 8968 8581
F: 020 8968 8591
admin@sethstein.com
www.sethstein.com

Costs Standard rate is 15 per cent of contract value.
Travel Not an issue. He commutes between Geneva, Cornwall, India, South Africa and Italy on a monthly basis. But has half a dozen projects going on in his neighbourhood (Notting Hill).
Size of job His criteria are: 'If the project is interesting and the client is nice, I will consider it.' Most projects are £5 million plus. Having said that, he will turn work away.
Attitude Always learning.

The slim, meticulous Stein, aged 44, is moving up the ladder fast. Clients include the designers Clements Ribeiro, Lucille Lewin, founder of Whistles, Peter Mandelson and Denise Kingsmill. Stein is a consummate modernist with a clear vision of what he wants. Much of his work is high-end residential but he's beginning to do art galleries, stores and new builds. He's presently building a house in Cornwall, and has already built a prefab house from scratch with a £100K budget on an island in Finland and another in the Turks & Caicos Islands. He also consults for MFI. 'An architect is someone who can manage expectations,' he says. 'He has to be able to be practical and follow a brief but he also has to help the client visualize.' He has to be firm, too: 'Many clients think they can make changes until the very end.' His company is still small – four associates – which means clients get his full attention. His greatest project to date is Kelso Place, his former house in Kensington, one of the first modernist houses built in London.

What the clients say
'Seth's great strength is in identifying that one transformational idea which, uniquely, can infuse a space with both excitement and integrity.' Louis Elson, client
'When I met Seth he was about to take off on a pilgrimage to Mexico City to see Barragan's work. This seemed a highly intimidating reference point for the stuffy Victorian townhouse we had just bought, yet somehow he managed to bring in light and colour to our home within the severe constraints imposed by English Heritage. He is very exacting and clear as to what works, yet listens to the practical needs imposed by two harried working parents with two young boys. We were able to leave it all in his hands and not worry, which I think says it all.' Mala Gaonkar, client

Stickland Coombe
258 Lavender Hill
London SW11 1LJ
T: 020 7924 1699
F: 020 7585 2201
M: 07939 155 928
mail@sticklandandcoombe.com
www.sticklandcoombe.com

Costs Middle to high end. Are used to generous budgets.
Travel Most of work is in London but have done jobs in
Scotland, Sussex and Wiltshire. Happy to work overseas and
have done work in Jamaica.
Size of job £100K–£1 million-plus.
Attitude This is fun.

Jonathan Stickland (front funny man) and Nick
Coombe (efficient, take-the-back-seat man) are an
unusual duo: both 46-year-olds (Jonathan studied at
AA but never finished and Nick at the Royal College
of Art) are modernists who set up shop in 1991,
specializing in making old (traditional) into new
(modern). They have a smorgasbord of clients: Lord
(Lucas) White on the one end, the artist Grayson Perry
on the other. They have respectable clients (Sir John
McTaggart) and edgy clients (Tim Attius). Their work
ranges from swanky refurbishments to conceptual
exhibitions for the Arts Council. They think micro (their
smallest project – a window – won them a RIBA award)
and macro (new builds for John Napier in Sussex).
They are very brief-driven, which makes their style
hard to pin down. 'I suppose our common theme is
that our designs are not always the most fashionable,'
says Coombe. 'We design for the client and for
longevity. Some of our clients have houses done 15
years ago and they still look current and are cherished.'
They rarely fall out with clients and have a great sense
of humour. The best compliment for any architect is if
he is asked to come back and design another house
(which is what they're doing at the moment for
Normandie Keith and Lucas White). They recently
secured two more major awards (RIBA and FX).

What the clients say

'Absolutely wonderful. Every time we have done anything we
have used him. Jonathan has a great eye for design. Does
wonderful kitchens and bathrooms. He's very easygoing and
laid-back. Doesn't mind if things are changed. I love him. He's
part of the family now!' Caroline McTaggart, client
'We're hugely fond of Jonathan. He is an extraordinarily
intelligent and gifted man. Complete and utter joy to have around.'
John Napier, theatre designer

Studio Kap
Central Chambers
Suite 308, 109 Hope Street
Glasgow G2 6LL
T: 0141 564 1247 / 0141 548 3004
F: 0141 564 1248
mail@studiokap.com
www.studiokap.com

Costs They refer to the RIBA scale. Depends on the project and
client. Usually work out a cost per square metre.
Travel Done projects in Orkney as well as Germany.
Size of job Take on a lot of domestic projects, large or small, but
try to avoid jobs smaller than £100K.

'You're buying a pig in the poke when you hire an
architect,' says Rod Kemsley of Studio Kap, a young
up-and-coming practice in Glasgow. Both partners
Kemsley and Chris Platt, who is also Director of the
BSc (Hons) course in Architecture at Strathclyde
University, worked in Berlin for years before hooking
up. They do mostly residential work (this includes
warehouses) but says Kemsley: 'We don't have a
prescribed solution but work in a contemporary idiom.
Every project brings a different set of challenges.'
They've already won several awards and regularly
appear in the architectural journals. Clients are varied
(no celebs), though one of their biggest jobs for the
American pioneer of eye surgery came through RIAS,
the Scottish RIBA. Their emphasis is on quality. 'We're
young enough to really care but too young to turn
work away,' says Kemsley.

What the clients say

'Our expectations were high. We wanted a design that delivered
functional and modern living space and a hugely child-friendly
environment at the same time. Studio Kap delivered both and we
are thrilled with the end result.'
Andrew and Jo Waddell, Waddell House
'Chris added a large extension onto our house using maple,
beech and Canadian cedar. It's very modern and contemporary
featuring the maximum amount of light. The project was
technically quite complex due to the slanted site but he had
a very good team working for him and there was a minimum
of disruption to us. He is an up-and-coming star on the scene
with high standards; he won't take second best. He was
highly attentive to our needs and I have no hesitation in highly
recommending him.'
Lesley and Alan MacFarlane, Macfarlane House

45

T–U

Templeton Associates
5 Archery Close
London W2 2BE
T/F: 020 7224 5766
s.templeton@btinternet.com

Theis and Khan Architects
22A Bateman's Row
London EC2A 3HH
T: 020 7729 9329
F: 020 7729 9341
mail@theisandkhan.com
www.theisandkhan.com

Costs Fee scale of RIBA; small jobs charged at 14 per cent, bigger jobs at 9 per cent.
Travel Spends a lot of time commuting back and forth to Ireland.
Size of job 'I'm easily tempted,' he says. From £150K upwards. He's too young to turn work away.
Attitude Sensitive rock star.

Costs Average budget is £500K Normally charge between 10 and 15 per cent.
Travel Have done a hotel in Spain and a house in San Diego.
Size of job No minimum budget. 'It's got to be interesting,' says Theis. 'There has to be a spark between us and the clients.'
Attitude Cool cats.

Simon (40) is more rock than rigid. This is glam architecture if ever there were such a thing. With his charming Irish accent, long hair and Vivienne Westwood suits, he looks as if he should be up on stage. He's just as glamorous, if not more glamorous, than the clients he works for, who include Harry Enfield and Jim Kerr of Simple Minds. He is creative enough to see three solutions to every problem: this comes from rigorous training – eight years' worth, in fact – under the master, Nicholas Grimshaw. Past projects include the Hotel Tipperary in Cashel and Carrigacunna Castle, Killavullen in County Cork.

Simon is not your average modernist architect. He won't suggest the usual diet of glass, stone and wood: it's more likely to be resin or copper or something you didn't know existed. His happiest clients (professionals in music, law, medicine, members of the Irish upper class, rock stars) are those who let him get on with his work. But he really cares, enough, for example, to come over and personally clean up a dirty gully (to avoid any possibility of flooding). He is charming, creative and easy but he won't be pushed around. This has led to a few falling-outs. His creative mind works at three times human speed.

Martin Amis and Isabel Fonseca were Patrick Theis (42) and Soraya Khan's (44) first clients. I must have been their second (though not intentionally. The architect we originally hired subcontracted the job to them). This was nine years ago. Since then, they have grown up and now have pretty serious clients (bankers, heads of law firms and advertising gurus).

Established in 1995, Theis and Khan have a distinctly modern take on architecture (glass, wood, straight lines, though they like colour), but with four children of their own, they understand how real people live. They come up with original touches that aren't in the usual modernist mould.

Their own house has been selected for a Channel 4 makeover series, along with one of their wealthiest private clients. They are intelligent, gentle, softly spoken, not prone to temper tantrums. When one job went wrong, they made an effort to patch things up (this is very unusual). They're still young enough to want to make a good impression.

What the clients say
'Simon is just faultless. It really was the most delightful experience and we are friends now. The work he did was superb, and it was a pleasure discussing the project with him.' Dr Susan Tanner, client
'Not only is Simon an architect who has interesting contemporary ideas to bring to classical London buildings, but he is also a man of great compassion and integrity.' Gerald Parkes, developer

What the clients say
'They were incredibly committed and weren't prepared to accept just OK. They went on to find the best solution. Great eye, inspired and open-minded.' Mrs AC, client
'Intelligent, sensitive, hard-working, creative. The major work they did in our house a few years ago gives us pleasure every day, and we are delighted to have these architects back to carry out a further phase of improvements.' Kate Bucknell, novelist

Urban Salon Ltd
Unit D
Flat Iron Yard
Ayres Street
London SE1 1ES
T: 020 7357 8800 F: 020 7407 2800
mail@urbansalonarchitects.com
www.urbansalonarchitects.com

Costs Too young to be expensive.
Travel Anywhere.
Size of job From £150K upwards.
Attitude Rocker meets maths professor.

Urban Salon is going places fast. The innovative, multi-disciplinary young firm was hired by Marks & Spencer to come up with the concept for their new stores. Urban Salon were the only design group to survive the regime change and are now in the process of building seven stores.

Enthusiastic future/eco-thinking Alex Mowat (34), director of architecture, and Diana Cochrane (35), director of interior design, set up in 1997. They built Orange's House of the Future (a laboratory to see how we will live, which was tested out by members of the public). They also do product design, collaborating with some of the most cutting-edge companies around. They also teach at the Royal College of Art. Their approach is – in their own words – 'one of logical optimism: bringing a logical approach to problem solving and an optimism to what is possible for the future.' This ten-man firm likes technological challenges. Aside from Orange's wire-free domestic technology (in the House of the Future), they have built 450 cottages on the edge of Exmoor, incorporating passive and active technologies. They can handle a boardroom or a bored housewife. One of their briefs was to 'build a house that is a Landrover, not a Mercedes'.

What the clients say
'Alex is an excellent, passionate and committed architect. When we first met about our home he came in and we went through a lot of architectural books determining what we liked. It was an excellent way for both sides to begin to understand what the project entailed. He was open to hear our vision and what we loved. Very nice guy who works hard.' Matthew Gwyther, editor *Management Today*, and Victoria Whitbread, designer
'They took a derelict space and made it into something really beautiful. The attention to details was amazing. They took a whole Saturday just to discuss colours. I love to cook – somehow they turned a tiny kitchen into something that appears huge. They underlit the bathroom. They think of absolutely everything.' Rosa Baden-Powell, barrister

Ushida Findlay
1CH
Arup
13 Fitzroy Street
London W1T 4BQ
T: 020 7755 2917
M: 07879 423 609

Costs Charges RIBA rates.
Travel Anywhere.
Size of job She needs a budget of at least £250K to realize her vision. But will work on something small if it's interesting enough.
Attitude I follow my own path.

Disclaimer: At the time of going to press, Kathryn Findlay was made bankrupt after a dishonourable – I should say corrupt – client failed to pay her firm's fees. As this was her principal source of income, she had to close her office and start again.

Business skills are one thing; talent, another; character is a third. The first is something you can buy in, the rest you're born with. Findlay's up there with the greats, but the soft-spoken Scot is no Rottweiler. 'Kathryn Findlay has the extraordinary ability of great architects for design that is both rigorous and free' says Jil Ritblat, a long-time admirer. 'She has a rare sensibility that combines the natural and historical with the new and radical. She is determined and capable and will be back!'

Findlay's had a couple of sheikhs as clients, and has exhibited at the British Pavilion at the Venice Biennale. She spent years in Japan where she ran a practice (Ushida Findlay) with her former husband, and has a particularly organic style. The often humorous buildings not only look like nature but also often have bits of nature hanging off. Perhaps the most publicized of her projects was the award-winning Grafton New Hall, a house in the shape of a starfish, which never got built.

Her work was spotted by a leading British developer who commissioned a house in southern England. The thatched roof, glass-encased pool won a RIBA award and made the cover of the RIBA magazine.

What the clients say
'Unlike most architects, Kathryn is not a control maniac. She is warm, giving and such a visionary. She made a beautiful, elegant, witty and friendly building for us at Perch Hill. It's very cool, done with efficiency. We love it.' Adam Nicolson, writer
'We worked together on a project called Homes for the Future in Glasgow (a project about urban rejuvenation). She's very exciting to work with and very excited by the work.' Andrew Burrell, The Burrell Company

Watson, Bertram & Fell
5 Gay Street
Bath BA1 2PH
T: 01225 337 273
F: 01225 448 537
mark@wbf-bath.co.uk
www.wbf-bath.co.uk

Costs Charge £100 per hour and/or RIBA rates.
Travel Surrounding area, home counties, Yorkshire, Devon.
Not too much abroad.
Size of job 'I'm not worried: We'll take on something from
£20,000 to a million.' Back extensions welcome. They have
also built many timber-framed houses.
Attitude Charming. Charming. Charming.

You know someone's a charmer when you start
convincing yourself that you need him even though
1) you don't own property in Bath and 2) have always
sworn allegiance to the bible of modernism.
　　Mark Watson and I chatted endlessly and when
I asked (discreetly) who the clients are, out came: the
Prince of Wales, Princess Anne, Captain Mark Phillips
and James Dyson. 'Oh,' he said. 'and we built Cliveden
Hotel.' Don't despair – most of WB&F's clients are people
who just want a nice house, preferably a nice traditional
house, as well as an architect who will ease the pain of
doing it up. The firm was recommended by the designer
Emma Sims-Hilditch, who used Mark Watson for her
own house (with a normal mortal's budget to boot).
James Dyson worked closely with partner Peter Fell.
　　Mark Watson, 55, spends 80 per cent of his energy
on residential projects. He would put himself in the 'arts
and crafts' mould ('That's where my heart is,' he says),
but this doesn't mean he can't do other things. Most of
his work is around the Bath area – all of it comes via
word of mouth. He draws the old-fashioned way: 'with
a pencil. I guess I'm a bit of a Luddite,' he says. The
practice employs three architects, four associates and
three surveyors. Watson's idea of a falling out is
disagreeing over where a window should go. Amusing.
He enjoys his work and his clients. And vice versa.

What the clients say
'Peter has a good understanding about when to restore and
when to build anew. His architectural knowledge and his
patience with English Heritage and the Listed Buildings Officers
allows him to be able to do the best for buildings and clients!'
James Dyson, inventor
'Mark's doing cottages one day, palaces the next. He's the best
you can get.' Emma Sims-Hilditch, interior designer

Wells Mackereth Architects
Unit 14 Archer Street Studios
10–11 Archer Street
London W1D 7AZ
T: 020 7287 5504
F: 020 7287 5506
hq@wellsmackereth.com
www.wellsmackereth.com

Costs Charge RIBA rates.
Travel Have worked all over the country – Bristol Wales,
Scotland – and are currently working in Cardiff and New York
(where they are working on Bumble & Bumble's product
headquarters including the café/gallery).
Size of job Won't consider a job worth less than £150K.
Attitude Cool

James Wells and Sally Mackereth are rock and roll
architects. They use materials that their contemporaries
would never consider, such as leather, felt, pony hide,
shagreen, even snakeskin. This ability to add glamour
to all the glass and stainless steel that most of their
contemporaries favour has made them stand apart.
They have many A-list clients, such as Michael Grade
to Miranda Richardson and Formula One driver Jody
Schechter. Thirty to forty per cent of their work is
domestic but, says James, 'we're selective'. They're
more design orientated than most: 'We've done glass
engravings even,' says James, who, unlike most of
his contemporaries at the Bartlett and the AA (Sally's
school), has even indulged in paint finishes. Wells
Mackereth have done the Pringle Shop in London,
This Works boutique for Cathy Phillips, as well as East
at West Street and Smiths of Smithfield. Both are
married to PRs (Sally is married to Julian Vogel of
Modus PR, a top fashion outfit, so they run with the
cool crowd). This is a fashionable cutting-edge firm,
so not for beginners.

What the clients say
'We felt lucky to have Wells Mackereth. They were never
patronizing and spent many hours going through tiny details
such as where the foldable T-shirts should go. We have an
amazing cantilevered glass room at the back of the house,
which they suggested.' Francesca Grade, client
'It was a great working relationship. They didn't force their
ideas at us, as some architects do. James and Sally were very
involved at the design stage, though a senior architect ran the
day-to-day site. We are very pleased with the results.'
Lucy Hoosenally, client

Yeates Design and Architecture
74 Clerkenwell Road
London EC1M 5NL
T: 020 7251 6667
F: 020 7251 6668
enquiries@yeatesdesign.co.uk
www.yeatesdesign.co.uk

Peter Yiangou Associates LLP
Whittington
Cheltenham
Gloucestershire GL54 4EX
T: 01242 821 031
F: 01242 820 193
admin@yiangou.com
www.yiangou.com

Costs Good value. Charges 15 per cent but never gets it. 'I feel guilty when the money grows; mostly I end up getting 10–12 per cent of the contract costs.'

Travel Gladly. Has done Sussex but says he hates North London, though: 'I'm a Tunbridge Wells boy.'

Size of job Will take things on from £75K upwards, such as back extensions, etc. Not used to getting billionaires.

Attitude Marital counselling comes for free.

Talk about word of mouth: the very jolly Nick Yeates's name is passed around from friend to friend (someone mentions him on the school run to a friend, who drops his name in conversation at a weekend house party and so on). The Sheffield-trained architect, who set up shop 12 years ago, often sits up until one in the morning working through designs with clients. 'I like how clients think and how they come to the conclusions they do,' says the sparky son of an architect, who was the son of a builder, who was the son of a builder. This is non-scary classic modernism that normal folks like. Having said that, Yeates was asked to design a 'White Box' in Farnham for a client who grew up in a Frank Lloyd Wright House. He has raised two boys of his own and therefore understands normal life. Oh, and he wears leathers because he rides a motorcycle.

He says things like: 'I hate working on houses that are not Victorian,' which explains why he is so popular among the traditional English set who want contemporary – but 'cosy'. He also does development on the side. He employs six people but is 'Mr Boss'.

What the clients say

'Working with Nick was a good experience. He listens to what you want, as opposed to thrusting his ideas down your throat, and will always look at cheaper options. The job he did for me was relatively small (bedroom and bathroom) but the whole house job he did for a friend was superb. All in all, a nice man with young kids. Sensible.' Kim Hurd, client

'Jeremy did a fantastic job for me. It was a Georgian rectory and he managed to get planning permission, which wasn't easy. He has great vision in terms of space. The project was better than expected.' Jeremy Aitchison, developer

Costs Average budget is £50K–£5 million. Will customize fees (hourly, percentage) for clients.

Travel Based in the South Midlands – projects to date have been up to about a 100 mile radius of Cheltenham.

Size of job Projects between £50K–£10m.

Attitude Thinking big.

Peter Yiangou is an 'it' architect. The Gloucestershire-based architect gets the really big jobs with big budgets and ambitious hopes (he was recommended to us by Property Vision). Of Cypriot extraction, he was educated in South Africa and at the AA before starting his practice in 1981.

Yiangou does mostly private residential work: swanky new builds and refurbishments, which veer toward the opulent and classical. Clients are bankers, businessmen (Peter Mullen of Thomas Pink Shirts), landed gentry, new money. He's got six CEOs and three celebrities on his books at the moment. This is mon-eyed world, and he fits neatly into it. But he also does commercial work: hotels, museums, etc., all in the Cirencester, Oxford area. Clients like him because he's gentle and takes a brief.

This is a fair-sized practice with 13 people and four architects.

What the clients say

'We worked closely with Neil Quinn in the practice. There were quite a few hiccups (not of their doing) and they dealt with them efficiently and immediately. Neil is very tenacious. Notes would come in within minutes of conducting a meeting.'
Peter Mullen, founder, Thomas Pink

Collett-Zarzycki Architects and Designers
Fernhead Studios
2b Fernhead Road
London W9 3ET
T: 020 8969 6967
F: 020 8960 6480
mail@czltd.co.uk
www.collett-zarzycki.com

Costs Top end. They take a percentage of the project and also charge an hourly fee, which varies depending on whether they are being asked to fly off for a day to France to see a client's new house or draw an elevation of a television cabinet.
Travel All over the world.
Size of job No minimum budget, but think of them as Balenciaga as opposed to Gap.
Attitude: Talk about Breakthrough Service.

This three-man practice (with 25 employees), run by Anthony Collett, Andrzej Zarzycki and Tim Flynn, does both architecture and design. Two out of three directors were born in Africa, which makes their style – neo-classical/modern, with the odd animal skin thrown in – a welcome relief. The level of detail is astonishing: clients get budget breakdowns and progress reports that would make any accountant weep. Those who come here – Hugh Grant, for example – want Cipriani Hotel-style service. 'We give our clients everything,' says South African-born Anthony Collett 'and our mobiles.' Collett – who trained in fine arts at the Royal College of Art – draws everything (in water colour). 'Some people talk, I draw,' he says. Most of their work comes via word of mouth, though they have also designed commercial projects, including the Spa at the new Grove Hotel (for which they received no credit). Their style is faintly American (tongue and groove detailing) with clean lines, wood panelling and simple textures (having said that, they can be very jazzy as well). Everything is made to order, which is why no two projects look the same.

What the clients say
'I worked mainly with Tony. I was most struck by his creativity and sensitivity. He quickly understood the kind of energy we wanted to create in our home and the way in which we live our lives. He has an amazing eye and a great sense of style and occasion. He places high emphasis on quality craftsmanship, but also recognizes that he is running a client-driven business and can be pragmatic when necessary.' Nina Kheraj, client
'We go back a long way. They designed my house in London and we are now doing up a flat in St Moritz. Tony Collett is highly professional. The builders said he was the best they had ever come across both in manner and in the drawings he produced. He's not a prima donna. Chantal Hanover, client

CAROLINE PATERSON INTER
EMMA SIMS-HILDITCH CHAF
FELICITY THORPE INTERIOR
NICHOLAS ALVIS VEGA JOA
JONATHAN TUCKEY FRANC
CATHERINE PAWSON AND J
GARUDA DESIGN LIMITED C
ANTA SCOTLAND ANN BOY
PAUL FIDGEN PARK GROVE
DRUMKILBO DESIGNS SCOT
BELLHOUSE & COMPANY W
PRECIOUS MCBANE ART AN
FRANCESCA MILLS NICHOL

RS CHARLES RUTHERFOORD
TTE CROSLAND INTERIORS
LUCY MANNERS INTERIORS
NA PLANT MARK GILLETTE
CA **DESIGNERS** INTERIORS
IETTE BYRNE SUSIE BEART
OLINE SANDON INTERIORS
DESIGN CARDEN CUNIETTI
ESIGN TODHUNTER EARLE
MADDUX ILSE CRAWFORD
DO WORKS TARGET LIVING
DESIGN PARTNERSHIP JKP
ALVIS VEGA PAUL FIDGEN

DESIGNERS

What is an interior designer? Good question. For the most part, a designer is someone who worries about what happens on the 'inside' of the house. This can mean anything from choosing fabrics for curtains to managing 70 Estonian builders in Bermuda.

Most architects, if they had their way, would fill your house with Donald Judd-style furniture and paint the walls brilliant white. Designers, on the other hand, care about whether the 1940s wooden coffee table next to the Christian Liaigre sofa is the right height for the lamp they commissioned in Venice. But here's the confusing bit. There are 'interior architects', 'interior designers' and just plain 'designers'. The former tend to have more schooling (most top American interior designers are qualified architects, for example; this is not the case here). The closest thing to a regulatory body in Britain is the BIDA, short for the British Interior Design Association. If a designer has those four letters after his name, it means that he or she has some sort of design diploma (at least one year's worth), plus one to four years of experience (associates have less, full members more), though even BIDA admits that experience matters more than anything.

Warning: some designers slap on mark-ups like there's no tomorrow. Some (big firms) put an 80 per cent mark-up on fabrics alone (plus 20–50 per cent for upholsterers, builder's tender, furniture purchased on your behalf). If they introduce you to a fly, you will be charged.

This is what matters

Does she/he have ideas? Is he/she on your wavelength? Do you like him/her? Does he/she listen? Are you speaking the same language when it comes to budgets/time/style? What's his/her house like? Is he/she fun to be with? These are the people you will spend the most time with, so you'd better like them.

How to find a designer

There are two ways. Number one is to go to a well-established interior design firm, such as Fox Linton Associates, Nina Campbell, Joanna Wood, Veere Greeney, Chester Jones, David Collins, Reed Creative, Alidad, Kelly Hoppen, Colefax and Fowler and so on, and buy their 'look'. The majority provide an excellent service for the most part, though they are not in the book because no one needs any help finding them. Having said that, Robert Kime and David Mlinaric were recommended so many times that we made an exception. Watch out, though: large practices (with large overheads) tend to be expensive (we found they were also quite secretive about how they charge – rumour has it they charge according to your postal address) and snobby. Many of the so-called 'style gurus' will turn you down unless you're 1) rich, 2) famous or 3) about to be one or the other. Some designers would hardly speak to us until we dropped a few famous names ourselves.

Skip the humiliation and ask around (as we did). A good interior designer should:

1. Be grateful that you called. She/he should work around you, not the other way around.

2. Follow your brief, unless you don't have one.

3. Be enthusiastic and show you things that you didn't know existed but not scare you away.

4. Be organized and professional (and/or have a good assistant). Humility is a bonus.

5. Be price-conscious. It's easy to choose the most expensive fabric under the sun.

6. Have a wealth of great sources that you don't already know about.

7. Be original. You don't want the same house as your best friend, do you?

You should not have to chase a designer. He or she is paid to be organized and on top of suppliers. Some designers virtually carry you into the bedroom, having chosen the thread count of your Egyptian cotton White Company sheets. Others act like bankers, producing fabric swatches instead of spreadsheets. Some are used to dealing with squillionaires, others are young and hungry. They can be hip or traditional or both. Look at their portfolios and websites by all means, though it's gut instinct that counts. Chemistry is everything.

What to expect

If you want mood boards, elevations, scale drawings, miniature models, say so. If you want CAD (computer-assisted design) drawings, make sure they have the training and resources (they often bill for this). You are the boss. They can take you shopping or shop for you (they will bill for this, too). Think of them as chefs giving you menus to sample.

Dos and Don'ts

· Don't hand them 300 magazines with post-it notes. They hate that.

· Do look at the size of the practice. Do you want the designer or his assistant?

· Do take their advice.

· Don't assume that you can undercut them by doing the legwork yourself.

· Do be decisive. Changing your mind costs money.

· Don't assume this is an easy job. It's not. It's fiddly, stressful and frustrating. You are paying them to relieve you of the burden of having to ship materials to the upholsterer and find the perfect shade of mauve. What's your time – and sanity – worth?

· Do make sure they are qualified to do the job. An interior designer is not an architect, no matter how fancy his or her title. Many designers (such as Ann Boyd) employ architects in-house.

· Don't think that just because a designer has celebrity clients that he or she is too grand for you. Most would love normal clients who know how to say please and thank you.

Money

Don't be English: ask how much everything costs before agreeing. One designer charged her client for 'thinking' about the job over the weekend. Some charge for postage stamps. We have ranked them reasonable, middle, high end or a mixture of both, to give you an idea.

This profession is still in the Middle Ages. Some designers charge by the hour (from £45 upwards). Some take a cut on the difference between trade and retail prices. Some take a percentage of the whole thing. Make sure you know exactly what will cost what (one metre of fabric sounds reasonable but 100 metres of anything will make you faint). Remember VAT. Ask whether they carry indemnity insurance, though this is not critical (unless it is a commercial project).

Finally…

There is a great deal of co-dependency in this business. Designers know whether you have a drink problem, are being unfaithful or have bad breath. Discretion, psychological skills, patience, not to mention taste, are absolutely essential. Never be afraid to say: 'I don't like it.' Remember: they work for you.

CAROLINE PATERSON

Caroline Paterson Interiors
9 Milner Street
London SW3 2QB
T: 020 7584 6890
F: 020 7584 5830
M: 07768 534601
cpinteriors@btopenworld.com

Costs Reasonable. Very transparent; thinks trust is important in this area. Charges £75 an hour and produces extensive timesheets. For fabrics she charges a 25 per cent mark-up on trade prices.
Travel Has worked from Bermuda to the small Scottish island of Islay.
Size of job Would consider one room as it has always led to more in the past.
Attitude This is fun.

We chose Caroline as our pin-up because she has everything: talent, energy, tact, efficiency and a great eye. She is transparent about costs and puts her clients (one of whom was very ill throughout the project) first.

Caroline Paterson has an enthusiasm for her *métier* that draws everyone in, including clients. She has a big personality ('She's very funny,' says a client, 'you quickly become friends') and a passion for art. After studying history of art in Florence, she joined Christie's furniture department, where she spent seven years 'cataloguing in a Dickensian warehouse'. She exhausted her travel bug, returned to London and went to work for Chester Jones at Colefax and Fowler, whom she credits for teaching her everything she knows. Her clients are families with houses in London and the country who need some creative and practical guidance. The fact that Paterson has three children, and understands the needs of a modern family, makes her particularly attractive. Her style is eclectic: she likes to mix art with quirky objects. But she believes you have to get the bones right before starting to add colour and interest. She works with an interior architect and has two assistants.

What the clients say
'Caroline is absolutely wonderful. I have been thrilled with everything she has done for me. I originally had her do my country house and now she is doing a huge project for me in London, which involves knocking together three penthouses to make one home, and I trust her completely. Caroline is quite unique in style and has an amazing eye for colour. She was happy to have input from me, and the result is a beautiful family home that doesn't look overdesigned.'
Alice Coptcoat, client

'Caroline completed two houses for me, one in London and one in the country. She's enormously energetic and has an adventurous eye. She created two completely different looks for both houses. Her schemes are fresh and contemporary.'
Alexandra Ferrari, client

The perfect client according to Caroline Paterson

A good client:
- Pushes the boundaries, trusts you and respects the fact that this is a job.
- Explores new avenues.
- Is open-minded to unexpected solutions to design and space planning.
- Pays invoices on time and doesn't constantly lose them.
- Does not have preconceived ideas.
- Shows appreciation for your effort and says thank you.
- Understands that there are lead times and that real decorating is not *Changing Rooms*.

A bad client:
- Calls you ten times a day and leaves endless texts over the weekend.
- Shows your scheme to 50 of her closest friends and then comes back riddled with doubt and indecision.
- Marches you into her best friend's house and says: 'This is exactly what I want.'
- Introduces you to her architect and says: 'You'll get on fine.' You know he wants to do the whole thing himself and wishes you a million miles away from site.
- Uses their 'pet' architect from another country outside the EU to specify all electrical and sanitaryware, when they do not understand what the latest EC regulations have done to us!
- Asks you to decorate their house off-plan in some far-flung country without flying you out there, and then promptly gets divorced.
- Gives you a brief, which you then execute, only to arrive at the meeting to be presented with what they have put together.
- Goes behind your back and contacts one of your suppliers direct.
- Allows the children to be 'designers'.

A – B

Anta Scotland
Fearn, Tain
Ross-shire
Scotland IV20 1XW
T: 01862 832477
F: 01862 832616
sales@anta.co.uk
www.anta.co.uk

Costs Expensive. Very precise about prices.
Travel Mostly Scotland, but are currently renovating
a dilapidated castle in Italy. Globally for the right job.
Size of job From a room to a housing development.
Attitude Highland hospitality.

Annie Stewart (of Anta), whose clients include the late
Queen Mother, is the best-known designer in Scotland.
She and her architect husband Lachlan Stewart are trying to promote old-fashioned skills, and much of their
work revolves around their Highland weaving mill,
where they produce the highest quality woollen carpets and classic weaves, including tartans, herring-
bones and tweeds. They give it a modern twist, but it
definitely says SCOTTISH. Some of the merchandise
(tartan printed coffee mugs, tartan printed bags, tartan
printed carpets – you get the picture), which they sell
in their three shops and website, is kitsch but clients
swear by their taste. One client calls Anta the 'Robert
Kime' of Scotland.

Annie describes her company's philosophy as
'low key, minimal, functional and robust'. Most of what
they do is on a grand scale: they restored Castle Mey
for the late Queen Mother and are presently working
on a 90-flat development in Fort Augustus.

What the clients say
'Annie and Lachlan Stewart are at the forefront of the Scottish
craft revival movement. They have an enthusiasm and a passion
for what they're doing that is contagious. It's stimulating to work
with champions.' Philip Hooper, interior designer
'They were not clear on how the carpet should be laid but the
end result was smart and contemporary.'
Helen Fraser

Antiques & Interiors Limited
Lazonby Manor
Lazonby
Penrith
Cumbria CA10 1BA
T: 01768 898 073 F: 01768 898 072
serena@serenawe.co.uk

Costs High end. Charges £120 an hour, but has no minimum value
for a job. Works on a percentage basis for larger projects.
Travel Moves around all the time. Has worked in Yorkshire,
France, Canada, Ireland, etc.
Size of job Used to substantial projects.
Attitude Mucks in.

You don't come to Serena Williams-Ellis for off-the-
peg design. She may wear red All Star tennis shoes
and act like a bubbly art student but she can do luxury
like few others.

Hers is an almost entirely bespoke service (she
even has the sofas made). It's all-encompassing: from
drawings to tendering to building works to follow-up.
Once the house is finished, she's still there, fixing the
broken tiles, restoring an old carpet, sourcing a new
coffee table. She started at Christie's and then moved
on to become an antiques dealer specializing in English
and Continental 18th-century furniture. Much of her work
was with decorators in New York. Her British charm
and enthusiasm made an impression: one client asked
her to do up their house and, the next thing you know,
she parachuted into the billionaire league, servicing
people with yachts, private planes and country houses
that make Blenheim look like a shack.

Her style is: 'Whatever the client wants. I can do
country or I can do pared down.' She is perhaps the
most naturally charming designer you will ever meet.
She's also completely hands-on: 'Clients come for me
and not an assistant,' (of whom she has three) she says.
She works from her home in Cumbria, which she shares
with her husband, the sculptor David Williams-Ellis, but
spends a great deal of time in cars, trains and planes.

What the clients say
'Serena worked closely with us for two years. Her principal
contribution was all the antique furniture. She is incredibly
efficient, all the i's are dotted and the t's crossed. Fantastically
capable, easy and fun to work with, has great taste and
a reasonable commission.' client

Susie Beart
63 Albert Bridge Road
London SW11 4QA
T: 020 7223 3676
F: 020 7223 3531
susiebeart@sbid.fsnet.co.uk

Bellhouse & Company
33 Kensington Park Road
London W11 2EU
T: 020 7221 0187
F: 020 7792 0467
bimbi@bellhouseco.fsnet.co.uk

Costs: Reasonable. £75 an hour for building design and project managment. There is no mark-up on other contractors, so the price is completely transparent. For fabrics and furnishings, etc., the cost is estimated on retail prices, which are a mark-up on the trade prices. She works with an architect on larger projects.
Travel Has young children, therefore won't go too far afield, but is happy to do most of Europe.
Size of job Would consider one room but it would have to be financially viable – mostly does whole houses.
Attitude Does it before you ask.

Glamorous down to her kitten heels, Susie Beart is unlikely to be seen in a hardhat and caterpillar boots, but this is where she excels. She estimates that she spends at least 90 per cent of her time on building sites: it's only the last six weeks of a project that she gets to have fun sourcing fabrics.

Beart is a real person's designer: though she spent many years working for Joanna Wood (and still freelances for her), whose clients are so wealthy that they need houses just for their shoe collection, Beart is down to earth. She will incorporate granny's furniture into a contemporary scheme and deal with the dog, children and a mother-in-law with opinions of her own.

Her style is elegant contemporary but she can do English chintz, minimal and 'East meets West'. She doesn't impose her taste but will manoeuvre you away from yours (if it's bad). The developer of the show flat she is currently working on interviewed both Kelly Hoppen and Jane Churchill but rejected the former for being too minimal and the latter for being too traditional, so Susie falls neatly into the middle.

What the clients say
'I simply can't speak more highly of Susie. She took on the complete refurbishment of our Georgian house in Ireland; it was an enormous project and she didn't let us down once. Her professionalism was second to none, and the house looks exquisite. Susie takes pride and care in perfecting even the smallest details.' Clare Reid Scott, client
'We have worked with Susie for over ten years. She is excellent at liaising with the clients. She always has a good sense of a client's requirements.' David Lloyd Davies, architect

Costs Reasonable. There is no design fee, though it makes no sense to come here unless you intend to use the services and fabrics.
Travel Around the corner or around the globe.
Size of job A pair of curtains to a complete manor refurbishment.
Attitude Headmistress

Bellhouse & Company is a Notting Hill institution. Ladies from Kensington spend hours sampling the fabrics and swatches and discussing the finer points of their domestic refurbishments. The company, started in 1979 by the formidable Bimbi, has grown to incorporate every aspect of the home. Bellhouse can supply you with anything from a few metres of fabric to the total refurbishment of a large country house or hotel. In fact, Bimbi's latest projects include a chalet in Gstaad, a plantation house in Georgia and the new Ballantyne Cashmere flagship store on Westbourne Grove. Everything is executed by her team of craftsmen, which includes upholsterers, curtain-makers, specialist painters and gilders. Bimbi offers something between trade and retail on fabrics, which makes the truly English feel comfortable. She will advise on design, but really this is for people who want to do it themselves.

What the clients say
'We know she has amazing suppliers. If she says the blind will come in two weeks, it does. Bimbi gets things done.'
The Kirwan-Taylor family (father, mother, son and sister-in-law) have been clients of Bimbi's for two generations
'I am a big fan of Bimbi's. We have used her services for a long time. She's terrific, has a good network of people who provide services, and they have been with her for a long time.'
Mrs Van Niekerk, client

Ann Boyd Design
Studio 8
Fairbank Studios
Lots Road
London SW10 0NS
T: 020 7351 4098
F: 020 7351 4090
ann@annboyd-design.co.uk

Costs Upper end of the spectrum.
Travel All over the world. Has recently worked in Moscow.
Size of job Whole flats or houses.
Attitude Perfectionist.

Ann Boyd has the eye of a stylist. She studied fashion design at Central St Martins, then went on to work as an assistant to Hardy Amies. She moved into fashion journalism before being head-hunted by Ralph Lauren as his creative director. Everything she does is just so: three vases lined up together, two perfectly matching lamps on equally matching tables. It's still life as seen through the eyes of the camera. The new school of asymmetrical chic this is not. Boyd runs a proper design office with five employees, and tends to manage the whole show in a highly professional manner.

In 1994, Boyd's flat caught fire and she was forced to move out and redecorate. It gave her the opportunity to demonstrate her abilities and effectively start a new career.

'It prompted me to explore my taste, which my friends started responding to,' she says. British *Vogue* photographed the apartment and it went from there. Stephen Marks of French Connection was amongst her first clients, then came Nicole Fahri and Alan Cleaver of Byblos. Recent projects include a flat for the designer Jasper Conran, and the Vogue Cafe in Russia.

Her style is characterized by symmetry, muted colours, lack of clutter and a sense of calm. She likes to throw in a Sanskrit prayer wheel or an artwork made from a deconstructed African necklace for individuality.

What the clients say
'Ann has the ability to easily translate her vision so that people can understand and share in her thought process. She has a great sense of humour – an invaluable asset when dealing with highly stressed home owners in the middle of a complete refurbishment! Ann is very intuitive – I sometimes think she can read minds. To put it simply, she has completely changed our lives – we now live in a gorgeous house where everything works in complete synergy.' Howard Shaughnessy, client

Martin Brudnizki Design Studio Limited
Unit 2L Chelsea Reach
79–89 Lots Road
London SW10 0RN
T: 020 7376 7555 F: 020 7376 7444
M: 07768 511 623
studio@mbds.net
www.mbds.net

Costs Expensive. Complicated but breaks it down to: £150 per hour for him (less for others) plus a percentage of the job (15 per cent if commercial). This needs to be negotiated upfront.
Travel Anywhere, gladly. He's worked in the US and recently completed Daphne's Restaurant in Barbados, so he's pretty familiar with BA.
Size of job Ideally several rooms to a whole house.
Attitude Straight Scandinavian.

If you can't quite afford Jonathan Reed or David Collins, try Martin Brudnizki, a 37-year-old Polish/Swedish/German interior architect who has worked for them both. MBDS is still relatively small (five in-house designers, two architects) but big enough to have landed the lucrative contract to design the Strada restaurants (owned by the same people as the Ivy), a five-star hotel in Frankfurt owned by Sir Rocco Forte, and the redesign of Browns, everyone's favourite clothing boutique. The style is high-tech enough to be cutting edge and low-tech enough to allow curtains and cushions and a bit of colour (though Reed's influence shows – there's a lot of boyish brown). He calls it Minimalism Deluxe. This is grooming as much as design. About 50 per cent of the work is residential; the rest is developments and commercial, restaurants, etc.

The firm does everything: 'from implementation to completion'.

Clients are banker types with the odd scattering of celebs like Leslie Ash and Lee Chapman of Teatro fame. Blond-haired and 6ft 3in, Martin is moving fast. He's service-driven, ambitious, good-looking and very nice. 'He's going to be huge,' says a member of his enthusiastic team.

What the clients say
'I have known Martin for four years and have a high opinion of him. He is incredibly talented, reinterprets well, listens and is supportive, flexible and confident about what he does. He is quick to make adjustments and takes your money seriously.' Ana-Elssy Martorell, client

Charlotte Crosland Interiors
Unit 36 Pall Mall Deposit
124–128 Barlby Rd
London W10 6BL
T: 020 8960 9442
F: 020 8960 9714
mail@charlottecrosland.com
www.charlottecrosland.com

Carden Cunietti
83 Westbourne Park Road
London W2 5QH
T: 020 7229 8630
F: 020 7229 1404
cc@carden-cunietti.com
www.carden-cunietti.com

Cost: Middle. Charges an initial design scheme fee, which she usually breaks down per room, giving the client the option to scale down if necessary. She then charges 10–20 per cent of the overall job.
Travel Would travel globally for the right job.
Size of job Would consider a single room, depending on its location and size and how big their workload is at the time.
Attitude Your wacky aunt. But it all comes together at the end.

Charlotte Crosland, sister of fabric designer Neisha Crosland, seems to be on a winning streak, picking up award after award. She's very much a darling of the media, as is her sister. After getting a degree from The Chelsea School of Art, she went to work for the architect's practice Marius Barran, where she honed her drawing skills. Later she moved to Charles Hammond, where she was taught to place fabric orders and took on her first clients before starting her own business in 1987. She works with a draughtsman named Paul, whose perspective drawings are often framed by clients.

Her greatest projects are her own houses, which she changes frequently. They are filled with bold fabrics and wallpapers (her sister's): it's not quite busy but minimalism this is not. It's really a modern take on chintz. Most clients want a similar look.

What the clients say
'Charlotte has turned our dull '70s townhouse into a smart family home. We chose neutral colours with some flamboyant touches to give definition, such as a broad striped linoleum floor in the kitchen and a bold wallpaper designed by Charlotte's sister Niesha Crosland to liven up the corridor and stairs. The overall result is a clutter-free contemporary house with an abundance of comfort and interest.' Alison Moodie, client
'The apartment that Charlotte Crosland designed with Neisha Crosland for the Brahm Portfolio of Properties is a celebration of rich colour and bold pattern. Charlotte has combined her creativity with respect for the budgets, timescales and proportions, and demonstrated fantastic spatial creativity and planning. The sole reception room, for example, has been designed to simultaneously work as four separate rooms – a study, TV room and den, dining room and drawing room. I have enjoyed working with Charlotte and hope to continue to do so in the future.' Pierre Brahm, client

Costs Middle to top end. Upwards of £40K. Budget varies, depending on the job.
Travel Work on projects across the UK, Europe and USA.
Size of job One room to an entire house.
Attitude Nice version of Trinny and Susannah.

These are rock-and-roll designers. Robbie Williams used them for both of his London homes, and they show no signs of slowing down. Eleanora Cunietti and Audrey Carden are the Notting Hill designers of choice: theirs is a bohemian meets Park Avenue aesthetic that combines one-off objects sourced from around the world (which can be found in their shop on Westbourne Park Road) with luxurious materials, unusual colours and contemporary French furniture. It's eclectic, glamorous, and, like most things in Notting Hill, consciously un-self-conscious. But you don't get in with the celebrity crowd by being dictatorial. They insist that their style is whatever the client wants. Scottish Audrey Carden will probably have dissuaded Robbie from having a jukebox in the middle of his living room. Her style is more diplomatic than the Canadian-American Eleanora, who looks and acts like a bit of a rock chick herself. Clients often choose one or the other.

What the clients say
'Audrey and Eleanora have a great bedside manner. They are enthusiastic and completely professional.' client
'Carden Cunietti were incredibly easy to work with, they really listened to all my ideas and translated them into something that is so much more then I could have imagined on my own. They budgeted precisely down to the last penny and were often even one step ahead with the timing. They really are fantastic!' Tracy Brower, client

C–F

Philip Hooper at Sibyl Colefax & John Fowler
39 Brook Street
London W1K 4JE
T: 020 7493 2231
F: 020 7499 9721

Ilse Crawford
studioilse
4th Floor
41 Great Guildford Street
London SE1 0ES
T: 020 7928 0550 F: 020 7021 0438
ilse@studioilse.com
www.studioilse.com

Costs Expensive. Hooper charges his time out at £135 an hour and sizes up the job before giving the client a real sense of costs. Once the client goes forward, they have a rolling fee.
Travel London, the home counties, the USA and the Caribbean. Distance is not an issue.
Size of job Projects range from £100K to £800K.
Attitude You're the boss.

He cuts a dashing figure in his tweed jacket with a silk cravat tied just so. Philip Hooper is one of the most experienced interior designers in London: he was the design director at Stefanidis before joining Colefax three years ago. Though affiliated with a traditional organization, Hooper prefers modern interiors. His palette is clean but sensual, with a tendency towards subdued colours, dark silks and luxurious materials. He uses the best: joiners, decorators, upholsterers, gilders, etc. 'The key is to be able to decorate in a modern way but without losing a sense of the past,' he says. You get the whole shebang with Hooper: colour boards, perspectives, as many drawings as necessary (he trained at Canterbury College of Art, so they will be good). It's the top to toe approach. Hooper's in the big league – he doesn't get published often, which means that his clients (investment bankers, landed gentry, tycoons) don't want publicity. He has the bedside manner they like: he's a bit shy, very polite and amusing when he lets his hair down.

Things run smoothly with Hooper and, unlike many of his peers, he doesn't think he's grander than the client. 'He's a real sweetie' is how one of his repeat clients put it. 'It has to be an enjoyable process,' Hooper replies.

What the clients say
'Philip is extremely reliable and flexible. He can do Colefax or super modern. He follows your brief. He's efficient and has an excellent team. He responds at the drop of a hat. We were small fry compared to some of his clients but everything was bang on time.' Jonathan Green, MD Richard Green Gallery
'Philip has been fantastic. He's highly professional and has great vision. He focused on what I wanted and was always on the ball. He's more than just an interior designer; he can do 3D sketches off the cuff. We really clicked.' Caroline Pereira, client

Costs Expensive, though Ilse is driven by curiosity rather than cash.
Travel She teaches at Eindhoven Academy in Holland, so is a regular commuter.
Size of job Would love more projects (such as hotels) in the UK.
Attitude Big sister – warm, patient, interested.

Think of Ilse Crawford more as a consultant than a designer. She won't go and pick out curtains for you but she'll let you in on her bohemian vision of the world, which is very special. The mixing old and new aesthetic that is all the rage is largely Ilse's invention. It was as launch editor of *Elle Decoration* (in 1988) that she started what became her trademark look. It consists of placing a tribal rug from Morocco in front of a B&B sofa with a Venetian chandelier overhead. 'I make modern cosy,' is her famous line. Donna Karan spotted her book *Sensual Home* and brought her to New York where she launched her home collection. One day Crawford bumped into Nick Jones, who asked her to design Babington House. Soon the cool, let-it-all-hang-out, never-look-like-you're-trying-too-hard school of design was born. Clients like Dave Stewart (male half of Eurythmics) wouldn't dream of choosing anyone else. She loves velvets, wallpapers, textures; if Ilse orders a modern sofa, she will make sure it's covered in mohair or something tactile.

Crawford has worked as a creative consultant for both Swarovski (she is the brains behind the highly acclaimed chandelier collection) and Marks & Spencer. She consults all over the world about unlikely things such as boudoirs. Her advice can be counter-intuitive but it's always on the money. Highly articulate and gentle, she is the top of the design tree.

What the clients say
'Ilse sees all that is out there and is able to put it together in a way that makes it reachable and touchable to real people. She links the design community and the consumer.' Donna Karan, fashion designer

Drumkilbo Designs
Whitberry House
Tyninghame
East Lothian
Scotland EH42 1XL
T: 01620 861 400 F: 01620 861 414
M: 07721 389 744
willa@drumkilbo.demon.co.uk

Paul Fidgen
36 Leinster Square
London W2 4NQ
T: 0797 107 3142
paulfidgen@btinternet.com

Costs Reasonable. Price is usually trade plus 30 per cent.
Travel Happily. But presently seems to work mostly in Scotland.
Size of job One room often leads to a whole stately, so she's willing to start small. 'If a client wants a new pair of curtains, that's fine, too.'
Attitude Could be the Queen's niece.

Willa Elphinstone (Lady Elphinstone) of Drumkilbo Designs is used to living in great big country houses in Scotland – not surprisingly, she is the designer of choice to the landed nobility seeking second or third homes (the Duke of Westminster, for example). She knows about things that normal mortals don't, like how to work with a trust and how to navigate complex tax issues. Based south of Edinburgh, she looks after big rambling houses that need everything doing to them. She doesn't have a style *per se*, but she doesn't really need to. Her clients know their taste (old-fashioned, grand, plenty of antiques): they just want someone to make it happen. Elphinstone has done a certain amount of commercial work, such as the Ballathie House Hotel in Perthshire, but her business is mostly word of mouth. She project manages as well and works with a clerk of works, which is Scottish for quantity surveyor. If someone aspires to Scottish upper-class style, Willa is their woman.

What the clients say
'Our house is from the fifteenth century and basically hadn't been lived in for decades. Willa helped, starting at the architectural stage and then decorating all the rooms. It was hugely successful. She was courageous in her choices for the house. She made the modern children's rooms work with the rest of the house, which was quite a feat. She is hugely professional, enormously fun to work with and has a warm and generous spirit.'
Mrs Anita Anderson Green, client
'Her ideas were superb. We had very little time, needed to have everything lined up in advance and we were finished a day early. She didn't put a foot wrong.' **Mr Christopher Longdon, managing director, Ballathie House Hotel**

Costs Middle. Either charges a percentage (20 per cent or less, depending on the project).
Travel London
Size of job Will consider anything interesting.
Attitude Lateral. Can see everything at once.

His hair is bleached blonde and he writes travel books in his spare time. He isn't trained as an architect but no one seems to have the slightest hesitation to take the charming 34-year-old's advice. He has ideas coming out of every pore: within minutes of walking into my house, he wanted mirrors everywhere and suggested I paint the ceiling a shade of mushroom-brown. 'I'm not Colefax and Fowler,' he says. That's for sure. He hates curtains, loves black and won't touch any furniture unless 'it's honest'. Could be precious but instead is straight to the point. He oozes creativity though, oddly enough, he began his career doing palaces in the Middle East. 'I worked for a huge company that was conveyor belt design but I learned a lot,' he says. He's done apartments and nightclubs, anything that takes his fancy – if he's not busy writing, that is. He beat some pretty hefty architectural firms (including Sophie Hicks) in a competition.

What the clients say
'Paul Fidgen worked for us as our architectural surveyor on the conversion of a church hall to a residential home, involving a completely new design and build of 5,000 square feet. We found him to be extremely competent, efficient and always accessible at short notice.' **Lucy Morris, client**
'Paul has an incredible talent for working with space and exploiting it to create something beautiful as well as functional. He perfectly balances his strong creative vision with the client's desire to shape their own environment.'
Natalie Fellowes and Simon Jones, clients

F–H

Katharine Fortescue Limited
3 Towns Farm Workshops
Sixpenny Handley
Salisbury
Wiltshire SP5 5PA
T: 01725 552 000
F: 01725 552 707
katharine@fortescue.co.uk

Costs Hourly rate of £50 (plus usual mark-ups). But will do set fee negotiated at the start.
Travel Mainly London, Wiltshire and Oxfordshire but has done jobs from Switzerland to Washington DC and will travel anywhere but war zones.
Size of job Anything from a consultation on one room to a hotel or whole estate.
Attitude Neighbourly.

Katharine Fortescue was trained by one of the best in the world, Sister Parish – not a nun but the *grande dame* of American decorating. The client list was a who's who of American society. Basically, if you can cut it there, you can cut it anywhere. Fortescue returned to London and set up a shop in Chelsea Green with George Cooper (a member of the old George Spencer crew). Now she's based in Wiltshire and gives nice ladies with listed houses nice interiors. She provides a complete service, starting with floor plans and ending with the bed linens. 'I couldn't do minimalist but I love doing contemporary penthouses.' Clients are aristocrats and bankers. Madonna is her next-door neighbour, so perhaps she will soon be joining the list. Much of her work comes via word of mouth. Clients say she's great company.

What the clients say
'Katharine is excellent at making good use of space, structural details and coordinating builders. She has lovely ideas and is a pleasure to work with. I can't stress enough the great strength she has. She doesn't overdecorate. The work she has done in our house is much admired and a great success.'
Lady Clinton, client
'Katharine is simply fabulous. She worked with me on my homes in both London and Washington. She has great taste, gets things done and never bosses you around.' American client

Garuda Design Limited
Maxol Building
261–263 Ormeau Road
Belfast BT73 GG
Northern Ireland
T: 02890 692626 F: 02890 692627
info@garudadesign.com
www.garudadesign.com

Costs Middle/high. 'I charge according to personality,' she says. That's between £85 and £120 for a scheme, after which the client chooses whether or not to go forward.
Travel See above.
Size of job From one room upwards.
Attitude You'll be lucky to get me (but if you do, I'll be amazing).

From the Kremlin to Jim Kerr of Simple Minds, Belfast-based Suzanne Sundara Garuda has seen and done it all. She studied fine arts at Central St Martins and then moved to Belgium to study specialist painting. After a stint of work for the Sultan of Brunei she moved to Milan and spent a few years decorating the biggest and fattest villas in the land. This got her the commission of a lifetime: decorating 30 state rooms within the Kremlin. The rock-and-roll crowd in Dublin followed but then she decided to move back home and open Garuda, a design shop that carries all the goodies she sees on her many trips to France, Italy and Belgium. 'I defy anyone to have a better selection,' she says. There are also Chinese antiques and one-offs by Mark Brazier Jones and William Yeoward. Stylewise, Garuda is eclectic, adventurous, anything but boring. 'We're definitely glamorous,' she says. Her criteria are somewhat unorthodox: 'If the client is local, I'll do it; if it means travelling, I'm very expensive.'

What the clients say
'She's wonderful. She's a decorator who doesn't try to be an architect. She's tremendous with materials and colours. She's also very efficient. She gives people homes that they couldn't dream of putting together themselves.'
Simon Templeton, architect
'For the last six or seven years I have more or less used Suzanne permanently. She did my house in Dublin and my in-laws' house in Belfast. She's very creative and easy to get on with.'
Chantal McCabe, client

Mark Gillette
Grange Farm
Parkgate Road
Mollington
Chester CH1 6NP
T: 01244 851897 F: 01244 851898
www.markgillette.com
mark.gillette@breathemail.net

Teeny Hickman of Hickman Interiors
Unit 2, Osiers Industrial Estate
Enterprise Way
London SW18 1NL
T: 020 8875 1282
F: 020 8875 0695

Costs Expensive.
Travel Spends most of his time up north unless clients need him to sort out their second or third house.
Size of job He's used to big budgets but will consider anything.
Attitude Wrote to each of his contacts to mention that we might be calling. Impeccable.

All roads in the north-west of England seem to lead to Mark Gillette. He originally trained to be an art therapist with mentally handicapped people, and it shows. Everything about him says 'calm'.

Gillette left Colefax and Fowler in 1994 to start his own firm and now moves effortlessly through the world of the very rich, where interior budgets can run as high as £2 million. For this you get countless schemes in any dimension you like. His style is very traditional. 'It's my clients who dictate,' he says with the slight disappointment of a man who wishes he could be putting some black leather on the walls. He has done seven houses for one client – that's how much they trust him. It can be a brand new Macmansion or a 17th-century wreck – either style suits him.

Gillette is about service: there isn't one facet of his work that isn't perfect (a lovely northern quality).

What the clients say
'I first used Mark 20 years ago for a small job and now we are working on a huge project together, with 23 rooms on the first floor alone. His input is vital, he has phenomenal design skills and is very clever when it comes to scale and layout. A lot of money has gone into this project but Mark ensures that it is all well spent. He is so talented, I just can't say enough good things about him.' Mrs Gaynor Townley, client
'Mark instinctively knows what the client's requirements are before the client does. Every project is completely individual. He doesn't impose a look on you, he doesn't have a set style. He finds unusual pieces, fabulous fabric, furniture or something quirky and it just works.' Lady Barlow, client

Costs Reasonable/medium. For bathroom and kitchen design, Teeny doesn't charge for her drawings; the bill is for the actual merchandise and the profit is made in the mark-up.
Travel Will go global, and has previously done jobs in Barbados, Scotland and France.
Size of job One room to hotels. Will even do the downstairs loo.
Attitude Rolex-watch precision.

Teeny Hickman is a designer who also supplies everything you need for the bathroom (and oversees the installation as well). 'Most architects don't even know what's available on the market, they just give you the same old thing,' says the very direct Hickman, whose clients include King Fahd, the Ali Reza Royals (maximalists), Ralph Fiennes and Madonna. She works for the great and the good, often without meeting them. 'I work for the designers who work for them,' she says. Hickman is Miss Efficiency; she was once asked to completely furnish a client's rental property in ten days, right down to the teaspoons. The tenant was a director in town to film a Warner Bros movie: Hickman pulled it off, no sweat. She specializes in bathrooms (of any style) but has branched out to kitchens and general design as well. She recently received her importing/exporting certificate and can trace the trucks carrying her bathtubs anywhere in the country or continent.

Hickman originally read fine art and later worked in fashion. She helped to establish Colourwash, a bathroom refurbishing company, on Fulham High Street.

What the clients say
'She can source anything from a bed to a freezer, at a great price, and have it delivered the next day. If a problem arises, she is very quick to respond. I would recommend her highly.' Helen Fraser
'Teeny fitted out our whole house. She is terribly efficient and articulate. Her service is very personal; along with having a great sense of humour, she is easy to get along with. She gets the picture very quickly and I trust her implicitly.' Peter and Georgina Pejacsevich

JKL
T/F: 020 7289 1149
jkl@jkl.eclipse.co.uk

Louise Jones Interiors Ltd
52 Agraria Road
Guildford
Surrey GU2 4LF
T: 07769 976 654
F: 01483 569 993
louisejonesinteriors@yahoo.co.uk

Costs Medium. Charge a flat fee based on a percentage of the job (usually 10–15 per cent); offer sourcing days for £300 in which they take the client on a blitz of the stores and showrooms from 10am to 3pm and set them in the right direction. Minimum fee of £1,000; a consultation costs £500 and is deducted from the final fee if they are hired.
Travel Based in London but will go anywhere, providing the project is substantial.
Size of job From one room to entire houses. Will consider anything.
Attitude Jewish mothers.

Joanna Lindsay and Jane Keisner, two nice Jewish girls from north London, describe themselves as 'fixers' rather than decorators. They can help with anything, from basic 'hand-holding' to complete project management. They are about to embark on a television career, so watch this space. Their real skill is psychological: they can bully and be impartial at the same time.

Their job says Keisner is: 'To interpret what the client wants. It can be chintz or modern or a combination. We steer people in the right direction rather than impose our aesthetic. Most clients just need help putting it all together.'

They come across as rather polished ladies who lunch (in Prada shoes with Hermes Kelly bags) but are not afraid of getting their hands dirty. They don't carry portfolios because the best advertisements for their abilities are their own impeccable homes.

What the clients say
'They're the Trinny and Susannah of the decorating world. Not afraid to tell you what is wrong with your house and then to put it right. Pluses: they work on the minicab principle of agreeing a fee up-front rather than letting the meter run, so they race to get the work done; will scour the high street as well as mail-order, auction houses and junk shops to find what you need, and it all looks remarkably classy. Underneath the sassy, north London Jewish princess exteriors (leather coats and kitten heels), both have hearts of gold and can save marriages. No minuses.' Rachel Kelly, client
'They're brilliant at getting things done. No one would dare be late.' Private client

Costs Reasonable. Depends on the size of the project. Set fee for larger projects and monthly instalments. For a smaller project would put a small mark-up on the goods and charge an hourly rate.
Travel Based in Guildford but will go anywhere for the right job. Says that going abroad should never be a problem – that's code for would love to.
Size of job Happy to do one room.
Attitude Hungry. But she has just appeared in *House & Garden*, so might be relaxing soon.

Louise was an accountant before becoming a designer. She got bored with number crunching, enrolled at Inchbald, got a job with Emily Todhunter (for whom she still freelances) and then set up on her own three years ago. She calls her style modern but she loves Donghia and Jay Robert Scott fabrics.

What the clients say
'She was brilliant. Absolutely happy with her. Very professional and personable. Coordinated everything calmly and on time. Very creative and full of ideas.' Oksanda Kolomenskaya, client
'Louise helped me recently set up my house; she is terrific. The house has a great look and she understood what I wanted. If I were to do anything further in the future, I would definitely use her again.' Monkey Chambers, client

Robert Kime
121–121A Kensington Church Street
London W8 7LP
T: 020 7229 0886 F: 020 7229 0766

PO Box 454
Marlborough
Wiltshire SN8 3UR
T: 01264 731268 F: 01264 731203
www.robertkime.com

Costs Expensive. Charges per room scheme (price varies on size). He will look at every job and doesn't consider himself expensive, though clients do.
Travel Anywhere. He regularly moves between New York, the West Indies and France. And statelies all over the country.
Size of job His criteria for taking a job is: 'Will it interest me?' You might slip in under the net if he likes you.
Attitude Pull yourself together.

Robert Kime is perhaps the most famous designer in the land: after all, not everyone can boast Prince Charles as a client. He has the Royal Warrant seal of approval and gets the very grand, the very rich, the 'hush hush, don't want my name in print' brigade, but, occasionally also the 'not so rich' (because they fell on hard times). He gets wannabes, too: people who aspire to aristocratic dishevelled chic.

He sees his clients, such as Andrew Lloyd Webber, through their many houses. 'I've worked with some for more than 30 years,' he says. The slightly dishevelled-looking Oxford graduate has no time for wishy-washyness. 'I am quite strict,' he admits. 'I don't like people who change their minds.' His style is faded aristocratic luxury: the idea is for a room to look like it's been there for ever, even though it was only installed at great expense yesterday. Kime offers more than just interior design. He also sells his own design fabrics, reproduction antique furniture and lighting, as well as artefacts he finds on his travels.

Kime has a devoted, polite, efficient team, all of whom make it their business to look after clients. 'My team can go anywhere,' he boasts, 'from a council estate to Highgrove.' He meets every client (this is not the usual practice in his league).

What the clients say
'He is the only designer I would recommend. He's phenomenal. He's very creative and can't stop himself. If something goes wrong, he never blames anyone else; he just comes and fixes it immediately.' client
'He is simply the best.' client

John McCall Designs Ltd
The Studio
Meadow House
Chapel Row, Bucklebury
Berkshire RG7 6NU
T: 01189 714 425
sales@mccalldesign.co.uk
www.mccalldesign.co.uk

Costs Top end. American and European clients tend to like fees and the English prefer an agreed percentage on everything.
Travel Will travel all over the world, not to mention the countryside – south of France, Japan, Greece, Spain.
Size of job From £30K upwards.
Attitude 'Of course.'

He sounds grand, and his clients certainly are, but McCall is a real pro with old-fashioned manners and few enemies. Very well dressed with wavy grey hair, he is the epitome of discretion and good taste. Clients (titled people, bankers) come back again and again: 'You don't change your dentist, do you?' he asks. You probably won't have heard of him because he (and his clients) are very publicity-shy.

McCall is generally on a very strict budget, which can be tough, given that his brief is to make houses look like they've been there for ever (though now the roof doesn't leak and the carpets are new but purposely faded to look old). He 'always has a chalet on the go!' His style is old money: expect chintz, swags and tails, whatever the client wants. 'I only give them a choice of two fabrics,' he says, 'and they usually love both.' He employs a small team but will bring in freelancers if necessary. With 30 years' experience under his belt, there is nothing that can faze – or delay – McCall. Clients say he never loses his temper or gets stressed.

What the clients say
'Johnny is extremely easy. He lets you think it's your idea when, in fact, it's his. He did both our house in London and our house in Oxfordshire, and works equally well with husband and wife. He's great at everything, whether moving furniture or choosing colours.' Verena Molson, client
'I have used Johnny on two projects and, put it this way, I would never use anyone else. Johnny is without doubt the best person to work with. He's got a fantastic eye, he gets on with everyone and he is totally straight when it comes to how he charges. His attention to detail is perfect.' Maya Adcock, client

Precious McBane Art and Design Partnership
50 Florida Street
London E2 6AE
T: 020 7729 2213
F: 020 7729 1292
M: 07970 533 007
mail@preciousmcbane.com
www.preciousmcbane.com

Scott Maddux
66 Enfield Cloisters
Fanshaw Street
London N1 6LD
T/F: 020 7684 2140
www.scottmaddux.com

Costs Middle. Daily flat rate and a percentage or 'handling'
charge. Price varies, depending on the size of the job.
Travel Based in London but will go anywhere.
Size of job Would consider one room, depending on size and
what needed to be done – mostly whole projects.
Attitude 'We could be artists but prefer creating interiors.'

Costs Reasonable because still small. Maddux either
charges a flat fee (negotiable) or adds a percentage to the
goods supplied at trade rates.
Travel Flexible, but mostly London-based.
Size of job Will consider anything. No restrictions. Window
treatments to total refurbishment.
Attitude Positive at all times.

The Central St Martin's graduates with offices on Brick
Lane and clients like 'the artist formerly known as
Prince', are a pretty groovy outfit. Precious McBane
collaborate with designer-of-the-moment Tord Boontje
and artists like Gary Hume and Tracey Emin. Their
Pom-Pom stools and Mongolian lambskin beanbags
made the cover of *Vogue* (with Kate Moss). Their
company motto is 'design, disrupt and delight'.

They have completed projects as diverse as
a private interior for pop diva Alison Goldfrapp,
The Zetter hotel in Clerkenwell and the make-up room
at Bloomberg tv studio. On The Zetter project they
worked with wallpaper designer Rachel Kelly, fashion
and fabric designer Eley Kishimoto, furniture designer
James Harris and specialist painter Charlotte Ingle.

They also act as colour consultants on The Mix,
a must-read for those who like to be one step ahead
of the trends.

What the clients say
'Working with Precious McBane was a lovely mixture of
informality and efficiency. We were allowed to be very
pro-active as clients, and Precious McBane were always
accommodating with our ideas – even though they usually
ended up steering us in another direction later on. I am now
using the company to do some work on my own home.'
Mark Sainsbury, director, The Zetter hotel
'I had followed the work of Precious McBane in the press and
always appreciated their wit. When I needed someone to
redesign my apartment (a blank, white loft), I tracked them
down. I had a very tight budget and they were able to stick to it.
They began by just hanging out with me; we discussed everything; we even went through and edited my possessions, so I
have ended up with a whole new way of living as well as a new
home. From the outset they listened to my ideas and made me feel
comfortable with the whole process.'
Eda Colbert, client

'Everything is up for discussion,' is the motto of
32-year-old Scott Maddux, a freelance designer who
moved to London from his native Tennessee ten years
ago. Hip, laid back and open to new ideas pretty much
describes both Maddux and his approach to design.
'I'm not confined to a particular style,' he says. 'I like
the idea of mixing old and new.' His isn't the school
of beige on beige: it's more likely to be black and
white stripes or rich colours, with the odd, unexpected
detail thrown in. Tables may not match: he has a
good-enough eye not to have to be symmetrical.
He never qualified as an architect but managed to
learn most of what is relevant.

Maddux has worked for A-list designers, such as
Ann Boyd and Herbert Zandburg (the former partner
of David Champion). He recently completed a private
apartment for the founder of the Bodas lingerie line
(he also added the finishing touches to her boutiques)
and the new spa/headquarters for Unlisted London.

What the clients say
'Maddux is exceptional value for money. He's edgy yet traditional
and completely diplomatic. He's on top of the suppliers. We
started with a brief but quickly moved in another direction.
What he gave me is 100 per cent perfect.'
Deborah Jean Farace, MD, Unlisted London
'Scott is prepared to discuss a fabric until two in the morning.
He understands that this job is about boring details. He will try
wild first and then settle for a happy medium. He is creative and
too young to be giving everyone "pink" walls because he can't
think of anything better. Can be slow but is very sorry.'
Helen Kirwan-Taylor, author, *Home UK*

Lucy Manners Interiors
The Old Imperial Laundry
71 Warriner Gardens
London SW11 4XW
T: 020 7622 3030 M: 07831 527 770
F: 020 7622 1060
lucy@lucymanners.com

Francesca Mills
63 Stradella Road
London SE24 9HL
T: 020 7733 9193
F: 020 7274 8861
Francesca@francescamills.com

Costs Reasonable/middle – open to discussion. Hourly rate £80.
Travel Works a lot in the country, anywhere from Sussex to Northumberland. Has done an apartment in Vienna and a house in Kuwait.
Size of job Would consider one room but mainly does whole houses.
Attitude Quietly efficient.

Lucy Manners grew up in a large country house full of antiques and dogs. Her style is undecorated, cosy, old world and classic, a bit like the house she grew up in. She's had lots of help from the pros, too, having worked for David Mlinaric, Victoria Weymouth and Alidad before setting up on her own. Her expertise is old-world England, but new England when it comes to chasing delinquent suppliers. She is always obliging (a real skill) and diplomatic (she's an aristocrat herself).

What the clients say: 'Lucy is sympathetic to her client's tastes.' Mrs Philip Dunne, client
'Fantastic work, incredibly professional and great taste. She is very patient, just the best!' Mrs Packard, client
'Lucy decorated our rented house in Sussex. She managed to take my modern taste on board while understanding what the landlord wanted. She shifted my choices without ever making me feel pushed. It was a smallish job but I never felt unimportant. She certainly knows how to use a measuring tape, which she brandishes like a whip.'
Helen Kirwan-Taylor, author, *Home UK*

Costs Middle. Flat fee £500 a day.
Travel All of UK, Jamaica and is currently working on a house in Portugal.
Size of job Will take jobs as big as £1 million.
Attitude Sigmund Freud meets Cinderella.

Francesca Mills studied psychology before becoming a television set designer and finally a designer. The reason she has the kind of clients she has (serious celebrities, big Hollywood names, fat cat bankers) is because she thinks clearly, speaks softly and never ever lets anyone get the better of her. 'Occasionally I have some big hotshot in the city try to negotiate with me,' she says, 'but I say: "No." They go: "OK then."' The 53-year-old is firm but fair. She would never raise her (soft) voice, even if a voice was being raised back. One (famous actor) client was in such a hurry to move into his new house that she hired set designers instead of builders. 'It was great,' she says, 'he was thrilled.' Mills also worked at Laura Ashley and has no shortage of great contacts in the business. She does everything, from overseeing the builders to moving the family in. On occasion she has taken a celebrity's child to school (because mum was still in bed having played too hard the night before). She will even shred incriminating evidence before the builders come in.

Mills' style is very easy on the eye. She calls it 'sensual minimalism'. It's comfortable and relaxed but luxurious. Knick knacks are allowed. 'My work is about the client, not me,' she says. 'I think it's not right to impose your ego on a project.' Her work comes entirely word of mouth. Celebrities know that she will never drop their name into conversation, no matter how tempting.

What the clients say
'She's brilliant! Extremely intuitive, sensitive and innovative. I got along really well with her and have passed her name on to loads of my friends.' Claudia Dorrell, Dorrell Management
'I loved working with Francesca. As a designer, rather than imposing her thoughts, she listens to your ideas, finds out how you live and works from there. I will be working with her again, and she is lovely company.' Alison Swinburn, client

Mlinaric, Henry and Zervudachi Limited
38 Bourne Street
London SW1W 8JA
T: 020 7730 9072
F: 020 7823 4756
info@mhzltd.com
www.mhzltd.com

Costs **Concorde. The service is bespoke and so are the prices.**
No one who uses them has to ask.
Travel **With offices in London, Paris and New York, they're pret-**
ty well equipped to take on projects all over the world.
Size of job **For an existing client they will take on a project as**
small as one room but for a new client it would probably need
to be more substantial.
Attitude **Are you being served?**

OK, you don't just hire David Mlinaric, Hugh Henry
(both based in London) or Tino Zervudachi (based in
Paris): you apply to the firm and hope that one of the
three directors might take pity on you. Adding a Sir to
your name might help or making the *Sunday Times*
rich list, or (says the architect Kathryn Findlay who
interviewed them for a project) just calling out of the
blue at the right time. Their clients might be aristocrats
and billionaires but they're not: they have a reputation
for impeccable manners and impeccable service. They
are at the top of their field largely because they provide
an excellent service. And they work weekends.

The good news is that if you are lucky enough
to make the client list, your project will be overseen
personally by one of the three directors and your
house will sit in a portfolio alongside The National
Portrait Gallery, The National Gallery and The Royal
Opera House. Stylewise, this is bespoke, gilded luxury.
Think of them as master Italian tailors: your suit will
come back with a silk lining and buttons made out of
pearls. One client told Mlinaric that her budget was
£500K to £1 million. He answered: 'My dear, that will
pay for this room.'

What the clients say
'They are amazing. I could only afford one room but they did
a brilliant job.' client

Catherine Connolly at Northwick Design
16 St John's Wood Road
London NW8 8RE
T: 020 7289 2555
F: 020 7286 0300
M: 07976 601 258
cathy@northwickdesign.com
www.northwickdesign.com

Costs **Reasonable. Her husband says she should register as**
a charity – in other words she's very good value for money.
She charges either £50 an hour or 10 per cent of the budget. She
often gives discounts on fabrics and has even been known to
reduce her fee if she really wants her client to have something.
Travel **Has done houses from Ireland to Barbados. Even set up**
an office in Poland whilst doing an executive office block in 1999.
Size of job **Would consider one room but has also done houses**
with 11 bedrooms and 11 bathrooms, entire office blocks and
development projects.
Atttitude **Audrey Hepburn school of natural charm.**

Catherine Connolly used to be a model, and it shows.
But she does get those long fingers dirty: she started
as an apprentice to Carolyn Benson, a specialist in
interiors finishes. Gradually friends started asking for
her advice on their homes, which led to full interiors
commissions. Clients include Irish tycoons, *Vogue*'s
Carol Woolton, Terry Wogan and many a nice lady in
the country with one room to decorate.

Initially, Catherine's style was very 'English
comfortable' until an old client commissioned a
Swedish-style country house. Now she says she is
happiest doing contemporary schemes using a few
beautiful antiques, luxurious carpets and perhaps no
curtains at all. 'The most important thing,' she says,
'is to be comfortable with your surroundings and have
pieces that are ageless, whether they are traditional or
modern.' One of her great strengths is colour: she can
make even the most conservative client experiment.

What the clients say
'Catherine was friendly, on time, incredibly efficient and hugely
tasteful. There really aren't enough positive superlatives I can
use to describe her. I had very strong ideas about what I wanted
but I left all the organization to Catherine, and she made my
ideas a reality.' The Hon. Mrs Finn Guinness, client
'Catherine is very down to earth and never overbearing.
She intrinsically knows what her clients need. She is amazing
with colour and actually physically mixed the paints for the
drawing room and bedroom for our house in the south of France
to ensure the colour was perfect. Catherine was just so easy to
work with and has actually become a good friend.'
Helen Wogan, client

Park Grove Design
14 Nant Road
London NW2 2AJ
T/F: 020 8731 6688
M: 07850 814 655)
info@parkgrove.co.uk
www.parkgrove.co.uk

Costs Reasonable. Hourly rate from £75, depending on type of job. Doesn't believe in percentages because it encourages designers to choose more expensive fabrics and objects.
Travel Will go anywhere.
Size of job Mostly mid- to large residential projects; has also done hotels and office buildings but missed the passion and intimacy involved with creating a home.
Attitude Could run IBM.

Lori Pinkerton-Rolet carries a briefcase and looks like she works in a bank, which is why people in banks employ her. You can put money down that she will never be late, never misfile a receipt and never lose her cool with a builder. She hands you her business card before you ask, the portfolio is open in front of you before you've even thought of it: in other words, she knows what you want before you do. She charges by the hour because she thinks percentages are unethical. She's as straight as an arrow: can you tell she's American?

Inchbald- and Chelsea-trained Lori Pinkerton-Rolet doesn't subscribe to any particular style, relying instead on her clients' requirements and taste to guide her. Her clients don't want rock and roll décor: they like their lamps to match and a bit of tassle in their curtains. They're busy people who let her run around the globe sourcing antiques on their behalf.

What the clients say
'I've used Lori for over ten years and can honestly say she has never let anything slip through the cracks. She has worked for us both in London and the US and is now updating individual rooms as our family's needs change. Lori doesn't delegate too much to her employees; you always feel like you have her complete attention. We've even gone away on holiday during a renovation, returning to find everything taken care of down to the last book on the bookshelves.' Debbie Hannam, client
'Lori is very thorough; she foresees problems and avoids them before they even happen; and is also very good at dealing with problems once they have occurred. I've been working with her for seven years now.' client

Catherine Pawson and Juliette Byrne Ltd
1 Munro Terrace
Cheyne Walk
London SW10 0DL
T: 020 7352 1553
F: 020 7349 7517
catherine@catherinepawson.com
Juliettebyrne@yahoo.com

Costs Middle/high end. Charge a set design fee or a monthly retainer on a larger project; they work like architects by taking a percentage of the overall costs.
Travel Based in London but will travel all over the world.
Size of job From one room up.
Attitude Avis – We try harder.

Pawson and Byrne have done 'ultra modern' in LA, 'English chintz' in Sussex and even 'chalet chic' in Megeve. Then there's the yacht, the marketing suites for big developments and the reception areas. They are so diplomatic that you're hard pressed to know how any decisions are ever made. Pawson is the wife of the minimalist architect John Pawson and (ironically) worked for Colefax and Fowler before renouncing all chintz. She paired up with Juliette, a graduate of Chelsea College of Art, to start what is an entirely word-of-mouth business (they hate the media, even though the media loves them).

'Nothing is too much trouble' is their motto. They employ only two assistants and are never more than a mobile phone away (clients develop a co-dependent relationship with them). They do absolutely everything (design, project manage, obtain planning permission) and anything (stock the fridge) at any time of day or night.

What the clients say
'Catherine was fantastic to work with. Not only does she have impeccable taste, she really understood what we were looking for. We were amazed that even with the distance to California, Catherine was able to be so organized and put together such a warm and lovely home for us. We would definitely work with Catherine again and can't say enough how much we enjoyed working with her in the past.'
Ellen Bronfman, client in Los Angeles
'I really enjoyed working with Juliette Byrne, and she has always been fantastically quick and efficient, and has a tremendous sense of style.' Annouschka Ducas, client

P–S

Joanna Plant
32b Heathfield Road
London W3 8EJ
T: 020 8993 4695
F: 020 8992 3934
M: 07909907927
jplantinteriors@aol.com

Charles Rutherfoord Ltd
51 The Chase
London SW4 0NP
T: 020 7627 0182
F: 020 7720 0799

Costs Very reasonable – £50 an hour. 'I don't want to intimidate my clients,' she says. 'Architects have seven years training. Let's not overestimate what we do.'
Travel Yes – working in Wiltshire, Oxford, France and Portugal, and has three projects currently in London.
Size of job Will consider anything – a bathroom, for example. No minimum.
Attitude PA and designer: What better combination?

This 30-something self-taught designer is a well-kept secret. She got her start working as PA to Ken and Nancy Berry, former chairman and vice chairman respectively of the Virgin Music Group. 'They had six houses to look after,' says Plant, 'and my job was to coordinate all the decorators. I got to meet them all: Paul Fortune in LA, Peter Farlow in London.' After a while, the Berrys said: 'Joanna, you know what we want, you do it,' which she did. She set up on her own five years ago and now has a steady clientele of repeat clients, such as the Beckhams (she's doing a house for them at the moment in France). She calls her style 'quietly elegant and chic' but she goes rock and roll when she has to. 'My job is really to please my client. I like to show them things that they couldn't imagine.' Plant calls herself a 'jobbing' decorator. 'I like to remain in the background. I'm not looking for a TV show,' she says. She is married to Nick Plant, one of the founders of Succession, the luxury leather upholstery makers. They often work together. Joanna is known for her effortless sense of style and perfect eye.

What the clients say
'Joanna and I worked very closely together. She is very professional and has great ideas. She made the process truly enjoyable.' Victoria Beckham
'Joanna has lots of ideas. Her style is contemporary classic. Knows fabulous people. She's so nice that she gets the best out of everyone.' Caroline Amrolia, solicitor
'Joanna is fantastic. She has extraordinary style and a great eye for beautiful things. Every day I walk into the house I am so pleased to have found her. The result is understated and lovely to live in. Also, her address book is fantastic.' Heather Manners, client

Costs Medium/high. Either charges a percentage of the overall cost (for larger jobs) or an hourly rate.
Travel Has completed projects as far flung as Oregon, Moscow and Riyadh, so will pretty much go anywhere.
Size of job From one room to a large house (mostly just complete projects).
Attitude He should teach it.

Every designer claims to pay 'attention to detail' but Rutherfoord will even measure your eye level as you sit in your armchair to make sure the rails of the windows don't block your view of the garden. He also designs unique pieces of furniture and has more recently taken on garden and planting design. His style is innovative with bold uses of colour and unusual finishes.

Rutherfoord trained in architecture at Cambridge and interiors at Kingston before setting up his own practice in 1984. He worked at Conran Associates, where he designed offices for the Minister of Arts, Lord Gowrie, in Whitehall, for Lord Carrington at GEC, and for the European headquarters for Seibu (the Japanese department store). He also worked at Christie's in the furniture department for four years, which has inspired some of his own designs. In other words, there isn't much about interiors that he doesn't know or can't do. He could feign grandness but he doesn't – his politeness makes a huge impression on all who meet him (including researchers on this book).

What the clients say
'I have known Charles for 20 years and when I needed to transform my poky flat he was the obvious choice. Temperamentally he is so calm and patient that he is a dream to work with. He was very quick to see the potential of the space and has transformed it from a dark, cramped space into a vast, light-filled apartment. Charles is a very stylish man and I'm sure that if you gave him carte blanche, you would end up with a definite "look", but I had my own very strong ideas on how I wanted the place to look and Charles really listened to me and made my ideas reality.' Mary Bonn, client
'Charles was delightful. He is a perfectionist and has a fantastic eye for colour. He has the most unique ideas and is particularly good at lighting schemes.' Diana Schofield, client

Caroline Sandon Interiors
Burnt Norton
Chipping Campden
Gloucestershire GL55 6PR
T: 01386 841 488
F: 01386 849 119
M: 07714 201771
carolinesandon@aol.com

Costs Medium. She charges either by the hour (£75), day
or 10 per cent of the contract.
Travel London, Gloucestershire and surrounding counties.
Also specializes in doing houses in Italy, especially Tuscany
and Umbria.
Size of job A pair of curtains to decorating a whole house.
Attitude Country lady who does houses for country ladies.

Viscountess Caroline Sandon knows what it's like to
live in a big country house because she lives in one
herself. She knows all too well that if you go overboard
with curtains, you will have to economize somewhere
else. With eight years' experience under her belt, the
former model specializes in helping people achieve
a look that feels like their own. 'I don't like cluttered
or fancy,' she says, 'but I follow my client's brief.' Her
clients are landed folk who want comfortable houses
in London and Gloucestershire. All her work comes via
word of mouth.

What the clients say
**'I would certainly recommend Caroline. She played a big part
when I moved from a house to a flat. She has a great sense of
colour and feeling. As far as getting the work done, she was
very efficient.' The Earl of Harrowby, client**
**'We refurbished a large country house and she got things
done in a timely fashion. I had very definite ideas and she was
someone who let my ego triumph. Everything she had made up
for the house was absolutely beautiful. I had a lot of fun with
Caroline; she was a pleasure to work with.'**
Mrs Martin Smith, client

Sieff Interiors
Studio C1
The Old Imperial Laundry
71 Warriner Gardens
London SW11 4XW
T: 020 7978 2422 F: 020 7978 2423
design@sieff.co.uk
www.sieff.co.uk

Costs Reasonable/middle. If a client already has a budget,
then Sieff charges a percentage. If the client has no idea of
the budget, Sieff will work one out. She also has a daily rate
for people who just need advice.
Travel Local and global.
Size of job Would consider a job involving one room,
depending on the scale of the project. Turns work down only
if she is overstretched.
Attitude Posh but down to earth.

Gloucestershire- and London-based Diana Sieff is
a lady designer. She is perfect in dress and manner
(she is discreet and won't drop names, though clients
include well-known personalities, such as presenter
Tania Bryer), and presents her portfolio in a beautiful
custom-made folder. She is not that different from the
clients for whom she works, which is why they let her
do everything from project management to hiring the
staff. She also runs her own shop, Sieff, near
Highgrove, which makes custom furniture, and is
currently working on the Lygon Arms Hotel, which was
recently privatized after being sold by the Savoy Group.
She has done everything from chalets to Grade 1-listed
manor houses to bachelor pads.

Her style is client led. 'I'm not aware of having
a personal style' she says, 'but friends and clients often
say that is so Diana.' Most of what she does is fetch and
carry, chase up and put up. Design is a fraction of the
job. The rest is organization, coordinating and listening.
'I live on the M4 and M5, between houses in London
and Devon and the shop in Gloucestershire,' she says.

What the clients say
**'Diana is very approachable. She has amazing ideas but
would never impose them on you and can adapt easily to your
needs. She has a wonderful way with colours and can put
together things you would never think of yourself. She is
incredibly efficient and is able to estimate everything down
to the last penny.' Lady Wolfson, client**
**'We had a terrific experience with Diana. She not only did up our
house but she project managed it as well. She has very elegant
taste but she never dictates. She listens to what you want and
meets you halfway. We have good memories of the project.'**
Tania Bryer, presenter

Emma Sims-Hilditch
The Studio
Old School House
West Kington
Wiltshire SN14 7JJ
T: 01249 783087 F: 01249 783400
emma@theinterior.co.uk
www.theinterior.co.uk

Target Living
6 Pont Street
London SW1X 9EL
T: 020 7823 2316
tara@targetliving.com

Costs **Reasonable – £45 an hour.**
Travel **Has worked all over the country, though her patch
is Oxfordshire, Wiltshire and Gloucestershire.**
Size of job **Will consider anything, though would prefer not
to travel across the country to make one set of curtains**
Attitude **Five star.**

Emma worked as a production assistant for the film
director Ridley Scott before turning her eye to curtain
making. That proved so successful that she started
doing up houses eight years ago. Her entirely word-
of-mouth clients are in the music world (Roland
Orzabel from Tears for Fears), the sports world and
most important, the real world. 'I've done "wild"
(leopard prints everywhere), glamour and classic
contemporary,' she says. She loves mixing
Scandinavian pieces with modern elements but is
'no Kelly Hoppen'. She has worked on a series of
developments and several restaurants in Bristol, and
is used to coming in on time and budget. She doesn't
get much publicity, so a bit of a find really.

What the clients say
**'Emma is Miss Microscopic Detail. Will research the world.
Remembers every thing you ever said, including fabrics you
turned away six months ago. Never met someone so organized
in my entire life. Draws beautifully: every vase is in the picture.
Reasonable, and has great fabric people.' Kate Cullinan, client**
**'Emma is great. She interviewed me at length, took me around to
see some other projects and took over (I was busy working in
London). She doesn't give you a stamp like some designers:
she's very adaptable.' Felix Appelbe, solicitor**

Costs **Mid- to high range: around £100 an hour.**
Travel **She's already in the private jet league and would gladly
take on foreign commissions.**
Size of job **Will consider anything interesting.**
Attitude **It-girl, minus the attitude.**

Let's be honest here: Tara, daughter of Elliot Bernerd,
one of the biggest developers in the land, could easily
be an 'it' girl, posing for photographers in tight Versace
dresses. Instead she's putting in 12-hour days running
a design business that includes a collection of furniture.
      She now employs three architects and a design
assistant. Her style is eclectic, groovy, well… Tara.
It means painting the room orange and sticking some
pretty wild cushions by Fake London on a B&B sofa,
flanked on either side by orange tables from best chum
Philippe Starck. It's not everyone's taste but it hasn't
kept her from clinching some pretty serious clients,
including Tony Pidgley of Berkeley Homes, Damien
Aspinall, Selfridges and Sir Terry Farrell. People come
to her for ideas. 'I would say we now have a style that
people want to implement,' she says. It was her own
loft in Battersea that first got her noticed; next she was
working on Yoo Too with Philippe Starck. She knows
everyone and everyone knows her. 'Need a reference?'
she asks. 'Call Norman Foster or Richard Rogers.'
Her reputation is for hard work and providing a high
degree of service. As a developer's daughter she also
knows a thing or two about business. She's about to
embark on some television work, so who knows what
may follow.

What the clients say
**'What I like about Tara is she's extremely talented, has a natural
feel for what she's doing and is hard-working. She has excellent
enthusiasm for her work.'**
Tony Pidgley, chief executive, Berkeley Homes
**'She knows and gives the client exactly what he or she wants.
We've worked together in the past and I was extremely
impressed, as was the client.' Mike Rundell, designer/architect**

Taylor Howes Designs Ltd
29 Fernshaw Road
London SW10 0TG
T: 020 7349 9017
F: 020 7349 9018
admin@thdesigns.co.uk

Costs Bespoke, high end. £95 an hour for senior designers;
£145 an hour for directors.
Travel Global. Have recently worked in Lagos, Ireland, India
and Saudi Arabia.
Size of job Whole houses only.
Attitude Goldman Sachs.

Karen Howes and Gail Taylor create the kinds of
interior that make you afraid to move anything even
a millimetre lest you ruin the perfect symmetry of the
room. Even the scatter cushions and textured throws
aren't really scattered or thrown at all, but artfully
arranged to be just so. A curvy Perspex chair echoes
the lines of a modern artwork behind it, six sculptural
trees on a balcony align perfectly with the wall-to-wall
windows of a sitting room and three oars mounted
on a wall have paddles that perfectly match the tiles
of the swimming pool they overlook. This kind of
perfectionism gets them big jobs such as Kings
Chelsea Development and the Aldwark Manor Hotel
and Health Spa. Taylor Howes are the kinds of
designers who get handed a set of keys and a blank
cheque at the beginning of a project. They hand them
back at the end with food in the fridge and a dog
(probably new, too) happily waiting by the door.

What the clients say
'Great, eclectic team. We had our own vision and didn't feel
dictated to. We would definitely recommend them.'
Vicky Beverley, client
'The reaction to our newly refurbished offices has been so
positive, and clients have been blown away by our super-slick
and chic interiors. PR is all about image and that is now the first
impression created when entering our premises. They are highly
professional and always react quickly and effectively. Karen
and Gail are so personable and stylish that you are guaranteed
a terrific result. They also have an address book of invaluable
and useful contacts for the home.'
Jenny Halpern, managing director, Halpern

Felicity Thorpe Interiors
89 Lower Street
Pulborough
West Sussex RH20 2BP
T: 01798 874 039
F: 01798 874 206
inquiries@felicitythorpeinteriors.co.uk
www.felicitythorpeinteriors.co.uk

Costs Middle. Charges a design fee based on the amount of
work required. Fabric is sold at retail prices. Most jobs are
at the higher end of the market (the average budget is £30K
a room). Did a property in Wentworth with a budget of £250K.
Travel Based in southern England but will go anywhere.
Size of job Would consider one room, as in the past has ended
up doing the whole house anyway.
Attitude Grad school.

It's nice to know that there are modern interior designers
outside of London.

Thorpe started the company in 1987 after studying
interior design and taking a course in CAD (computer-
assisted design) at London's Guild Hall. She thinks it's
important to study before becoming a designer and is
surprised when she reads about designers who just
'fell' into it without ever training. She offers a complete
service, from the initial schemes, lighting and floor
plans to elevations, scale drawings of curtain treatments,
project management and completion. Her style is what
the client wants: she has done a house in Tunbridge
Wells with swag tails and mahogany bookcases as well
as modern apartments in Brighton and London. Her
showroom in Pulborough stocks stock very modern
Italian furniture.

What the clients say
'She's very efficient and modern, which is a refreshing surprise
for the country. She has a very contemporary eye.'
Sarah Chappatte, client

Todhunter Earle Interiors
Chelsea Reach
1st Floor
79– 89 Lots Road
London SW10 ORN
T: 020 7349 9999 F: 020 7349 0410
emily@todhunterearle.com
www.todhunterearle.com

Jonathan Tuckey
246 Kilburn Lane
London W10 4BA
T/F: 020 8960 1909
design@jonathantuckey.com
www.jonathantuckey.com

Costs Expensive. There is usually a flat fee (paid monthly), related to the workload and budget. Todhunter Earle are very experienced at quoting budgets and pride themselves on their accuracy. The contract is a simple one-page affair. There is an extra charge for lighting design or specific joinery drawings, or if they take on a large chunk of the architectural work.
Travel Global.
Size of job Mainly whole houses and flats, as well as commercial properties.
Attitude Nickel-plated polish.

Emily Todhunter and Kate Earle's work is about luxury. Clients (who include Le Manoir aux Quat' Saison in Oxfordshire and people with long unpronounceable names from far away kingdoms) can afford it. The style is Park Avenue meets 1940s Paris. The curtains may
be cream linen but the lining will be made from an unexpected patterned fabric; the walls may have panelling but it will be nickel-plated – you get the idea. Their philosophy is that clients should never have to do anything but sigh with pleasure.

   Emily Todhunter originally trained as a specialist painter. She was in New York in the early 1980s when over-the-top decorative techniques were all the rage, and ended up designing the interiors at Au Bar, the New York equivalent of Annabels. She returned to London and started her own company, employing Kate as her assistant. They decided to form a partnership in 1994, and Todhunter Earle was created.

What the clients say
'**Emily has done three large jobs for me over the years and for two of those jobs I was pregnant and probably not the easiest of clients. She took it all in her stride, though, and was always sensitive to my needs. My taste is actually more traditional than Emily's, but that was never a problem; she didn't push or impose anything on me.' Arrelle Von Hurter, client**
'**Katie and Emily represent a unique marriage of sheer aesthetic genius and consummate professionalism. No two Todhunter-Earle commissions ever come out looking the same. In a market where so many top designers simply apply and adapt a signature style, it is refreshing to find such a dynamic and talented design team who give their clients unique and personal space.'**
Shanon de Boissard, client

Costs Medium. Depending on the job, works on a percentage basis like an architect or on a fixed fee, for which he would use RIBA guidelines. He adds 15 per cent to items brought for a client but usually these are discounted at trade prices anyway.
Travel Will travel anywhere for the right job.
Size of job Usually whole houses but has done single rooms.
Attitude No self-esteem problems.

The 34-year-old Jonathan Tuckey has an air of old fogyness about him. He wears pinstripe suits with Birkenstock sandals, more fitting for an Oxford don than the cutting-edge designer he is. Tuckey has been known to deliberately underestimate the hours spent on a project because he was embarrassed at how much time he actually spent debating and questioning each brief. He has worked in large practices, such as David Chipperfield and Fletcher Priest. His decision to set up on his own was partly motivated by the frustration he felt at the lack of personal service he was able to give clients. His style is clearly modern but he takes real life into account: he loves colours, fabrics, furniture and playing around with new materials.

   Though Tuckey is not an architect, he teaches architecture at Oxford Brookes and Greenwich University. He approaches a project from an architectural point of view, sketching and making spatial models before he even gets to colours and fabric samples. Clients come via word of mouth and tend to stick around. Tuckey is so precise and so businesslike that misunderstandings would be hard to imagine. Tuckey makes a big impression on clients: references were so long we had to cut them (see below).

What the clients say
'**Jonathan is just brilliant. He is inspiring, flexible, incredibly efficient and always on time. I have used him for two of my houses and have also recommended him to friends, all of whom have been completely satisfied with him. He is honest and decent and has become a good friend.' Max Edgar, client**
'**The work we had done by Jonathan was fairly limited but he was still able to be stylish, clever and imaginative. He grasped very quickly what it was we wanted and was able to deliver. He has become a friend and I would definitely use him again.'**
Peter Hughes, client

Nicholas Alvis Vega
9 Pont Street
Belgravia
London SW1X 9EJ
T: 020 7235 8423
F: 020 7245 9754
lizabruce@btconnect.com

Waldo Works
North Buildings
Holberton Gardens
London NW10 6AB
T: 020 8964 5294
F: 020 8964 5049
waldoworks@btinternet.com

Costs Medium/high. Usually works on a percentage of the budget, depending on the size of the project.
Travel Based in London but has worked in California, Mexico, Morocco, France, and will go anywhere for the right job. Joked about being interested in doing a mud hut in central Africa.
Size of job Would consider anything. Speedy service this is not. Clients are prepared to wait.
Attitude Unique character.

Nicholas Alvis Vega is an accidental designer. It was only when the house he shares with his wife Liza Bruce, the swimwear designer, appeared on the cover of the *World of Interiors* (as did her store, which he also designed) that the Central St Martin-trained artist began getting calls from interested clients. Mind you, these aren't ordinary people (Nicholas is hardly mainstream): they're people like Charles Saatchi with a big interest in art and design. Vega also designs furniture: his iconic gold Throne chair is already a classic. Donna Karan owns one. Margaret Thatcher was photographed sitting on it, on the cover of *Harpers & Queen*. This is haute bohemianism. Vega's house celebrates falling-down-ness – you have to be pretty brave to live the way he does.

Vega calls it 'exuberant minimalism with a touch of primitivism'. He may put a Louis IX chaise next to one by Mies van der Rohe with some African art to throw it all off balance. He'll use an Ecuadorean cushion on a minimalist sofa if that's where he's been lately. He'll design the pool, too, and the garden. The couple also own a house (this one is luxurious) in India and travel constantly.

Though fantastically charming and wonderfully creative, Vega is his own man. If a job is boring, he will turn it down. But if he does take you on, you will get something unique. Liza Bruce gets involved with everything as well: for some clients the best part is getting to know this fascinating couple.

What the clients say

'Working with Nicholas was a lot of fun. He is very original and sees things very quickly. What is so nice about him is that he takes in everything, from art to furniture; he even helped me with my landscaping. He has a deep understanding and such a good eye.' Lady McAlpine, client

Costs Medium/high. Charges £100 an hour but is negotiable. He will also work on a percentage.
Travel Happily anywhere. Loves the country. Is presently moving between Dubai, Moscow and Ibiza.
Size of job: Will take on anything interesting. No minimum budget, though back extension in Blackpool won't appeal much.
Attitude A total pussy cat.

If first impressions mattered, you might think twice about Tom Bartlett of Waldo Works. He's of the Notting Hill school of dishevelled chic, and his office near Ladbroke Grove is piled high with papers. You wonder if he knows where anything is, but this is all part of being a member of the cool brigade. Still, Jade Jagger doesn't ask you to design half a dozen showrooms for Garrard (the jewellers) if she doesn't think you can do it. Nor does her ex, Dan Macmillan, ask you to design his flat. The celebrities (including film folk) appreciate the fact that Tom never puts on a tie or combs his hair unless absolutely necessary.

Still, hiring a designer whose tutor at the Bartlett School of Architecture was Gavin Turk has its advantages: he gives you things you couldn't imagine, like a mirror and macassar ebony kitchen. He uses out-of-the-box materials: resins, velvets, silks, on walls that most designers run away from. At 31, he is only beginning his career but already has quite a strong and loyal following. Bartlett loves to detail things perfectly, joinery in particular. He is also great company.

What the clients say

'I have always worked really well with Tom, not just because he is extremely talented and is concise and strong about his ideas, but also because he is exceptionally good at listening to and understanding people, which allows the clients he works for and the people he works with to enjoy a truly collaborative design relationship. Most of all, though, he really makes me laugh.' Jade Jagger, Creative Director, Garrards
'He has done a couple of projects for us, one being a small hotel. He listens to clients and works with them, is very practical. He does put a bit of glamour and sparkle into his designs. He's very up to date and understands new materials. Great energy. I would definitely recommend him.'
Tracy Lowy, Director of Vienna Group of Hotels

CC CONSTRUCTION LTD GE
S & P CARTER SHOPFITTING
BERRY AND VINCENT LIMIT
REYWOOD CONSTRUCTION
STONEWOOD BUILDERS LTD
RBS BUILDING SERVICES S
CHELSEA CONSTRUCTION E
ALEXANDER MALTBY LIMITE
GILBY CONSTRUCTION JOH
SHEER DEVELOPMENTS ST
F A VALIANT & SON LTD P
JUSTICE AND SONS EATON
PETER GRABHAM ASSOCIAT

GE FOSTER CONTRACTORS
ECIALISTS LTD ATELIER ONE
JOHN PERKINS PROJECTS
D M J HARDING BUILDING
IME BUILDING SERVICES UK
MONDS KENSINGTON LTD
WNSTONE SIMON BROWN
BUZZ **BUILDERS** ROBIN ELLIS
GOWER DESIGN KOYA LTD
EN TAYLOR PARTNERSHIP
ER GRABHAM ASSOCIATES
TE BUILDERS W & A BAXTER
STONEWOOD BUILDERS LTD

BUILDERS

Architects reckon that the average cost of building work is somewhere between £150 and £300 per square foot (depending on finish). Rumours are rife that prices are coming down (many a client has said: 'We wish you a recession'), but this is where your hard-earned money goes: approximately £14 billion of it in 2003. the industry is increasngly becoming regulated, a must to any client's ears.

Don't blame me if it all goes wrong

Let me start with a big, BIG disclaimer: no matter how well recommended a builder comes, how many trade associations he belongs to or how many references you have checked out, something will go wrong. Building is an extremely imprecise art that depends on hundreds of subcontractors doing their job as well. One slip in the programme (the builder's mother dies) and your budget and timetable are stuffed. Design-wise, there are all sorts of building establishments: design and build, developer/builders, carpenter/builders, green builders and anal builders who can't do anything without 300 pages of paperwork. I have not included the builders Holloway Allom and White, or Taverners because, though recommended and excellent, they require a lottery win or at the very least a couple of trust funds. Taverners is so exclusive that they only work with repeat clients (go figure).

Three things to remember

1. Building is a triangle: price, money and quality. You can have two choices but not all three. You can't have cheap and fast and quality, for example. Good builders don't like to rush.

2. If you take something out of a contract, it will be reduced by 50 per cent. If you add it later, it will go in at 150 per cent. In other words, the bathroom you no longer want will reduce the overall contract by £10,000. If, however, you decide that you want a fourth bathroom (having previously specified three), expect to pay £25,000.

3. Builders by and large hate the architectural profession (they think they're poncey white boys who don't like to get their hands dirty). Builders depend on architects for building permission: after that they want to see the back of them. 'We annoy them,' says architect John Hood, 'because whenever we turn up they feel it costs them money. We show them what they've done wrong and make them change it.'

What makes a good builder?

'My best contractors,' says Hood, 'are the ones that seem dour and worried. You want someone who anticipates the future. He should always be worried about when he's going to be bitten.' 'Personally I don't trust a builder who wears a suit,' says Jeremy Pits, design director at Studio Reed. 'I am always wary of someone who does not have a trade. I would rather have someone who is a craftsman than someone who studied at Oxford.'

A good builder shows up on time and does what he says he's going to do, for what he said he was going to do it for. Simple as that. Cristiano Silvano of CC Construction, our pin-up builder, recently rescued a woman whose £90,000 quote for a two-bedroom flat refurbishment in Pimlico, London, had gone up to £150,000 and rising. 'It breaks your heart to see this kind of thing,' he says. A good builder pays enormous amounts of insurance (£5 million in CC's case) to make sure he (and you) are covered in case things go wrong, which they will.

Some builders started as labourers and pride themselves on showing up in a boiler suit. Some are businessmen and drive BMWs. I'm not sure any of this is relevant – pick your type and go on informed gut instinct. Of course, a BMW and a second home in Spain mean he's earning a lot. This could be because he's an excellent businessman or because he's charging you horrendous mark-ups. Again, it's a competitive business – getting another quote will give you a good idea. What matters is how involved he is in the project and how much responsibility he takes on. Larger firms like Holloway & White won't give you personal time (but it will be done as they said it will be done): smaller firms are more personal. But – and this is the rule of thumb – the more they subcontract, the more you're dealing with people they don't really know.

Beware the builder who started up in business last week. 'There is a real boom and bust cycle in building,' says Silvano. 'In the '80s a lot of builders were driving taxis. Now everyone is a builder or a decorator.' What matters is experience, attitude and, to a certain, extent background. Did they bother to go out and learn their new trade? Have they invested in insurance, an office, employee benefits? Can they communicate with their workers?

Some people say 'look at a builder's truck and it will tell you everything'. Yes, a tidy truck does a tidy builder maketh, but we all know anal slobs. 'It's a bit like saying look at someone's shoes,' says Silvano.

Things to keep in mind

Sucker Syndrome

Building is a male-dominated business. There is something evolutionary about it. Builders don't quite beat their chests like great apes, but they love to blind you with science and, more importantly, problems. 'You're looking at buying a new boiler there, madam,' they will tell you, sipping your organic decaff coffee, even though you didn't ask them for their professional opinion (because they were supposed to be hanging a door). This lovely quality is known as 'male answering syndrome' and or 'unsolicited advice disease'. Always get a second opinion before you agree to anything.

Let's make a deal

Let's be honest: everyone thinks they can slip under the tax radar screen, pay in Slovakian Koruna, or in kind (I'll teach you English in return for a new floor). But, warns the National Federation of Builders, beware the VAT-free 'deal'. 'A VAT-free "deal" means one of two things,' it says. Either the builder does not do more than £47,000 worth of business per annum, or he is avoiding his legal tax liabilities. The former means he's very small (so good luck when the project expands) or that he's cheating. When he disappears back into his hole, you will have no fall-back position.

Tax

The good news is that new builds are tax exempt. The bad news is that you can't ever get planning permission to start from scratch.

The environment

Architects are very aware of issues, builders less so. Polyurethane has to be stored in tanks because no one knows how to get rid of it, for example. Half of all energy produced goes into building.

You don't have to live in a mud hut, but there are many ways to save water and electricity. Construction Resources (www.constructionresources.com) can answer any questions, not to mention provide your builder with eco-friendly paints, wood, etc. There is usually a premium to be paid for this, but if you save water and electricity, you gain it back. Increasingly, there are firms that specialize in green (see Koya and Sustainable Property Group).

Associations

There are two main associations: the National Federation of Builders and the Guild of Master Craftsmen. Both aim to be representative bodies that vet builders but the truth is they don't. They're not helpful when things go wrong (say builders) and they don't check up: a recent investigative report showed that a guinea pig was accepted to be a master craftsman. Builders have to pay to belong and complain that they get nothing for their money.

Costs

The fewer overheads the builder has, the less you pay. On the other hand, the longer he takes, the longer you will keep paying. There is a standard JCT (Joints Contract Tribunal) contract that most builders adhere to. The most important thing to remember is: changing your mind is very expensive.

Getting started

1. Look carefully at other projects your builder has done, examining the finish closely.

2. Ask for estimates, in writing, listing the works and their individual costs.

3. If it's a bigger project, think of going to competitive tender. This means inviting several builders to price the job and submit their thoughts in writing. When they sign on a figure they have to stick to it.

4. Don't think you can be the foreman. The builders will eat you for breakfast (see Sucker syndrome). It can be the architect, the designer, the project manager, the foreman, even your children, but not you! It's like thinking you can run a restaurant because you know how to cook. Did you know that the contractor has control of the property until he's finished? 'We've had clients who were kicked off the site because they were arguing,' says Paul Hellier, Managing Director of D &T Electronics.

5. Builders are human: if you throw your weight around and don't pay them, they will go bust. They often do – and reappear shortly afterwards with a new name. Many building firms declare bankruptcy rather than carry hefty insurance premiums.

CC CONSTRUCTION LTD

CC Construction Ltd
Cadogan Pier
Chelsea Embankment
London SW3 5RQ
T: 020 7376 7770
F: 020 7376 8880
info@ccconstruction.uk.com
www.ccconstruction.uk.com

Costs They guarantee their work for six months and have full liability insurance.
Travel Mainly south and south-west London, though all areas of London considered.
Size of job Normally between £100K and £1 million.
Attitude Two for the price of one.

These guys work hard: they pride themselves on being contactable seven days a week. Cristiano Silvano and Chris Edwards, both 34, met at Epsom College, Surrey. They subsequently went onto Oxford Brookes, where Silvano studied surveying and project management while Edward began (but never finished) his degree in architecture. They started as a limited company in 2002 and now handle all forms of refurbishment, project management and construction work (they also like to dabble in design). They are known within the design trade (see below), which is as good an endorsement as you can get. Most of their work veers towards the modern where details count for everything. There are seven full-time employees with up to 45 available on demand. Clients are media types like Amy Somerville, Shakespearean actors and City types.

What the clients say
'Chris Edwards is fabulous. He hand-holds you the whole way. If there's something he can't tackle, he'll get someone else and redo the estimate.'
Gerri Gallagher, associate editor, *Tatler* magazine
'Great to work with – stuck to the job until it was finished. Warm, friendly, personable and diplomatic.'
Rebecca Weir, Light IQ

Insider Information from CC Construction
Do
1. Do appoint a quantity surveyor or architect to administer the project as a third party. This will ensure the work is carried out to a good standard at a fair price.

2. Do ensure that all work carried out is with the approval of your local authority. This requires you or your agent to submit a Building Notice. It will enable you to satisfy any future purchaser as to the standard of the work on structural, plumbing and electrical jobs.

3. Do try and use Corgi-registered plumbers when carrying out any work involving gas installation.

4. Do ask for two or three references from RECENT clients of any builder.

5. Do consult a structural engineer if any structural work is being carried out. Structural calculations will be required from your local authority surveyor if you submit for local building authority approval.

6. Do agree a payment schedule.

7. Do agree a defined retention period (typically between three to six months), plus a percentage of your total contract sum. For example, if your works will cost £50,000, agree that 2.5 or 5 per cent will be held back for a period of three or six months, at which point the builder will return to rectify any minor problems.

8. Do check whether the planned works need party wall awards if you are part of an apartment block (all floors and ceilings will). This protects both parties from any damage claims, as a survey is taken prior to any works and agreed upon. At the end of the works a second survey inspects any damage, which is made good.

Don't
1. Don't pay too much up front.

2. Don't cut corners with electrics and plumbing.

3. Don't forget to tell your neighbours. You may require a party wall award.

4. If you require a total design, don't leave all aspects to your builder – consult an interior designer/architect.

5. Don't forget to inform your insurance or leaseholder of your plans. You may need their permission.

6. Don't start your project without a clear overview of your objectives and a specification for your builder to quote against.

7. Don't be too price-driven: often the cheapest is the cheapest for a reason.

8. Don't use a builder/contractor who is not able to offer you references.

9. Don't get upset by small mistakes or problems. Always take a step back and assess the bigger picture.

ATD (UK) Ltd
26 Wilberforce Road
London N4 2SW
T: 020 7503 3481
M: 07979 341 011
tomd@post.com
andrew@debertodano.net

Alexander Maltby Limited
109 St John's Hill
London SW11 1SY
T: 020 7207 3502
F: 020 7207 3527
info@alexandermaltby.co.uk
www.alexandermaltby.co.uk

Costs From £50 to £100K.
Travel London, Gloucestershire and Oxfordshire.
Size of Job From a leaking tap to a full town house refurbishment.
Attitude 'You can count on us.'

Costs His bigger work tends to be in the region of £2 million. This is grown-up: he sets up a site office on location, which produces paperwork on a daily basis.
Travel Generally works within greater London.
Size of job Takes on jobs from £300K upwards.
Attitude Maitre d' at the Ivy.

Andrew de Bertodano (brother to the journalist) and Tom Daukes are not your usual builders. For one, they're very young: for another, they're posh (Bertodano went to Eton). The two met on a building site and soon were being asked by acquaintances to do small jobs. They decided there was a gap in the market and started ATD two and a half years ago, specializing in small jobs – though they now are getting calls for bigger projects, such as the acclaimed Stag gastro pub in Hampstead. 'I think the reason we're successful is because it's very hard to find reliable people who can take on smallish jobs. It's easy to find big reliable building companies, and it's easy to find small unreliable building companies. We're the exception, I guess,' says de Bertodano. What ATD have going for them is the fact that they know how to pick up a hammer, better yet drive a bulldozer. Their reputation is for coming in on time and budget. 'If it's going to be hard to do it or if it's going to be really tight, we just won't do it,' is their motto. Clients are in the law and media, north London intelligentsia.

Gentleman builder Alexander Maltby graduated from Edinburgh University and proceeded to teach himself the building trade. Twenty years ago he started out as a one-man operation, calling himself a Residential Refurbishment Specialist: now he's doing million-pound projects for people like Jasper Conran. 'We can do anything, and we frequently do,' he says. 'We knock down the house and we hang up the pictures.' If there's something that his 50 permanent staff can't do, he'll go to one of his 100 specialist subcontractors. If they can't do it, he'll find the best person in town, vet them personally and train them up. The buck stops with him.

Maltby is considered one of Britain's best builders because he really cares. 'If you were to visit all our sites over a three-year period, you would recognize every person,' he says. Clients know him as well as he knows them. Many have worked together for over 20 years.

What the clients say
'We had a very tight budget and a very tight schedule and they worked very hard to make it happen. What's more, they made it a very exciting place to be while the job was on-going.'
Barbara Horsely, manager, Stag gastro pub
'They kept to the timescale they'd promised, and the standard was very good. They cleared up after themselves and were very clean. They were marvellous in every way, and I couldn't fault them.' Mrs Ben Howkins, client

What the clients say
'They have been very good. They're focused on the process from the client's point of view, understanding the importance of early decision-making. There is a solid methodology in place. Alexander and Stuart are a good double act: Alexander is the project manager and Stuart is the hands-on supervisor. Pro-active and have good subcontracts.'
Patrick Theis, architect
'They're a good firm whom we've worked with for many years. He's an honest builder trying to do a good job. One of an exceptional breed!' Peter Wood and Partners, architects

RW Armstrong & Sons
Armstrong House, Aldermaston Rd,
Sherborne St John, Basingstoke
Hampshire RG24 9JZ
T: 01256 850177
F: 01256 851089
info@rwarmstrong.co.uk
www.rwarmstrong.co.uk

Costs **Normally negotiated with the client or through
architects and surveyors, though a certain amount of work
is obtained through competitive tendering.**
Travel **Within a 50-mile radius.**
Size of job **£100K–£5 million.**
Attitude **Country builders.**

Just look at the client list: the Palmer-Tomkinsons,
the Guinnesses, the Hambros, Hugo Vicker, the de
Carvalhos, Paul Smith and Sarah King, and you get
the message. These are high-end, meticulous, service-
orientated, country builders whose clients are happy
to have their name on a website. Most come to soft-
spoken Nigel Armstrong, who took over from his
grandfather, through architects and surveyors. They
do everything: refurbishments, extensions, new
builds, kitchens, swimming pools – they even build
fireplaces. They specialize in Grade II listed buildings
and townhouses.

What the clients say
'Bloody good builders.' Simon Morray-Jones, architect
'Armstrong are high-quality builders who specialize in domestic
work. We have worked with them for many years and continually
recommend them and are never disappointed.'
Robert Adam, architect

Atelier One
4 Goodge Place
London W1T 4SB
T: 020 7323 3350
F: 020 7636 3350
mail@atelierone.com
www.atelierone.com

Costs **£13K – £450 million (a commercial project in Melbourne).**
Travel **All over the world – Melbourne, Singapore – but have
done the pods basically in London.**
Size of job **Will replace a beam or build a skyscraper.**
Attitude **Legoland.**

For those who can't stomach having builders around,
this may be the answer. The engineering firm Atelier
One are makers of pods, factory-made structures that
are simply craned onto an existing building (like the
White Cube Gallery) or lined up side by side or one
on top of another to form a house. Pods are steel
frames fitted out with bathrooms and kitchens (or
anything you desire, really). The outside can be clad
in anything the client wants, even wood.

Pods are more expensive than traditional building
methods (10 per cent more, but prices will go down
as demand increases), but they're also much faster,
neater and stress-free. All the technicians have to do
is plug them in. Atelier One's two MDs, Aran Chadwick
and Neil Thomas, are structural engineers who started
their career by doing touring exhibit structures. One
client suggested they make a permanent one and that
started the pod business. They now have lots of fancy
clients, including Jay Jopling, Damien Hirst and the
artist Mark Quinn. About 10 per cent of their work is
residential: they have just built two penthouses in
Fulham and Wandsworth.

What the clients say
'I have had the pleasure of working with Aran on several
residential projects where we have gently tried to push the
boundaries of innovation. Aran Chadwick is a brilliant structural
engineer. He has a supple and flexible approach to the vagaries
of the brief and to collaboration with the client and the design
team, whilst always maintaining a rigorous and clear-sighted
integrity to the overall design concept.' Pierre D'Avoine, architect
'Over the past ten years I have worked with Atelier One on
a number of challenging projects, and we are currently working
together on a large project at Heathrow Airport. I am often
inspired by their innovation and the quality of solutions proposed.
I would definitely recommend them to anyone who enjoys
collaborative working on unusual and stimulating design.'
Hilary Clark, senior design manager, Virgin Atlantic

Baxall Construction Ltd
Eastlands Estate
2 Maidstone Road
Paddock Wood
Kent TN12 6BU
T: 01892 833 344 F: 01892 834 816
info@baxall.co.uk
www.baxallconstruction.co.uk

Costs High but still priced competitively.
Travel London and the South East, i.e., Kent, Sussex, Essex and Surrey, with 50 per cent of work in central London.
Size of job £250K–£10 million.
Attitude We know what we're doing.

Malcolm Clarke, managing director of the family-owned company, was chairman of the National Federation of Builders. In other words, this is a grown-up firm, with a turnover of £12 million a year, largely because Malcolm runs a tight, efficient ship and has clients such as Queen Nor and Lord White, who won't accept anything less. He may have 250 workers on site at any given time, but he still takes the client's calls himself. He's not really that different from the bankers who employ him. His wife also happens to be an interior designer who worked for Nina Campbell and Nicky Haslam. All in-house, so to speak.

What the clients say
'They were amazing. We chose them out of six who tendered. Very polite and thoughtful, and very good with numbers. Not cheap but very thorough.' Victoria Sharp, client
'They were hugely reliable and trustworthy. Very clean and non-destructive. Nothing was damaged. Everything is beautiful, top notch. Also very clever finishes, and they teach you how to look after it all when they've gone.' Mr and Mrs Michael Baulk, chief executive of Abbot Mead Vickers BBDO
'Amazing character with very nice flair for contemporary design.' Simon Foxell, client

W & A Baxter
269 Gunters Bridge
Petworth
West Sussex GU28 9JJ
T: 01798 342561
F: 01798 342275
home@wabaxter.go-plus.net

Costs From £500 upwards.
Travel The Sussex-based outfit will travel within a 25-mile radius of Petworth – though if 'bribed', perhaps a little further.
Size of job Large ones come in at £1.5 million.
Attitude Should teach others how to do it.

It was a tie between W & A Baxter and CC Construction for pin-up status in this section.

W & A Baxter is the kind of building company Britain was once famous for. Alexander (Sandy) Baxter, 52, shows up in a boiler suit and works seven days a week. Clients often hire him before they've even bought the house. He doesn't tender for jobs because he doesn't need to. This originally father and son partnership started out as agricultural contractors. Now they employ 23 people and do everything from water gardens to full conversions for repeat clients. Sandy is known to be a workaholic. 'He takes Sunday off, that's about it,' says a client. He is a perfectionist who takes his time: one client calls him a 'wonderboy'.

What the clients say
'They are careful and considerate. The men are well behaved and will work seven days a week. Expensive but will travel a whole day to see an ironmonger.' Duncan O'Kelly, architect
'I have worked with Sandy for the past seven or eight years on both large and small projects. He is extremely good at attention to detail and operational set-up. The level and quality of service is the best in the market right now.'
Philip Acton, Philips Charters Surveyors

Berry and Vincent Limited
18 Union Road
Crediton
Devon EX17 3AS
T: 01363 772814
F: 01363 772814
berryandvincent@btinternet.com

Costs **Very competitive.**
Travel **10–15-mile radius of Crediton.**
Size of job **£10–£300K. Try to avoid the £10 jobs but nonetheless do a lot.**
Attitude **'We're part of the family.'**

This is a very old-fashioned company established back in 1770. They do all the joinery themselves and have workshops in Crediton, the local town. John Metherell, a former bricklayer, co-owns the company with his brother. John is always popping in to check on clients even though he finished months ago. 'These are proper craftsman with old-fashioned values,' says client Katie Rowan. There are 18 employees who specialize in listed buildings.

What the clients say
'They have the ideal old-fashioned set-up offering all the trades under one roof – although in their case under several roofs, as the practice comprises a couple of specialist workshops spread out throughout town. John has a very good eye for design and proportion. They are very nice country builders of the old school who aim at keeping their great reputation in the area. Very sincere, honest and trustworthy.' Mike Innes, architect
'John runs one of the most established and respected building firms in the area, and I use them whenever possible. Apart from being reliable and thorough, they can also put their hand to pretty much anything, from huge contracts to listed building refurbishments to high-quality extensions.'
Phillip Thomas, Arthur Palfrey Partnership Architects

Simon Brown
Weyside Cottage
Bepton
Nr Midhurst
West Sussex GU29 OHZ
T/F: 01730 810 353
M: 07973 512 607
smbrown@macunlimited.net

Costs **From £400–£1 million.**
Travel **London, Chichester, Guildford area.**
Size of job **Whole refurbishments.**
Attitude **Nice enough to invite for dinner.**

Simon Brown, 41, started life as an estate agent and a film producer before turning into a developer/contractor, which is what he has been for the past 15 years. Attractive and well spoken, Brown acts as though he really wants the job (which is more than many builders we spoke to). He has a few grand clients (Esther Tree, granddaughter of Colefax and Fowler, has passed his name around), some hot shots in the City, but mostly clients are normal people (such as Nicholas and Kim Hurd) with families and limited budgets. Brown does mostly refurbishments (and development on the side) for the London and Sussex set. He is a builder you can sit down with over coffee and have a really nice chat. The fact that his name gets passed around the neighbourhood is a good sign. He's has eight full-time employees and on average has 30 men on any given site.

What the clients say
'Simon Brown ripped out my house and rebuilt it in conjunction with the fabulous designs of architect Nick Yeates. He always had a smile on his face (even when under pressure or bearing bad news), he has good-quality workmen, and finished on time… nearly.' Nicky Granville, director, *The Good Web Guide*
'I suppose you could refer to him as a gentleman builder. He's a project coordinator with a full team of builders, etc. Easy to get hold of on his mobile and is good at returning calls, refreshingly. Can get help round to you in a crisis very quickly. Good sense of humour and sensible price policy. Very useful that his wife Bridget is an interior designer and does curtains and soft furnishings. A very different type of builder!'
Kim Hurd, client

Brownstone
30 Crediton Road
London NW10 3DU
T: 020 8969 1142
F: 020 8969 1164
M: 079840 33214
nathan@brownstone-uk.com
www.brownstone-uk.com

Costs Reasonable: £50K–£350K.
Travel Covers the whole of west London and greater London,
although W11 is his 'area'.
Size of job From a loft design to a full house renovation.
Attitude Zen master.

Nathan Brown is a new age builder: he spent six
years studying feng shui with the master Chan Kun
Wah (where he learned that 50 per cent of doors are
hinged the wrong way) and can regularly be found
practising sun salutes in the kitchen. Brown started
as a party organizer and a fashion photographer: his
building career took off when he did up his brother's
flat. Soon friends were asking him to do the same. He
enrolled on a building course (starting with carpentry
and working his way up) and now does refurbishments
around London. His commitment to Eastern practices
makes him a particularly empathetic builder: he is
usually more concerned with the details than the
clients. He is also capable of 'whipping up a kitchen'.
And he finishes what he starts. 'When we commit
to an end date, we meet that,' he says. Clients are
journalists and media types – Queen's Park is his
stomping ground.

What the clients say
'Nathan is sometimes to be found on site with his feet in the air.
But he's only taking a quick yoga break. Forget mounds of fag
ends, builders' tea, broken deadlines and overshot budgets.
He would never do the classic builder's trick of starting a job
and then disappearing to another one. On four occasions we
dropped by at our house, which he had gutted. It was after 11pm
and Nathan's tiler, John Hill, was still hard (and happily) at work.'
Caroline Phillips, writer
'He excels at three things: attention to detail, ability to deal with
clients, and to date, every job that I've done with him has been
completed on time and on budget. Excellent credentials for any
builder, I think you will agree.'
Ian Hume, architect, Totem Design

J&P Buildec Ltd
Albion House
Albion Street
Aylesbury, Buckinghamshire
HP20 1RD
T: 01296 436832 M: 07770 393 457
www.jandpbuildec.co.uk
email: info@jandpbuildec.co.uk

Costs Budgets from £20K upwards.
Travel Across the country. He has worked in Glasgow, south of
France and Portugal.
Attitude We get things done.

When you walk onto one of Jim Brennan's sites, you see
something unusual. Though there are men everywhere,
none of them bother looking up. They're all too busy,
even though you (me in this case) have just pitched up
with the client. You need only look at the site office to
get an idea: papers are meticulously lined up. There
are to-do lists on the whiteboard. 'Everyone comments
on how tidy the site is,' says a client.
   Brennan has been in the business for 23 years.
'I've done every trade there is, from sweeping the floor
to laying bricks,' he says. 'I'm qualified as a contracts
manager,' he says, 'but I have worked on sites all my
life.' His no-nonsense-tell-it-like-it-is attitude makes
him very popular with clients (who sometimes span
a generation – see below). He has his share of celebs
(James Nesbitt, etc.), but most clients are normal
families. The company has a £5 million turnover
and employs 24 people (90 per cent of them are
longstanding employees).
   J&P Buildec also do commercial work (for *Forbes
Magazine*, Tele West) and office refurbishment.

What the clients say
'I would trust Jim with anything. He knows every man's job and
has worked his way from the bottom up. He really cares about
his clients but is also a very good manager. He knows how to
get the best out of everyone.' Sarah Elson, client
'We came across Jim 15 years ago. He's very involved in the
job himself and has become a friend. He is always immediately
available to crack anything that goes wrong. He's an exceedingly
caring and compassionate man, who understands the trauma
of building a house. Even this morning one of his people was
here fixing something. We have total confidence in him. He's
like a family GP.' Ambassador Edward Elson, client

JND Building Services Ltd
Unit 18
Cirencester Business Estate
Elliot Road, Love Lane
Cirencester, Gloucestershire GL7 1YS
T: 01285 640 287 F: 01285 650 160 M: 0797 756 4451
info@jndbuildingservicesltd.com
www.jndbsl.com

Cost Reasonable: £19 an hour–£500K.
Travel 40-km radius of Cirencester.
Size of job Renewing a door to completely restructuring and
refurbishing an ancient building.
Attitude Home-grown talent.

JND is a real Cotswold firm. Jonathan Davies is the son of a Cotswold architect who learned his trade in the Cotswolds, starting as a labourer and working his way up to bricklayer, foreman and finally to director of a 50-man firm that has everything in-house, including interior designers. They do both modern and traditional (Cotswold) houses and never have to advertise: in fact, they don't even bother putting their phone number in the local directory.

All work comes from recommendation. Every job, no matter how small, is worthwhile. 'It's very important for me to maintain relationships because that is my business,' says Davies. After-service is a strong point.

What the clients say
'A good old-fashioned respect is borne out of ten years of working together. Building is never easy or cheap so it may as well be professional, fun and end with the right result. J N Davies are all the above and I find their "after service" second to none.' William Yeoward, designer
'Jonathan is straightforward, conscientious and keen to try new things. We have worked with him and his team over the past ten years and can't imagine a better relationship.'
Honor Riley, publisher

The Building Works Ltd
59 Harvist Road
Queens Park
London NW6 6EX
T: 020 8964 0918

Costs £35K – £500K
Travel Will work all around London and home counties.
Size of job From 'moving Patsy Kensit's car' to a complete
refurbishment.
Attitude Mr Perfect.

The utterly charming 40-year-old Alexander Cullen fell in love with building at 15 while working as an apprentice on a barn conversion at St John's College, Oxford. He set up Building Works originally with his brother in the early '90s and soon found his niche at the top end of the market. Clients now include Patsy Kensit, Conran & Partners and Anoushka Hempel (he built Blakes as well as her house). Cullen has also built oak timber houses on the Godwin-Austen estate (Robin Godwin-Austen is his father-in-law) and for Peter Van den Bergh (Alderbrook Estate). Mr Proper, he's very polite and extremely helpful. So helpful, in fact, that Kensit did the very unusual thing of thanking him when her house was featured in *Vogue*: 'I have great builders from a company called The Building Works.'

Cullen recently relocated to Surrey with his family, where, as might be expected, he knocked down his cottage and rebuilt it. Word got around and now he regularly renovates 14th- and 15th-century houses as a lucrative sideline. He employs 40 people.

What the clients say
'Building Works have done all my homes and are brilliant at dealing with demanding women like me.'
Patsy Kensit, actress
'They come in on budget and on time. Alexander Cullen is fantastic. They don't look for extras.' Francesca Mills, designer
'Alexander's is an extremely well-organized company that prides itself on workmanship and finishes. They provide both an excellent service to the architect and client, as well as good site organization.'
Daniel Campbell, Stiff and Trevillion Architects

Buzz Build Ltd
296 Latimer Rd
London W10 6QW
T: 020 8969 8588
F: 020 8969 8688
M: 07961 354222
inquiries@buzz-build.com
www.buzz-build.com

S & P Carter Shopfitting Specialists Ltd
162–164 Abbey St
London SE1 2AN
T: 020 7231 7995
F: 020 7231 8901
M: 07802 949 639
spcarter@btconnect.com

Costs Reasonable for the quality. Hazlett will do something
if he feels like it. He'll turn work away if he doesn't like or
distrusts the client.
Travel Central London – mainly around Notting Hill, Holland Park
and Kensington.
Size of job 'What starts as a piece of string can quickly become
a piece of elastic,' he says.
Attitude Existential.

Costs £ 100K– £3.5 million.
Travel Has worked everywhere but the Far East. Would
work anywhere.
Size of job Will look at anything interesting.
Attitude Marlon Brando before he went off the rails.

New Zealand-born David Hazlett was an accountant,
a chef and a film producer. He looks like someone you
might meet at a Grateful Dead Concert with his round
glasses, long hair and oversized black T-shirts. Clients
consider him a friend. He met one, Karen Mulville, of
the Talk Back Production team, at the school gates.
He's creative enough to be able to make design
decisions without an architect.

Hazlett also has his own joinery workshop, which
means: 'I can do fun stuff like build curved walls
designed by Piers Gough.' Hazlett is witty but very
serious about detail and quality. You get the sense that
clients like having him around (he's got some wonderful
homegrown wisdom, which he's happy to share).
There was a lot of smiling on the site when I visited.
He seems laid back but that's not what his (on-the-ball)
Lithuanian foreman says. A very together firm.

Pat Carter has a difficult reputation to live up to: many
architects and clients consider him to be the best
builder in London. But with the best you get
idiosyncrasies. Carter does not like paperwork (in fact,
he hardly ever fills out forms); he chooses whom he
works with and he has gone insolvent before (this is
not necessarily his fault). The 60-year-old from Leeds
started his career as a shopfitter more than 40 years
ago. Since then he has clinched some of the best jobs
in town. He has built the KYX gym, the Gucci and YSL
boutiques, and houses designed by architects Rick
Mather and Eva Jiricna. Clients include the very grand,
like Lord Rothschild, or anyone Carter likes (he decides
there and then whether he likes you). He has 40
employees and considers himself a bit of a dinosaur.
If he doesn't think the architect is good enough, he'll
tell you. He is obsessive about details and, despite his
unwillingness to fill out forms, always comes in on
time and budget.

What the clients say
'David is very bright and very creative. I found in the past that
many builders' priority is is to do things the easiest way
possible, David is not like that. He is professional, unflappable
and flexible. He did up a rental house for us in six weeks, and
the quality was amazing. I would definitely recommend him.'
Karen Mulville, Talk Back
'David is a trustworthy contractor and a lovely person to deal
with, who is capable of delivering an extremely high finish. He
and his team are familiar with all the issues associated with
high-quality residential projects, and are also resourceful when
it comes to executing bespoke architectural details.'
Anita Sen, architect

What the clients say
'He's a great builder. One of the reasons is that he's always
there. He's not poncing around in a fancy car. He gets things
done quickly and resolves problems that architects can't.
He has a very good eye.' Chris Adair, director, Cornflake
'Pat is one of the last gentlemen builders. He intuitively
understands the language that architects use doing modern
buildings. The finished product is unbelievable, extremely
high quality. He takes pride in his work and everyone loves
to work with him.' Jonathan Clark, architect

Chelsea Construction
Unit 10a
Charterhouse Works
Eltringham Street
London SW18 1TD
T: 020 8870 9020
F: 020 8870 9050
chelsea.construc@btconnect.com

Costs **From £100K though they do maintenance work for
existing clients.**
Travel **They are generally based in London (Chelsea,
Knightsbridge, Belgravia, Kensington and Notting Hill with
a few jobs in Hampstead) but should a client want to use them
for their country house (e.g., Ringo Starr), that's OK, too.**
Size of job **Average job is £300K and average time span
16 weeks.**
Attitude **The Professionals**

You should feel confident with builders whose clients
are designers such as Nicky Haslam, Emily Todhunter
and Mary Fox Linton. In fact, it was Haslam who
suggested to Managing Director Andy Langridge that
he set up on his own (he was previously at Eaton
Gate). Clients include Ringo Starr, Anne Robinson,
Collin Montgomery and slews of European bankers.
They now employ seven people and some of the best
subcontractors in the business. The sites themselves
are impeccable, as are the trucks (always a give-away
for a company). One client gives Andy all of his alarm
codes: he's happier to pay Chelsea Construction £150
to change a few light bulbs than a cheaper handyman
whom he doesn't know and doesn't trust. Andy is the front
meeter and greeter, but director Avis Hirani is the
hands-on, day-to-day man. Because they work mostly
for designers, they're used to pointing technical things
out or just doing them before being asked.

What the clients say
'They've done a lot of work for me and produced an absolutely
superb quality of finish, leaving no stone unturned. Their other
outstanding quality is timing: if they say they'll be out in three
months, they'll be out in three months. Not only do they do a
tremendously good job, but nothing is too complicated for them
it seems. Although they'd never claim to be the cheapest, they're
exactly what you'd hope from a construction company, and they
do it extremely well.' Chris French, investment banker
'I don't think I can recommend them highly enough. Every single
person they employ is a joy to work with, and not only do they do
a fantastic job, but they also follow up on absolutely everything.
The kind of company that will come to see you two months after
a job is done, just to fix a faulty light switch. I'd use them again
and again and again.'
Beverley Buckingham, Sotheby's, Private Client Services

Chester Row Project Management
2 Lower Belgrave Street
London SW1W 0NL
T: 020 7730 6650
F: 020 7730 1131
M: 07721 563302
www.chesterrowgroup.co.uk
info@ chesterrowgroup.co.uk

Costs **From £60K – £1 million.**
Travel **Kensington, Chelsea, Belgravia.**
Size of job **Whole houses.**
Attitude **John Wayne.**

Jolyon Prowse is a property developer who spent
years putting together a great team of builders.
He takes on only five to seven jobs a year. 'I only work
for clients who are recommended to me, I don't do
competitive tender and I hire architects rather than
work for them. I like to be in control of the whole
project,' he says. He qualified as a chartered surveyor
and knows everything there is to know about getting
planning permission for a building, listed or otherwise.
He's strict: he won't take on a project if the occupants
are in the house, for example, but once on board, he
sorts everything out from home entertainment to
carpets; he'll even hire the interior designer for you.
He has slews of great contacts who can do things like
make kitchens at a third of the going rate (in his friend's
East End workshop). He is known to save his clients
money, which is why they don't hand his number out
too frequently. Clients are mostly City types.

What the clients say
'Jolyon is an extremely reasonable, flexible human; it's like
talking to your husband. Always available and easy to talk to.
He doesn't send in a million invoices and knows exactly what
everything is going to cost. He's done three houses for us and
my husband's office. He is a star.' Kate Cullinan, client
'Jolyon has huge practical experience, which simplifies things
by not needing as big a team. He has a large network of people
to draw from. He doesn't tender, which means flexibility with
changes, and you don't need to write up a specification
document. He is extremely professional, very thorough and
knowledgeable. Specializes in Central London buildings.'
Vickie Wormsley, client

Clarkson Builders Ltd
Unit 85, 342 Queenstown Road
London SW8 4NE
T: 020 7720 4444
F: 020 7720 7201
clarksons1@btclick.com

Construction Resources
16 Great Guildford Street
London SE1 0HS
T: 020 7450 2211
sales@ecoconstruct.com
www.constructionresources.com

Costs Considered good value for the quality.
Travel London – as far west as Ealing and as far south
as Wapping.
Size of job From £50K–£1.5 million.
Attitude Servant's heart.

John and David Clarkson work for people who won't
work with anyone but them. 'Our clients want to see us
when they come on site; they want us when they call
the office,' says John Clarkson (45), a former carpenter.

The two brothers used to be subcontractors to
other builders and decided to pull out and do it for
themselves. They are known for very high-spec, high-
finish work for demanding clients (public figures who
absolutely don't want to be named). Clarkson work for
designers such as Jonathan Reed and Robert Carslaw,
again people with high standards. They have stayed
purposely small to remain exclusive. They look after
existing clients and do accept that being in the service
industry means changing light bulbs when required.
Straight talking and to the point, they try only to
employ British subcontractors. 'It's a health and safety
issue as much as anything else,' says John.

What the clients say
'Cute and charming. Great service. Amazing finishes… can
do most things, small and large, and not outrageously
expensive… yet!' Carolyn Lahiff, architect
'John and Dave are very good-quality builders. They're
conscientious. They really appreciate finish. It's the quality
of work that is under the skin that matters, and they really
understand this. They don't come in late without good reason.
We recently worked on a very difficult project together and
they were very diplomatic.'
Jeremy Pits, design director, Studio Reed

This is the kind of place that yoga-loving, algae-
popping, green-tea-drinking home owners shop for
building materials. You will find nothing toxic or bad
for the environment here. In fact, you're likely to bump
into Ben Goldsmith fingering the all natural paints
and good-for-the-planet insulation. They also conduct
workshops that enlightened clients may want to send
their builders on.

Desert Oak Ltd
Units 7 & 8
Briar Close Business Park
Evesham
Worcestershire WR11 4JT
T: 01386 765 451 F: 01386 765 055
camel@desertoak.co.uk
www.desertoak.co.uk

Costs Can be very competitive but price varies according to project.
Travel Nationwide. Presently have work in Dublin and Hull.
Size of job £50K–£1.5 million.
Attitude Cool cats.

This is a pretty cutting-edge firm that uses the latest technology. The three top men, Jim Ditchfield (chairman and founder), Andy Wood (managing director) and Barry Downey (associate director), are almost as cool as the name of the company. Clients include Stella McCartney and Chris Evans, not to mention Porsche Cars Great Britain (for whom they built four dealerships). They do both contemporary and traditional projects (40 per cent of their work is domestic) and take safety issues dead seriously. They try to use as much local labour as possible. They employ 50 people which, says Ditchfield, means: 'We are small enough to look after clients and get involved with them, but big enough to do large scale projects.' Their motto is: 'If the money's there, we'll do it.' Have a small works department as well.

What the clients say
'I have used them for basic projects for which they were reliable, not expensive and they showed up.' Nick Lee, architect
'Brilliant! They are very professional, meticulous and put up brilliantly with very difficult clients.' Mike Rundell, architect

Robin Ellis
Chalcot Yard
8 Fitzroy Road
London NW1 8TX
T: 020 7449 4252
post@robinellis.co.uk
www.robinellis.co.uk

Costs From two digits to six.
Travel Have worked all over UK and Europe.
Size of job 'It's not economical for us to go below £200K,' says Meckin.
Attitude Smooth operators.

You can't miss Robin Ellis's bright signs that hang on all the right houses in all the right neighbourhoods. Ellis is a trained architect who offers one of three services: design, design and build, or just build. They have some pretty nifty clients: David Bowie for one; the owner of Ted Baker, the clothing chain; and the developer Harry Handelsman of the Manhattan Loft Company, who used them for his own famous penthouse loft designed by Piers Gough, even though he's in the contracting business himself. Ellis do both commercial (such as the Princess Diana Memorial Playground, the Royal Festival Hall) and residential work. Clients are the trust-fund set, jet-setters, celebrities and lots of bankers. ('We love them,' says director Sean Meckin. 'They're the only ones who want to move in after Christmas once their bonuses have been paid.') Up to 75 per cent of their work comes via professionals (architects such as David Collins, Jonathan Reed and the very famous American designer/architect Peter Marino). They are up there in price but this is a quality firm. 'Yes, we give workers slippers,' says Meckin, apropos of the cleanliness factor. They've got 100 employees, 15 site managers and a £15 million turnover. They are no pussycats, though: if you don't pay your bills, you'll know about it.

What the clients say
'Robin Ellis is really good and hard-working. The firm will tackle things that no one else will do.' Paul Fidgen, designer
'I've worked with Robin on three separate projects. The firm has always been very helpful, very amenable and really a pleasure to work with. They have a relaxed but efficient way of handling a building contract, and are sensitive to the needs of private clients, which is unusual when it comes to builders.'
Craig Hamilton, architect

F–G

George Foster Contractors Ltd
83 Upper High Street
Broadway
Worcestershire WR12 7ALM
T: 01386 853 362
F: 01386 858 408
reception@geo-foster.com
www.geo-foster.com

Costs Not cheap. £50K–£5 million.
Travel Gloucestershire, Worcestershire, Warwickshire.
Size of job Will consider any job.
Attitude Uncle Podd.

Martin Podd is possibly the most charming builder you will find in the Cotswolds. He was originally trained as an architect but found the fees he was earning were not enough to 'put three children through university'. The builders he frequently used (George Foster) suggested he join them, which he did. He worked for a while as their in-house architect, then eventually became MD. He still does all of their design work and occasionally 'sketches for friends'. He uses a quill pen, refuses to learn CAD and is gifted at water-colours. Clients are lords and ladies: the firm have also worked on Sudeley Castle.

At 75, Podd works only three days a week, 'though my wife says I manage to bring six days' work home,' he says, but his team of 20 full-time people are there to offer as much support as he needs. All work comes via word of mouth. Martin's advantage is that he really knows how to design and can charm his way past local planners. The firm does mostly period restoration work, very hands on, offering a high level of service. Says Podd: 'This isn't London. If you need me on a Sunday, that's fine.' He has his opinions: 'I don't intrude on women's kitchens', and 'I loathe designer houses where every book has to be laid in the right direction. I like lived-in houses with dogs' hair on the sofas.' He follows Lutyens' motto: 'Tell me what you want to do or tell me what you want to spend, but don't tell me both.'

What the clients say
'We are doing up an old house that is part 17th and part 19th-century. We wanted an architect with artistic flair. We found Podd sympathetic to our views. He's a real character. A younger architect will tell you what to do but Podd listens.' Mr Andrew Malim, musician and venture capitalist
'Martin Podd is an expert in Cotswold restoration and building. He is an architect by training, and has an excellent team of workmen who have done both recreational building work and conversion. I could not recommend him more highly.' Lucy Morris, client

Gilby Construction
The Surrey Canal Office
Rope Street
London SE16 7SY
T: 020 7394 9444 F: 020 7394 9452
gilby@btconnect.com
www.gilby.co.uk

Beckside Hall
Middleton-in-Lonsdale, LA6 2NE
T: as above

Costs The very top end of the market.
Travel Within the M25 and Lake District, but anywhere really if the project is interesting.
Size of job £300K–£3 million.
Attitude Post-modernist.

This is a cutting-edge business with offices in London and the Lake District and a big interest in eco design. Clients include include Jay Jopling and Sam Taylor Wood (they did their home and her studio), Richard and Emma Curtis (they built the famous house with the blue door in the film *Notting Hill*), a few big industrialists, not to mention famous architects like Edward Cullinan, whose Cookson Smith House has graced many architectural magazine covers. Paul Gilby, now 45, hails from Lancashire. He wanted to be an architect but dad, a builder, persuaded him to follow in his footsteps. He's done pretty well for himself. 'I find this work immensely satisfying,' says Gilby. 'You start from the ground and end up with something real.' He still talks to all of his clients, which is a rarity in this world. Quality is said to be pin-sharp, say clients. About 40 per cent of his work is residential (this varies from year to year). He's not cheap but in his words: 'If you want good service, you have to pay for it. Clients only delude themselves if they think they can pay less and still get good quality.'

What the clients say
'It's not often that you remain friends with your builder. Paul Gilby is very good.' Jay Jopling, White Cube Gallery
'The fact that I have employed them to do my own house must say something about them. They did a dramatic house for Ted Cullinan on the river, which was very well received. Very keen on innovation. They push the designers forward rather than the other way round, which is very unusual.' Julian Stock, architect, Stock Woolstencroft

Peter Grabham Associates
The Kidlington Centre
High Street
Kidlington
Oxford OX5 2DL
T: 01865 841550/07802 630003
F: 01865 841597
petergrabham@petergrabham.co.uk

Costs **£90 per hour.**
Travel **Home counties, central London and Oxfordshire.**
Size of job **£150K upwards.**
Attitud **'I'm in your service.'**

I was introduced to Grabham (a former quantity surveyor) after suffering a disaster at the hands of my architect. His client, the Labour MP Shaun Woodward, warned me: 'Start with Peter,' but I didn't listen. Of course, now he's big time: clients include Liz Hurley, Hugh Grant, a Russian oligarch or two. He is a complete charmer and never flaps (even in our case when he was brought in to prepare for litigation). He gets the high rollers like Pierre Lagrange, but also the nice lady down the street. 'I met a woman today with £150K to spend – I'm just as happy to work with her,' he says. He sees his job as preventing problems: 'An architect will say "great", but then I will hear that he's starting a big job in six months – the clients should know that.' He does everything from hiring the architect to representing his clients in court. He is known for coming in on time and on budget, meaning his fees cancel themselves out. Grabham is diligent and also very good company.

What the clients say
'Peter plays a GP role. He comes in and says "it's going to
be alright". We brought him in when the building project
was out of control. He went up to builders and says "this
is what we're going to do", there's no hemming and hawing.
Things run like clockwork.' Barbara Abt, client
'Peter is very good, very serious. He's expensive, but well
worth it. We've been working so long together that we are
now friends.' Barbara Myers, client

Grove Court
69a Peckham Grove
London SE15 6DN
T: 020 7252 5535
F: 020 7252 7070
grovecourt@fireflyuk.net

Costs **£100–£250K.**
Travel **Work within central London.**
Size of job **Fixing a window to remodelling a whole house.**
Attitude **Peckham pride.**

This one's a find. In the early '70s carpenter Bill Fancourt opened his first atelier in the heart of Peckham. Today the joinery shop (with ten full-time carpenters) is still there, making 'top-end bespoke furnishing at well below top-end prices' for everyone from MPs to supermodels like Kate Moss (who used them for her dressing room) and Charles Spencer. Bill was joined by his son Nick a few years back, and now the two have moved into smaller-sized building projects, though about 60 per cent of their workload is still bespoke kitchens, wardrobes, bedroom, bathroom and office furniture. They've done well enough to land Damien Hirst's houseboat (recently featured on Channel 4's *Grand Designs*).

The Fancourts pride themselves on being flexible. 'If you need us to do up a room, we'll be happy to design it for you, although we usually work with an architect if we're remodelling anything bigger than a kitchen or a bathroom,' says Fancourt. This is a friendly firm that says things like: 'We have a fantastic client base that we like to look after. Usually we'll end up working for their friends, their children and hopefully pretty soon, their grandchildren! Isn't that what a family business is meant to be?'

What the clients say
'I have used Grove Court for the last ten years to make bespoke
joinery and kitchens. They not only produce meticulous work of
the highest quality but also collaborate fully in the overall design
process, which ensures that pieces remain fully practical as
well as beautifully made.' Mike Rundell, architect
'I've worked with them for 30 years, and it must be said that they
are excellent. Their principal, Bill Fancourt, is so experienced
that his help in design and working detail is invaluable, even to
an architect. Follow this up with good workmanship and what
you have is one of the best builders in the country.'
Russell Garner, architect

Alfred Groves & Sons Ltd
Groves Industrial Estate
Shipton Road
Milton-under-Wychwood
Chipping Norton
Oxfordshire.
T/F: 01993 830302

Brian Hannon
105 Weston Park
Hornsey
London N8 9PR
T/F: 020 8348 2163
M: 07956 819 829
bpphannon@aol.com

Costs **From £100–£2 million.**
Travel **20 miles from Chipping Norton area.**
Size of job **Projects start from £25K.**
Attitude **'We're old school.'**

Alfred Groves popped up a few times in conversations, most recently with Ruby Wax (who intends to use them) and David Astor (who has used them). The firm founded in 1660 is 300 years old and well known in the area for its restoration work (they were originally timber merchants). Roger Rawlins (with 50 years experience), managing director, now partly retired, is also known for his ability to design. They employ 26 people. The firm has grand clients like Prince Michael of Kent and Henry Dent Brocklehurst as well as ordinary weekenders who want a barn converted. Will do smaller jobs for existing clients. Princess Anne was recently overheard praising them at a dinner.

What the clients say
'They are very good builders with a special skill for restoration. Efficient and reliable. They were recommended to me. They come back anytime I need something doing.'
Sir Peter Miles, client
'A very solid, reliable old fashioned firm. Very good at traditional Cotswold houses.' Peter Grabham, project manager

Costs **Job by job basis. No hourly rate. Depends on where the work is, size of project, etc.**
Travel **North and north-west London.**
Size of job **Anything up to £300K.**
Attitude **'You're the boss…'**

Putting up a picture for a fiver in the evening or walking the dog are fine by Brian Hannon, a builder with 35 years experience. Building is in his blood: his great grandfather did it before him. This makes him fairly sanguine about the whole thing. 'I don't mind if a client changes their minds,' he says. 'I'm used to it.'

He does private domestic jobs in London for mostly repeat clients who trust him enough to leave him their dog – that tells you something. His reputation is for being tidy, on time and on budget (which means – surprise, surprise – that's he's also very much in demand). He was born, raised and still lives in North London. His clients are professionals who don't have time to chase wayward builders. He has 12 employees.

What the clients say
'I have always found them to be entirely trustworthy and honest when dealing with other people's homes. Brian remains very flexible, always willing to make changes and revisions as the project develops. His priority is client satisfaction. I would thoroughly recommend him to anyone who wants to remain involved and hands-on in the decision-taking.'
Simon Templeton, architect
'He was great to work with, very amenable and very patient. He also had an extremely jolly team. Not only is his work excellent, but he is also very hands on and good with the personal service. I highly recommend him to anyone needing a builder.'
Liza Meir, client

M J Harding Building Contractors
89 Sandy Lane
Cheam
Surrey SM2 7EP
T: 020 8642 1502
M: 07767 206666

Terry Harris & Sons
Watergates, Trelights
Port Isaac
Cornwall PL29 3TJ
T: 01208 880 434
steve@harris5911.freeserve.co.uk
www.terryharrisandsons.co.uk

Costs Extensions are priced on a metre by metre basis. He often calls in quantity surveyors to help price up the bigger jobs.
Travel South-east region and London.
Size of job £30K–£1.5 million. They will happily fix the broken door of a former client.
Attitude No blemishes here.

This is the builder that super-specialized 'take-no-hostages' designer Teeny Hickman uses for her very detailed projects (such as putting in fancy bathrooms for designers with clients like Madonna). This means de facto that he is detailed and very precise. Having finished his carpentry apprenticeship at the youthful age of 19, Matthew Harding set up by himself. He has been running his development, refurbishment and extension business for the past 20 years and now employs a team of 30.

What the clients say
'I have worked with Matthew for roughly three years. Their standard finish is excellent. All the work is fantastic and they use the most up-to-date ideas, anything that's new and good. Honest as the day is long.' Teeny Hickman, designer
'They're a very professional and reliable company with a very high standard of work. I've known them for 15 years and there's no doubt that they're one of the better firms out there.'
David Hardwood, Fulham Timber

Costs Average hourly rate is £14/hour.
Travel North Cornwall area.
Size of job Large projects as high as £1.7 million.
Attitude Matter of fact.

This is truly a local family concern in the best of Cornish traditions: family in the sense that it is run by Terry and his two sons Steve and Julian; local in the sense that they seldom travel more than six hours from their HQ. 'Basically we build very interesting, high-quality second homes,' explains Steve. 'Our main office is based in Rock, the place where the Princes take their holidays, which gives you a pretty good idea of our client base' – i.e., a lot of bankers, accountants and people in the entertainment biz. They do a lot of refurbishments, extensions and new builds. They particularly like modern design, and were recommended by a local architect, Roger Dongray. They have recently got into development. 'We're building five new houses on the coast, which we hope to sell on,' says Steve, 'and it looks like it will be the last development of its kind, as legislation has come in that will make it very hard to put up anything new in this area.'

What the clients say
'A family firm with a proud tradition of high-quality workmanship. Terry Harris has set a great example to his two very capable, forward-thinking sons.'
Ruth Jackson, film producer
'Having worked with Steve Harris and his family building firm over the past five years, we are most impressed with the service and attention to detail that he gives the project and the personal attention he provides the clients and consultants.'
Peter Sutton, Harrison Sutton Partnership Chartered Architects

G–L

John Gower Design
Unit 2
Southdown Farm
Yarnscombe
Devon EX31 3LZ
T: 01271 858 855

Justice and Sons
85 Netley Road
Ilford, Essex
IG2 7NP
T: 020 8518 4443
F: 020 8518 6166
M: 07831 310073
justiceandsons@aol.com

Costs 'Expensive is when you pay more than something is worth,' says Gower, who once spent two years building a kitchen. He considers himself reasonable.
Travel Has been asked to work in France because they wanted British craftsmanship. Mostly does the Cornwall/Devon area.
Size of job Will consider small jobs.
Attitude Self-reliant.

You don't find many builders like Devon-based John Gower anymore. For one, he's articulate and dresses like an architect (white shirt plus faded jeans). Two, he's the son of an architect and, three, he was trained as a carpenter. When clients kept asking him to do more, he turned into a builder and now employs six people and has some pretty fabulous contacts. Gower designs and makes furniture, kitchens, cabinets and tables, as well as entire houses. He is now constructing a modern timber house for the architect Seth Stein in Cornwall. He never turns clients away but is always busy – somewhat implausible but, then again, Gower, a tall and obviously confident man, has an air of total authority about him. 'I give the client what he wants,' he says.

What the clients say
'John is precision. I know from having done up another house that his work is a different standard. It's absolutely to the letter.' Mary Sandelson, client
'Their background in architecture and joinery gives them a very intuitive understanding of building that results in something rather special.' Andrew Abdulezer, Seth Stein Architects
'Resourceful, flexible, nice.' Seth Stein, architect

Costs RIBA scale.
Travel Greater London, south-east region.
Size of job Smallest £20K up to £700K.
Attitude Up for the challenge.

They built Janet Street Porter's house and have a following of loyal architect clients (Guy Stansfeld, Anita Sen and Piers Gough). Ray Justice, 50, has been in the business since he was 15 and now employs 10–15 people, many of whom have grown up within the firm. They can do very modern (always tricky), as well as English Heritage work. Clearly a nice guy, Ray also gives his services to a charity that converts warehouses into studios for artists (his daughter is an artist). All of his work comes via word of mouth.

What the clients say
'This traditionally English company is a pleasure to work with. They are good with clients, very well organized, prompt and good with costs. Gladly work with them again'.
Guy Stansfeld, architect
'I have completed six projects with Justice & Sons ranging from large-scale basic refurbishments to small-scale high-specification fit-outs. I can highly recommend them as an established and well-organized firm of builders who devote a level of integrity and care to each project that is not easily found.' Anita Sen, architect

Koya Limited
84 Furley Road
London SE15 1UG
T: 020 7639 6255
F: 020 7277 7918
M: 07968 728 678
treharris@compuserve.com

John C Lillywhite Ltd
Gravel Lane
Quarry Lane Industrial Estate
Chichester PO19 8PQ
T: 01243 781 911
F: 01243 780 168
office@johnclillywhite.co.uk
www.johnclillywhite.co.uk

Costs **Medium-sized projects. We're looking at £250K – £2.5 million.**
Travel **90 per cent of work is within 100 miles of London. One project was in France.**
Size of job **From a small house to a block of flats/ industrial development.**

Martin Hughes is a Cambridge-educated architect, as well as a designer (he also studied at the Central School of Art), who is as close to an eco-builder as you can get. He spent his formative years studying under Walter Seagal (the man who encouraged Britons to build their own houses), and now builds houses made of renewable materials that use less energy and 'don't kill the occupants'. He is too modest to say much about his clients: the singer Sade, the film producers Richard Loncraine and Patrick Uden, and architects such as Sarah Wigglesworth (of the famous Straw Bale House). Koya will design the house, pick it up mid-design or build it for you (he has since converted many un-eco-friendly builders to his methods). He goes back to Cambridge twice a year 'just to see if they've learned anything'. Once warmed up, you're dealing with a complete charmer who cares about the planet.

What the clients say
'Right where it's at. His heart is absolutely in the right place.'
Sarah Wigglesworth, architect

Costs **£100K – £1.5 million.**
Travel **All of Sussex and as far as Southampton in Hampshire. Will travel further for a special project.**
Size of job **Small refurbishments to major new build.**
Attitude **'Ethical' is how one client put it.**

The company started 32 years ago in John Lillywhite's garden shed. They now occupy a 7,000 square foot space, employ 24 people and have a reputation for integrity, not to mention a good eye for detail. They've won slews of awards and were shortlisted for a RIBA award for a house on stilts, as well as architect Kathryn Findlay's thatched-roof pool. They have also won the Sussex Heritage Award for the refurbishment of the Council Chambers in Chichester. Clients include the journalist and broadcaster Sarah Raven.

David Hobson, the MD, was an education manager before marrying the boss's daughter. (His managerial skills are a huge asset to the company.) They have in-house joinery facilities and all kinds of sophisticated computers for quick estimates. They're skilled at both contemporary and traditional, and 75 per cent of work is residential. All of the site staff are NVQ-(National Vocational Qualification) trained.

What the clients say
'They're fantastic. They're incredibly conscientious about their work and achieve the best results by not spreading themselves too thinly. They could easily work further afield but they choose to stay local, so that they can provide clients with the service. They're what you would like to think a small builder would be, which I think is, in part, due to Dave Hobson, a director of fantastic integrity.' Kathryn Findlay, architect
'They're ultra efficient with superb management. They can turn a hand to every type of joinery and have a stunning foreman, Ian Rudkin.' Duncan O'Kelly, architect

Lucking Bros Ltd
North End
North Street
Petworth
W Sussex GU28 9NH
T: 01798 342 365 F: 01798 342 933
lucking.bros@virgin.net
www.luckingbros.co.uk

Mica Projects Ltd
258 Station Road
Addlestone
Surrey KT15 2PU
T: 01932 828613
F: 01932 828614
info@micaprojects.com
www.micaprojects.com

Costs Medium/expensive. 'Anything up to £1.5 million.'
Travel 'Up to 30 miles from Petworth, although we do some work in London. As a rule, we are competitive anywhere from Sussex all the way to the south shore of the Thames.'
Size of job 'We'll replace a pane of glass for someone today, on the off chance that they, or someone they know, will be buying a mansion tomorrow. The majority of our work comes through recommendation, and this just doesn't happen by turning work away.'
Attitude Got to where we are because we try hard.

In 1965 the Lucking brothers formed a company that is now considered to be one of the best building contractors in the south. 'We don't promise the cheapest price, but we do promise the best quality,' says David Lucking, son of one of the founding brothers, who now runs the company with his three brothers. A very old-fashioned firm: 'This has always been a family business and although we employ about 50 people now, we still insist on politeness, cleanliness, tidiness and all the other qualities you'd expect from a good contractor.'

Around 80 per cent of their work comes through architects, but should a client go to them directly (which they often do), they will happily supply a designer.

What the clients say
'Very pragmatic and happy to do small jobs. They have their own workforce and know how to do things well.'
Duncan O'Kelly, architect
'They converted a barn for us and I found them very professional. We looked at a number of builders and we're delighted with our choice and what they achieved. They struck an excellent balance between traditional skills and service, and very modern methods and materials.' Guy Spurr, client
'I looked at four builders and they were the most reasonable. They're very good at restoration work (we bought a flint house), very organized and the perfect size. '
Richard Fawkes, property developer

Costs £100K–£1.4 million.
Travel Mainly London and home counties, though have worked as far north as Glasgow.
Size of job Fixing a window for a client to fitting out a whole office block.
Attitude We don't mess around.

Shopfitters are building companies that specialize in quick commercial jobs where details mean everything (they are usually masterful at joinery and finish, and often cutting edge). Many architects, such as Seth Stein (who uses Mica for most of his projects), prefer working with shopfitters for the simple reason that they have a high degree of finish and they know how to get things done on time. Mica have done the Timberland and the Whistles shops as well as other commercial work.

The company was started in 1991 by Neil McCulloch, a former quantity surveyor. He's serious, good with numbers and obviously good enough to be used by modernist architects such as Stein. Clients are bankers, celebrities, publishers, with £1 million plus to spend on their refurbishments. There are six full-time people working in the office with many trusted subcontractors.

What the clients say
'Extremely professional and very attentive to the details of the work. Capable of pulling out all the stops for the client and the architect when they need to.'
Andrew Abdulezer, Seth Stein Architects
'They're essentially fit-out merchants who do some construction. They're very professional, highly organized and are impressively fast. They don't hang about. We use them in the health-care industry because things need to be done "like yesterday". Traditional contractors tend to do a bit and then disappear for a few weeks. These guys understand the meaning of "fast track".'
Nigel Azis, architect, Nigel Azis Limited

NRL Property Facilities Management Ltd
37 Nork Way
Banstead
Surrey, SM7 1PB
T: 01737 355 777/07703 186 949
F: 01737 363 456
simon.payne@nrlproperty.com
www.nrlproperty.com

Costs **Up to £600K.**
Travel **London only.**
Size of job **From replacing a ball valve to a full
house refurbishment.**
Attitude **Relief.**

It was only because I gave a client of Simon Payne's
a lift home one night that I now have his valuable
number. Payne describes the unusual and much-
coveted service he provides as 'reactive and
preventative facilities management'. This translates
to 24-hour crisis-management domestic service for the
residents of south and west London. If your heating,
plumbing, electrics or anything else go belly up, these
are the guys who will come and fix them. The fact that
theirs is the number that Foxtons, Chestertons and
Wellingtons call when they have a problem should
be good enough. Payne started the business 15 years
ago (he was originally an electrician) and now employs
25 people. He is also a builder in his own right.

What the clients say
'Utterly reliable and always meets deadlines and budgets.
A member of a very rare breed of clean, courteous and efficient
small London builders.' Richard Pears, developer
'Simon is fantastic.' Gemma Graham, estate agent

Norman & Gardiner Limited
37a Clacton Road
St Osyth
Essex CO16 8PA
T/F: 01255 820 270
johncarney@o2.co.uk

Costs **Mid-range.**
Travel **Within a 35-mile radius of base.**
Size of job **From £4K – £350K.**
Attitude **We do what we do, and we do it well.**

Recommended by architect Rodney Black, this is an
old-fashioned practice set up in 1896 by brothers-in-
law Norman and Gardiner. The company was bought
in 1992 by John Carney and now specializes in
refurbishments of listed buildings – typically the country
retreats of high-earning barristers and solicitors. They
also have a joinery shop capable of providing bespoke
kitchens, etc., for the more demanding projects. They
employ 12 full-time staff. Of late, they have been
known to slip behind.

What the clients say
'They've been our builders for about 15 years. They've done all
sorts of fantastic things for us, and I can't imagine using anyone
else.' Mr and Mrs Watson, clients
'They have done two major projects and a fair number of smaller
projects on our home. The first large one was gutting the entire
inside and redoing it. The second one was to do the outside.
They are our first choice in contractors. They have a very skilled
workforce and are very good at dealing with older properties
that need sympathetic treatment. They are outstanding.'
Mr and Mrs Adams, clients

O–P

Mark Van Oss
The Office
Arlington Manor
Arlington, Bibury
Gloucestershire GL7 5NG
T: 01285 741 161
F: 01285 741 162
markvanoss@mvoal.co.uk

P & N Homes
Suite 9, Redan House
23–27 Redan Place
London W2 4SA
T: 020 7229 4344 F: 07000 176 329
M: 07771 700 901
office@pnltd.co.uk
www.pnltd.co.uk

Costs Charges a flat fee and no mark-ups.
Travel Anywhere a client needs him, though most are in London and Berkshire.
Size of job Budgets from £200K–£4 million. Will take on small jobs because they might lead to bigger things.
Attitude It's the client that matters.

This project manager/consultant/builder/designer was literally sweeping up floors for a Czechoslovakian decorator when he started thinking about the fact that decorators are always squeezed in at the last minute. He started his own decorating company. 'Then people kept asking me for advice on building, which I readily gave out for free.' Finally, he started doing it for a living and is now considered one of the best. His clients count on him for absolutely everything: from running the show to coming in with the cleaner before the clients move in. There are lots of nice gestures. Van Oss will build a life-size model that the client can walk around before finalizing the architect's proposal.

This is a handholding-plus service. 'Everyone thinks they're spending a fortune,' he says. 'My job is to give value for money.' He'll do anything for clients: this includes hiring decorators and sending in a marble specialist. He has hundreds of people on his books. He is often the one to be found on site at 2:30 in the morning the day before a client moves in.

What the clients say
'Mark is excellent and I would recommend him to anyone. He is very efficient, helpful, etc., and the joy is that all accounting is transparent – he takes a fee on the whole contract sum but you pay all contractors direct, with no mark-ups and backhanders.'
Susie Beart, interior designer
'He completed our house absolutely beautifully and to the highest standards, and all these years later he still turns up at my door whenever I need him. My brother-in-law just had his house completed by Mark, and he's equally happy. I think it's very telling how the guys who worked on my brother-in-law's house are the same ones that worked on my house four years previously. I've done many projects in London and New York, and not one has been as successful or enjoyable as the one I did with Mark, so I wouldn't do anything in London without him.'
Daisy Keevil, client

Costs He is considered moderately expensive.
Travel Mostly west and north London but has done houses in Hampshire and Kent.
Size of job £150K–£2 million. From £150K in London, but it has to be £500K-plus in the country. 'I can't deliver a service unless I am on site,' he says.
Attitude Refreshing.

Danish-born Claus Thottrup is in the enviable position of being fought over by architects and clients like screenwriter Richard Curtis. He is known for the high quality of his finish and a Scandinavian approach to work. 'I am very direct,' he says. His firm (between 80 and 140 people) is growing rapidly and tends to service high-end clients with a modernist bent. Typically, he will use a lot of limestone and wood, often cantilevered, which means it has to be precise. Work comes mostly word-of-mouth and is often with the same team of architects: Michaelis Boyd, Tom Croft and 3W Architects. He knows a lot about design himself, having built his own home. He is service-driven enough to have hired several Danish site managers to look after each client. He also offers his clients a maintenance service. 'There has to be an after service,' he says. 'It's always a struggle in London to find someone who can do something fast enough.' He speaks his mind, though, that's for sure. 'I'm a bit of a bull terrier,' he admits. On average he employs between 80 and 95 people. Claus is also a developer and runs an entirely separate building company that does commercial work. All this means he has to be pretty organized (though clients moan that he doesn't have as much time for them as he used to).

Claus had some problems in summer 2003 and nearly went into liquidation. But his clients continue to use him and asked me to keep him in.

What the clients say
'Claus is a good man who really cares. He grew too fast, which often happens to builders, but I would use him again.'
Paul Whalen, film director
'They are very detail-conscious and committed to handing over a well-finished product. I would definitely work with them again.'
Michaelis Boyd, architects

M. J. Partridge Ltd
Builder's Yard
Birdlip
Gloucestershire GL4 8JH
T: 01452 862 555
M: 07970 485 471

John Perkins Projects Ltd
171 Jerningham Road
London SE14 5NJ
T: 020 7639 9750
M: 07768 113 758
mail@johnperkinsprojects.co.uk
www.Johnperkinsprojects.co.uk

Costs **Considered expensive by some – 'competitive' is how they put it.**
Travel **Pretty local.**
Size of job **Like to stay small – won't go over £1 million.**
Attitude **We'll get a website and all that fancy stuff, but we'd rather do a good job.**

Costs **Still small. 'We're not the cheapest, but will give your job the respect it deserves.'**
Travel **Likes the East End but has also done Kilburn.**
Attitude **'I'll work my a… off.'**
Size of job **'We've done £400–£500 jobs but at the moment it's around £100K. We'll look at anything.'**

Chris and Robin Partridge are fourth-generation builders (the firm was established in 1919), whose 85-year-old mother still does the books. When they started listing their awards, I stopped scribbling – that's how many there were. Both brothers did their apprenticeship within the firm and now more or less work for everybody in the area, including Lord and Lady Vestey, Lord Liverpool, Michael Dobson and the designer Jane Sacchi. This is a proper firm with a £5 million turnover and 40 staff. They still use traditional carpenters, have yet to build a website and don't like to be rushed. Lord and Lady Vestey won't allow anyone else in their house. They say things like: 'When we say we'll do it, we do it.' Will also do maintenance after the fact. They usually get booked early and seldom go to tender.

What the clients say
'They are fantastic. Their quotes do not come cheap but they come in on time. Couldn't be more pleased.'
Jane Sacchi, Jane Sacchi Linen
'They are fantastic. When it came to the snagging list… there wasn't one. They put on extra people when needed and even found us a cleaning lady.' client
'Very talented and very good.' Rob Ashby, architect

This is the builder who did David Adjaye's Electra house. An Essex working-class boy, Perkins originally started out copying designer kitchens and then expanded to bigger things, such as bars for companies like the Breakfast Group and the Canteloupe Group, and cutting-edge houses for architects such as Adjaye, Tom Emerson of 6a and Jonathan Tuckey. He runs the business with his wife and focuses on what he wants. 'I want to do a very precise job, so I am careful,' he says. Music to anyone's ears.

He accepts that builders are the fall guys. 'We're scapegoats,' he says. 'What we find when you're working in the domestic market is that you have to be a psychologist. You become part of people's aspirations.' Clients vary from trust-fund billionaires to impoverished artists. One client described them as 'slow' but Perkins refuted it with: 'We just built a new build in 48 weeks!' Perkins is a real builder: he wants to be on-site rather than sitting in an office pushing paperwork.

What the clients say
'We've worked with John on five projects and we've just started another. Every building project has its fair share of difficulties and challenges. What I have always enjoyed about John is that he is always part of the solution. His prices are very competitive and his team produce work to a very high standard. Paperwork is not his strong suit but this is compensated for by the fact that John is extremely trustworthy and honest. He has genuine knowledge and interest in construction of contemporary design, which makes the whole process collaborative rather than confrontational. I think it's no accident that he has built so many of the most architecturally interesting small projects in London in the past few years.' Tom Emerson, architect, 6a Architects
'John Perkins Projects are first-rate builders… methodical.' Jonathan Tuckey, designer
'Cool, really cool builder.' David Adjaye, architect

107

Prime Building Services UK Ltd
572 Becontree Avenue
Dagenham
Essex RM8 3HR
T: 020 8595 1090
M: 07773 777 821

RBS Building Services Ltd
159 Mortlake Road
Kew
Surrey TW9 4AW
T: 020 8876 0052
F: 020 8392 9569
dave@rbsbuildingservicesltd.com

Costs 'I'm not the cheapest,' he says.
Travel London, Essex, Brighton.
Size of job From £50K upwards, but will take on smaller jobs
if they're in between projects.
Attitude Guru.

Costs Expensive. You don't get minimalist perfection for nothing.
Travel Hertfordshire, Glasgow, Manchester, Edinburgh, Bath,
Bristol, but mostly London – wherever the client needs them.
They will live in caravans for weeks on end if necessary.
Size of job Will take on any job – highest is around £1 million.
Attitude Curious competence.

Gwyneth got luckyHarji Bhudia learned the building
trade (carpentry) from his father. Now he runs a
(mostly Indian) firm that has done some of the most
challenging projects to date for architects like Patrick
McInerney and John Silver. One job they tendered
for was rejected by all the other builders because of
its quick turnaround time. 'We worked seven days a
week on that one,' says Harji, who always puts an
'OM' on his project sites to keep evil spirits away.
(The symbol of both the personal God and the
Brahman or Absolute, Om is regarded by Hindus as
the greatest mantra of incalculable spiritual potency.)
He had to put up a few extra on Gwyneth Paltrow's
house to keep the paparazzi away.

His team is largely made up of family members
(six to seven work for him at any given time). His wife
answers the phone. He was proud to tell me that he is
now limited. 'We used to trade £600K a year, now it's
£2 million.' He only takes on two or three projects
a year, or one at a time. 'Clients wait for us until we
are ready,' he says.

Dave Manchester is an unusual builder. When the
minimalist architect John Pawson hired him for the
Jigsaw store, the first thing Manchester did was jump
on a plane to New York to see the Calvin Klein store
(also designed by Pawson). 'Then he went off to
Amagansett for the weekend,' says Pawson. RBS
subsequently did Pawson's own house, which meant
closing down the street to crane in pieces of marble
and limestone – not your usual stuff, in other words.
'Minimalism is always a bit more of a challenge
because you have all the normal practicalities of
a building project but are hiding all the mechanics,'
Manchester says. Basically, if he can keep Pawson
happy – a man whose architecture is so pure that any
mistakes stick out like a sore thumb – he can please
anyone. The 20-year-old firm employs 30 people and
is used primarily by modernist architects such as
Pawson, Eldridge Smerin and Found Associates.
They've done the Hobbs shoe stores and have worked
on an award-winning house on Pilgrim Lane and for
Retreat Living on Great Portland Street.

RBS also employ Gary Whiskers, a quantity
surveyor and project manager, which means jobs
run smoothly.

What the clients say
'Harry is still there at 10 o'clock at night. He has a great rapport
with the clients. He tackled a project with me recently that all
the other builders said couldn't be done. We were finished
48 hours before the clients moved in. He really cares.'
Patrick McInerney, architect
'Harry is delightful to deal with. He provides very good quality
and is incredibly hard-working.' Charlotte Washall, client

What the clients say
'Dave Manchester is an unfailingly genial man who is genuinely
interested in the work. I knew he was the right man for the job
when he took himself off to New York to see the Calvin Klein
store on Madison Avenue as preparation for the Bond Street
Jigsaw project.' John Pawson, architect
'I find them totally reliable as contractors. One of the few
contractors that I have come across who are excellent builders
as well as first-class interior fit-out contractors. Dave
Manchester is very much a "hands-on" director with
a refreshing honesty seldom found in the building trade.'
Richard Found, designer

Reywood Construction Ltd
MacMerry Industrial Estate
MacMerry
East Lothian EH33 1RD
T: 01875 615 400
F: 01875 610 115
lesley@reywood.org
www.reywood.org

Costs **Variable hourly rate for existing clients.**
Travel **Edinburgh and the Lothians.**
Size of job **£10K – £2 million.**
Attitude **Family affair.**

This a real family firm where sister and mum took turns answering our questions. Steven Reynolds is now managing director (having joined his father, the firm's founder). There are 50 employees who do mostly traditional new builds, extensions and refurbishments. They enjoy working with architects who understand that 'sticking to a budget' is often high on the list of priorities of many clients. 'The perfect clients are those who are prepared to take advice on board when cut-backs are necessary to meet their budget.' They have done a fair bit of restoration and preservation works with The National Trust for Scotland and Historic Scotland.

What the clients say
'It's a good family-run company that is not claims-conscious and provides a high standard of workmanship.'
Ian Thompson, MRICS, Ross & Morton Surveyors
'We have worked on a couple of big projects with them. They are an up-and-coming company who are very well run from the top. Steven is hands-on and is on-site. They produce high-class work and their response time is quick. I have had no trouble with them at all.' John Murray, architect

J Rigg Construction and Development Limited
Parkside
Dumbleton
Nr Evesham
Worcestershire WR11 6TL
T: 01386 881071 F: 01386 881586
johnathanrigg@btopenworld.com
www.jriggconstruction.co.uk

Costs **£500K – £3 million**
Travel **Radius of 50 miles from Dumbleton.**
Size of job **A rectory extension to a complete country house refurbishment.**
Attitude **Crème de la crème.**

It's unusual to meet a builder with a degree from the London School of Economics. After graduating and dabbling in property for a bit, Rigg moved to Worcestershire where he landed in the world of the mega rich, and now spends his time hopping from island to island on clients' private jets. 'We're geared up for dealing with the larger projects, usually four or five at a time, so it's no surprise that our clientele tends to be wealthy and well known,' he says. Clients have long titles and equally long driveways.

Rigg has 35 employees and an army of subcontractors. J Rigg are specialists in Cotswold stone and Georgian red brick, but are willing to take on just about anything. 'We've completely remodelled substantial country houses and built some fairly significant modern ones. I've learned this means being ready for just about anything, from the numerous unusual swimming pools we've made to the bridge we built at Paxton Manor.'

What the clients say
'The smoothest gentlemen builder in Gloucestershire, the ultimate "master builder" with the most enormous amount of integrity.' Viscountess Sandon, designer
'I have worked with J Rigg Construction on many projects over a period of 15 years or more. It is a pleasure to work with them because Jonathan Rigg has a very good idea of what the client and we are expecting, and the members of his workforce have a truly "can-do" attitude.' Toby Falconer, architect

Seymour Projects Ltd
37 Richford St
London W6 7HJ
T: 020 8740 0724
F: 020 8740 4332
M: 07778 648 529
johnny@seymourprojects.co.uk

Sheer Developments
71 Walton Street
London SW3 2HT
T: 020 7823 9646
F: 020 7823 9645
info@sheerprojects.com
www.sheerprojects.com

Costs Middle. On tenders they will usually be in the upper half of the market, never the most expensive but not the cheapest either.
Travel They work in west London (especially Notting Hill), although they have also worked in Shoreditch and the City.
Size Projects are normally £100K – £500K. For contract work they average £200K – £500K.
Attitude Worldly.

Johnny Seymour started life as a photographer. He decided he wanted to try something else (having found a passion for building sets) and started his construction company in 1979. Pretty soon he had clients like Nina Campbell.

After a difficult spell in the '80s (when many builders went bust), he joined up with Steve Patten whose background was 'big sheds' – that's industry-speak for shops like Toys R Us. Since forming a partnership, they have done the Bush Bar and Grill, Woody's and many residential projects for people like the writer Sebastian Faulks, and architects Michaelis Boyd and Tchaik Chassay. Seymour's address book is teeming with names of specialists: French polishers, steel specialists, marble and stone experts. At 59 he has lost none of his enthusiasm: 'I really love the mechanics of building, the huge changes that go on from the start to the finish of a project.' Building is hard work and, as with all professions, I think you have to enjoy it to do it really well.' He employs two full-time people and subcontracts all other work.

What the clients say
'They were absolutely fantastic.' Veronica Faulks
'Excellent. Simply the best person to work with on any project. Seymour takes an enormous amount of pressure off the architect, he is steady, reliable and an all round good builder.' Tchaik Chassay, architect

Costs Top end. About 20 per cent more expensive than others. Size of job £100K – £5million.
Travel South-west London – have worked in Chiswick and Kew.
Attitude 'If I can't run Morgan Stanley…'

Italian Marco Pangherz, a 36-year-old former banker at Bank Paribas, was so impressed when he met builder Mark Steeds that they decided to go into business together. They started the Sheer Development in 2001 and now offer 'bespoke luxury' – in other words, very high-spec refurbishments. To give you an idea of how serious they are, they write to the next-door neighbours to inform them that they will be commencing a project. They make a point of washing down the pavement at the end of the day. If the client is looking for a new kitchen, Marco will fly out to Italy to source the best one for the best price. They do micro and macro: a whole house minus the client (because he's away making billions) or something bitty like a bathroom.

Needless to say, their clients are foreigners and bankers – people who simply will not put up with the usual incompetence and mess. Marco says things like: 'We are an aggressive little company that is growing slowly,' or 'Always at the end of a phone line' or 'A very well-oiled team'. Sounds like a banking pitch but they live up to it. They were recommended to us by an American neighbour who saw them in action. 'I mean – not a speck of dirt when they left.'

What the clients say
'From the start of our involvement with Sheer, I have been impressed with the speed, quality and professionalism of their work. Under severe time constraints, the site staff and administrative staff were able to complete the project smoothly and on time.' Geoffrey Makstutis, architect
'All you can ask of a company is that they deliver on time, to budget and to the highest standards. Sheer achieved all three and, on top of that, were a delight to work with. I'd use them again in a flash.' Justin Bairamian, audience researcher

Simmonds Kensington Ltd
4 Pembroke Place
Kensington
London W8 6ET
T: 020 7937 0122
F: 020 7937 0322

Costs **From £70 – £200K.**
Travel **West London.**
Size of job **Prepared to do small jobs.**
Attitude **On Her Majesty's approval.**

This is the man who built the Beckhams their house (though he is far too much of a professional to indulge me with any details apart from the fact that they were great clients). Two things about Simmonds: one, owner Roger Sinclair will call you back right away from a landline. Two, if there's anything you need, he will be on the phone the very next day confirming the appointment with the appropriate specialist. Roger Sinclair is the latest to own this established firm of Kensington-based builders (they have the Royal Seal of Approval), who employ seven full-time staff. Efficiency, neatness and politeness are the hallmarks of his business. They even have the courtesy to dustsheet the garden. Typical jobs include refurbishments, roofing and plumbing, though listen to this: they're prepared to do small jobs. Roger has many teams of builders to choose from and usually arrives with them. He is a straight-talking kind of guy whose relationships are based on trust – he does the work first and asks for money later. 'We check the clients out as much as they do us,' he says.

What the clients say
'Absolute, complete professionalism. Always on time, always on budget – 100 per cent reliable.' Joanna Plant, designer
'They turn up on time and ring before they come. They always clean up after themselves. Impeccable.'
Caroline Amrolia, solicitor

Stonewood Builders Ltd
Long Dean
Castle Combe, Chippenham
Wiltshire, SN14 7EX
T: 01249 782 293 F: 01225 744 519
M: 07971 022434
inquiries@stonewoodbuilders.co.uk
www.stonewoodbuilders.co.uk

Costs **£40K – £500K.**
Travel **Based in Castle Coombe, they work mainly in the surrounding Wilthshire area, taking in Swindon, Bath, Devizes and the closer parts of Bristol.**
Size of job **Big projects in the pipeline but would do smaller jobs for previous clients.**
Attitude **Honest.**

Stonewood built Gatcombe Estate, the home of Princess Anne, as well as Corsham Court. They've also worked on the Badminton Estates. Founded 35 years ago, they specialize in refurbishing and restoring listed country homes. The three directors – Tim Saunders, Matthew Aitkenhead and Neill Aitkenhead – employ 22 people.

What the clients say
'It is so important to find a builder you can trust to get the job done on time and on budget. The team at Stonewood run a professional business, but one that is also small enough to remain personal. Matt, who heads the firm, is young, enthusiastic and just a really nice guy!'
Emma Sims-Hilditch, designer
'They restored an 18th-century millhouse for us. They were incredibly straightforward and honest. Excellent work.'
Louise Turner, client

Strategic Construction Limited
Unit 10
Blackheath Business Centre
Blackheath Hill
London SE10 8BA
T: 020 8692 7700 or 020 8692 7200
paul@strategicconstruction.uk.com
www.strategicconstruction.uk.com

Costs You're looking at figures of between £1,000 and £1,500 per square metre, depending on materials. The average refurbishment probably costs around £300K.
Size of jobs A small refurbishment to a large new build: £20K – £3 million.
Travel Within a 50-mile radius.
Attitude Focused.

This is an ambitious, professional outfit that started up four years ago. Directors Paul Anderson, 42, a former site engineer, and Fred Yusuf, a former bricklayer, pride themselves on their business-like attitude. Clients get a written programme from the beginning and written notices when there is a delay or any change in costs. 'We're an open book,' says Anderson, who has worked (in his previous firm) with Sir Richard Rogers, Eric Felner, Alan Yentob and Jonathan Glazer, the film producer. 'I've always said reliability, integrity, no secrets is our motto. We have a rolling final accounts, and we pride ourselves on having little or no snagging,' he says.

The team of about six drive around on motorbikes, though Anderson is the proud owner of a Porsche Turbo, thanks to a very good head for business. Put it this way, he started with a £700K turnover and is now at the £5 million mark. Anderson is serious, straight and fiercely determined to be a success. They have some commercial projects, too, such as the Novotel and Ibis hotel chains and a restaurant for Michelin-starred chef Tom Aikens. To be on time means that Fred occasionally has to get off his motorbike and lay some bricks himself. Strategic also work a lot for architects such as Michaelis Boyd, Sasha Gebler, Stephen Turvill and Alan Higgs. They're Greenwich-based and work in central London, with many clients in the Notting Hill area.

What the clients say
'The great thing about Paul is that he is very organized, and his standard and quality are impeccable. You will never need to chase him, he is one step ahead… And he always finishes on time.' Carlos Calvo, property developer
'Paul and Fred run the company very, very professionally, and are immensely responsive to the client or architect. They do a great job and an excellent finish.' Steve Ashley, banker

Sustainable Property Group Ltd
Cowley Farm
Aylesbury Road, Cuddington
Buckinghamshire HP18 0AD
T: 01296 747 157 F: 01296 747 703
M: 07977 045 902
info@sustainable.uk.com
www.sustainable.uk.com

Costs £40K – £1.5 million.
Travel UK.
Size of job We're flexible.
Attitude Others should follow their lead.

This is an environmentally focused firm founded by Stuart Anderson 15 years ago. He himself is considered to be more of an artist then a builder. 'He can see things that no other builder can,' says client Michael Burrows. Another client is George Michael who is on his third project.

His son Darren recently joined him as MD. Darren has a masters in environmental management, which has a lot to do with the firm's commitment to saving the planet. Green issues are paramount. 'But,' says Darren, 'we don't stuff it down our clients' throats. Green doesn't mean mud and straw. You can use the latest state-of-the-art materials.' For example, Darren recently completed a barn conversion where a standard slate roof was replaced with photovoltaic slates, which now give the house 60–75 per cent of its electricity. About 50 per cent of the firm's work is green-focused development: the other is luxury renovations in London (for the likes of George Michael). 'Wherever possible we try to combine both,' says Anderson.

There are 25 employees. This is green bespoke: they handcraft their own oak roofs, rafters, etc., from local timber when at all possible. Their name is now getting passed around the celebrity circles – one happy celebrity means many more will follow.

What the clients say
'If I could work with Stuart every day of my life, it still wouldn't be enough. He's phenomenal. Apart from being bloody good at what he does, he's also one of the nicest people I've ever met.' Ann Boyd, designer
'Stuart Anderson is a joy to work with. He gave us a home (a barn conversion) that would have been unachievable by anyone else. There aren't many builders who have his style and sympathy for a building. He won't put in a fireplace, a floor, or even plaster a wall unless he thinks that's how it should be done.' Michael Burrows, businessman

Symm and Company Ltd
Osney Mead
Oxford OX2 0EQ
T: 01865 254900
F: 01865 254935
www.symmgroup.com

Stephen Taylor Partnership
40 Sisters Avenue
Battersea
London SW11 5SQ
T: 020 7228 9055
F: 020 7924 4082
M: 07831 647 138

Costs **Expensive. (They usually come way above other bids.)**
Travel **You need us, we'll get there.**
Size of job **Budgets from £250K – £15 million.**
Attitude **'The Business.'**

This is a heavyweight building firm – a fourth-generation, 100-year-old firm that exports its skills as far as America. The Symm Group is made up of several different companies: they do joinery, stone work and full building services, and are one of the few building companies left in England that still train apprentices (35 at any given moment). 'The builder should employ his craftsmen. He should train his craftsmen,' says 65-year-old chairman Malcom Axtell, a man who likes to take clients around the facilities personally. The company employ their workers full-time (they have 100 staff).

They are known for building exquisite traditional houses of stone or timber (they are specialists). 'We have people in the workshop who can trace the wood back to the 18th century,' says Axtell.

Symm also does contemporary: clients include the De Rothschilds and architects such as Allies Morrison and John Simpson (a favourite amongst the Royal family). They also got their foot in the door at Covent Garden, Daylseford House (belonging to Sir Anthony Bamford, head of JCB), Oxford University and the Queen's Gallery in Buckingham Palace.

Their clients are discerning professionals who want impeccable houses, but, says Axtell, they're not all filthy rich. 'If a project has been delayed, we will happily take on something smaller, a contract worth £100K perhaps.' The manpower gives them that kind of flexibility. They also do decoration and maintenance, not just as in 'if we have to' but as in 'this is a service we offer'.

What the clients say
'Impeccable, immaculate builders.'
Serena Williams-Ellis, interior designer
'They are very good with very good management skills. They are also good at sticking to a budget. There is a saying that you only go out to tender to find out who is the most expensive, then you hire them. You get what you pay for in the building trade.'
Lt Col Peter Browne, estate manager, Glympton Parke

Costs **Reasonable. 'Some are cheaper and some are more expensive, but at the end of the day you get what you pay for.'**
Size of job **Charges £30 an hour for maintenance work; projects up to £250K.**
Travel **Most of London.**
Attitude **'I could blind you with science, but I won't.'**

Stephen Taylor started his career as maths teacher. He then became a plumber. Eventually, he started adding bits and pieces – plastering and so on – until he became a fully fledged builder. Where the maths comes in handy is with his approach to the client. 'I won't start a job unless I can finish it,' he says. The 20-year-old company now employs ten people and boasts clients like Cath Kidston and Jack Dee. Taylor is prepared to do small jobs (in fact, he prefers them). This is an unassuming, straightforward builder who thinks before answering questions. He gets passed around from friend to friend, a bit like a chain letter.

What the clients say
'Stephen is that rarity – an intelligent builder. He shows great sense and workmanship in every job he undertakes and never cuts corners.' Cath Kidston, designer
'He is a gentleman builder who doesn't start what he can't finish.'
Rachel Meddowes, design editor, *Harpers & Queen*

T – W

Treliganus Limited
The Broich
Doune
Perthshire
FK16 6HJ
aly@lanrick.co.uk
T: 01786 841 866
F: 01786 841 134

Costs **£20K – £500K.**
Travel **Within Scotland.**
Size of job **Fitting a kitchen to building a new ten-bedroom house.**
Attitude **From a time gone by.**

'We're a very, very small company that does rather large projects to an exceedingly high standard,' explains Alistair Dickson with a certain satisfaction. Treliganus was launched 25 years ago with a flat conversion in London's Eaton Square. 'Even in those days I believed that the person who designs the scheme should build it as well,' he says. 'I saw that project through from inception to fulfilment, and have done so with just about every subsequent one.' Dickson, who trained at the Inchbald School of Design, often works with architects and designers; however, he believes in the benefits of having one person direct an entire project. Clients are lawyers, moneyed folk, professionals, etc.

Dickson and his partner Michael Mingay (who heads the project management side) specialize in the exclusively residential renovation of Scottish country houses. They employ three people directly and offer an in-house design service as well. They do mostly new builds and refurbishments (50/50). They pride themselves on being service orientated.

What the clients say
'**I have worked with Alistair Dickson a number of times over the years and he is always conscientious, helpful, hard-working and enthusiastic. You can depend on him and his team to have the work ready on schedule – a recommendation that cannot always be relied upon in this business, but in Alistair's case it can be.**' Willa Elphinstone, interior designer

F A Valiant & Son Ltd
36 Bury Road
Barrow
Bury St Edmunds
Suffolk IP29 5AB
T/F: 01284 810297

Costs **From a £50 call-out to £2.5 million.**
Travel **Suffolk, Norfolk, Essex and Cambridgeshire.**
Size of job **Replacing a roof tile to a complete new build.**
Attitude **We care.**

Managing director Roger Valiant, 58, is a third-generation builder. His great-great-grandfather built wells in the Suffolk area, and in 1945 his father started F A Valiant & Son, builders specializing in the restoration of historic and listed buildings. They are English Heritage-listed, which means they can take on any project of any period. The 30-man team is highly skilled in traditional crafts as well as modern methods. The carpenters are experts on oak frameworks; the bricklayers also do flint and stone walling, etc. This is an old-fashioned service that mostly restores churches and listed buildings. But they work for architects like James Gorst, so they can also go really modern.

What the clients say
'**He is unreservedly one of the best builders in Norfolk.**' **Richard Morris, banker**
'**Three generations of the finest traditional craft-based contractors in East Anglia.**' James Gorst, architect

Warriner Builders Ltd
19 The Lennards
South Cerney
Cirencester
Gloucestershire GL7 5UX
T: 01285 861 934
F: 01285 862 365
Michael.warriner@btconnect.com

Costs £20K – £400K.
Travel Within a 20-mile radius of South Cerney in
Gloucestershire.
Size of job Varies from a couple of hours' work to £400K
for full refurbishments.
Attitude 'Builders don't have to be the enemy.'

Softly spoken with a West Country drawl, Michael
Warriner is the builder of choice for those in the know
in these parts. At 53 he's seasoned enough not to
bother with contracts with repeat clients who, in his
case, are big wigs such as Barry Townsley and Howard
Hyman, plus lots of other bankers and celebrities that
he's too proper to mention. He's a bit of a workaholic
(he is no longer married). 'A client will suddenly want
to add a kitchen and you were supposed to be starting
another project,' he says. 'You sail close to the wind in
this business.' Warriner does mostly refurbishments
for London weekenders (these tend to be in the multi-
million price category). He employs eight people,
mostly stonemasons and carpenters. Clients often
come to him directly, at which point he finds them an
architect. 'I only work with good drawings.'

What the clients say
'Mick has been our builder for at least ten years. We've kept him
on because he's so good, because we can trust him, because
he's reliable and because he does the job properly. We have
a large new project coming up and we're going with Mick
rather than putting the job out to tender. Why? Because although
he may not be the cheapest, he IS the best.'
Paul Springate, Harnhill Centre of Christian Healing
'He has a brain and he uses it, he has experience and he
remembers it. He's sensible and he listens. An intelligent man
who does what he does well.' John Marsh, architect

G A Wildish (Southwest Ltd)
The Lower Yard
The Old Bodmin Jail
Scarletts Well Rd
Bodmin
Cornwall PL31 2PL
T: 01208 72 707

Costs Average £130 a day.
Travel 25-mile radius of Bodmin.
Size of job £25 for a small job to £300K for a large conversion.
Attitude If we're not busy, we're all yours.

Not every builder can boast he works from a jail. Dave
Smale says the cells are useful: 'That's where you go
when the bills don't get paid,' he says. He can spin
a tale all right and loves to amuse burnt-out London
folk with second houses in Cornwall. It's a fair-size
business with a £700K turnover a year – £100K of that
is 'bread-and-butter' work for Cornwall County Council.
The remaining is residential. Smale does mostly
traditional extensions and conversions and employs
15–16 people.

What the clients say
'They are reliable, honest and remarkable builders. I wouldn't
use anyone else.' Henry Hood, solicitor
'They were brilliant. Real old-fashioned gentlemen craftsmen
with values and honesty. If ever there was a problem, they
would phone me immediately with the solution. Ran to time and
didn't overcharge me. Even if I wanted a little extra, they tried to
cover it without extra cost. What's more, their subcontractors,
especially the plumbers and electricians, were just as
thoughtful. An outstanding firm who understand what it means
to take pride in your work.' Carrie Crutcher, client

M–N

R Williams Building and Groundworks Ltd
The Cider House
Halmore Lane, Halmore
Nr Berkeley
Gloucestershire GL13 9HQ
T: 01453 810 244 F: 01453 811 589
admin@rw-building.co.uk
www.rw-building.co.uk

Costs **£20K – £2 million.**
Travel **30 – 40-mile radius of base.**
Size of job **An extension to a whole house. They are also doing development work in the area.**
Attitude **Are you good enough for us?**

This is an exclusive building firm with clients like Prince Charles and the Princess Royal. Their website pretty much sums it up with 'traditionally built, high-quality homes'. Roger Williams, who started the company in 1992 with his enthusiastic wife Kate, offers a high level of service to clients who expect nothing less. 'We have 25 fantastic employees,' says Kate. 'If there's anything they can't handle, we work with all the best specialist craftsmen in the area, too. People expect the best from us, and we find that giving them the best tends to prevent a lot of hassle. Even though this makes us slightly more expensive than most, our clients truly appreciate the complete service.' They take on a small number of select projects (about ten a year) for a fairly discerning clientele (polo players, for example). They are considered eco-conscious (HRH would not use them otherwise). They will turn work away if it's ten miles past their patch, for example. The solution is to buy a house next door.

What the clients say
'Roger did the original new build on my house and has been working with me ever since. They've been just excellent. All the work has been of the highest quality, and so I'd be happy to recommend them to anyone.' Mr and Mrs Salter, clients

Koichi Yamaguchi
1 Percy Gardens
Worcester Park
Surrey KT4 7SD
T: 020 8330 2998
M: 07966 196 340

Costs **Middle to expensive.**
Travel **Central London but spent several months working for a Japanese company in Cambridge.**
Size of job **Ideal budget is £500K. Will also take on small jobs, e.g., maintenance, painting, roofing work, etc.**
Attitude **Far East precision.**

Nicknamed 'Gucci' by his workmen because they can't pronounce his name, this Japanese carpenter/builder/maintenance man with 28 years of experience in Britain is a real find. Not only has he built Stella McCartney's London houses (and physically built her famous roof-top shower) but he's there at 6:30 in the morning, long before the client has even woken up. He despairs of the wave of new 'cash-in-hand' builders who have no training and no insurance. 'I have to trust my clients and they have to trust me,' he says.

Koichi originally trained as a cabinet maker and had his own workshop (his father was a cabinet maker before him), but then moved into contracting and maintenance work. Having said that, Koichi still designs his fair share of kitchens and wardrobes. He has many loyal subcontractors, whom he dispatches all over London to do roofing, painting and electrical work. Though he gets asked to do the £3 million jobs, he prefers to work with modest budgets. His name was given to us by interior designer Catherine Connolly who considers his craftsmanship amongst the best she has seen.

What the clients say
'Koichi was working in the flat above me in Oakley Street. I was impressed by his work and asked him to do mine. He produced exact workmanship down to the ½mm. He wants everything to be perfect. If he says he's going to do something, he does. If something goes wrong, he will come back and fix it immediately. He is totally reliable. Not the cheapest, but you get good quality.' Richard Fawke, property developer
'Koichi did my shop. He is fabulous. I recommend him to everyone. To give you an example, something went wrong with one of the electric sockets. It wasn't even to do with him, but he came back, fixed it immediately and wouldn't accept any money.' Gregg Baker, Asian-art dealer

Zenon Builders Ltd
273 Abbeydale Road
Wembley
Middlesex HA0 1TW
T: 020 8998 5959 F: 020 8998 7272
M: 07775 733 734
kaczmarczyk@btinternet.com
www.zenonbuilders.com

Costs Can be pricey.
Travel North London is his beat, but will work anywhere in the city.
Size of job From £200K – £2 million.
Attitude I want to be the best.

Another potential pin-up, Zenon Kaczmarczyk is a Polish builder par excellence. He speaks beautiful English, which makes the usual language hiccups (and crazy hand gestures) unnecessary. He came over from Poland in 1987 and started work as a labourer. He set up his own company in 1992, and over the last seven years has built 50 houses using an all-Polish team. 'When you come on site there is no loud music, everyone is working,' says architect Nick Lee. Coffee breaks are unheard of here. Zenon imports materials from all over the world in order to get the best possible (he is now planning to open a hardware store). Quality is top (he also offers a joinery service and stone work), which can be pricey – though, says Zenon: 'For the service I provide I think I'm very cheap.' Zenon also does carpentry work and is meticulous with finish. 'He takes pride in his work. It's a point of honour,' says Lee. He has many fussy clients in the Hampstead area – South Africans in particular.

What the clients say
'Zenon was a pleasure to work with. I can't believe I actually enjoyed the process. We were a little over budget but that's because I kept adding things.' Karen Paul, client
'A very responsible builder. If the job is not right, he's one of the few builders who will rush over to fix it. An honest man who is very charming to work with.' Gidan Mousaieff, client

PAT GIDDENS CAMERON BRO
KINGS ROAD UPHOLSTERY S
THE CURTAIN CLINIC JON RHO
IAN SARGENT REUPHOLSTEF
WILLIAM FOUNTAIN AND CO
DOWNERS DESIGN LIMITED V
WILLIAM FOUNTAIN AND C
KIRSTEN HECKTERMANN THE
WILLIAM HOWARD CONTRAC
SUCCESSION WILLIAM HOW,
CAMERON BROOM KINGS RO
POWELL BLINDS DOWNERS
LYNN WESTWARD WILLIAM FO

M JON RHODES SASHA GIBB
CCESSION POWELL BLINDS
ES KIRSTEN HECKTERMANN
LYNN WESTWARD WALNUT
HN LEWIS EDGE INTERIORS
LIAM HOWARD CONTRACTS
PHIL GIDDENS ED WILSON
URTAIN CLINIC SUCCESSION
IAN SARGENT PAT GIDDENS
D CONTRACTS SASHA GIBB
D UPHOLSTERY JOHN LEWIS
ESIGN **SOFT FURNISHINGS**
NTAIN AND CO JON RHODES

People are very particular about their upholstery and curtains (see Kate Moss and Succession page 133). Designers wax lyrically about sleeping under curtains...

Who would have thought that making upholstery and sewing curtains is such a glamorous profession? I have heard tales of upholsterers virtually having to be blindfolded as they deliver thousands of pounds worth of silk-lined curtains (in unmarked vans) to large palaces belonging belonging to illustrious members of European and Saudi royal families. Most, of course, have no idea whose house it is. The paperwork simply says 'Project George'. Though New York has its fair share of curtain makers, too, many of the top designers still come looking over here. 'Curtain making is an old English art,' says Jon Rhodes. 'You don't find it in any other country.'

Most of those included in this section do things the old-fashioned way using wooden frames, horsehair, coils and feathers (none of this high-tech foam stuff). This means that Pat Giddens, our lovely pin-up, does not come cheap. This is the last of the world of the handmade. It's a dying art, they all tell me.

We have given the names of those who come highly recommended – that means in some cases that you will have to order your own fabric (they won't do it for you). If you can't be bothered, either go to John Lewis or one of the bigger retail firms. Don't forget that Anta Scotland and Bimbi Bellhouse (see pages 60-61 in Designers chapter) do upholstery as well.

How can you tell whether something is good?

'It's nearly impossible to tell a good upholstery job,' says designer Joanna Plant. 'A tidy job on the outside doesn't necessarily mean a good job on the inside – you cannot make a silk purse out of a sow's ear and all the other truisms. However, God is in the detail: always be alert to a beautiful finish – tidy and straight seams, no loose corners, untied threads, etc.'

'The physical feel will also tell you a lot about how it has been made if you push and prod,' says Sebastian de Groot of Ben Whistler. 'Failing that, if you take the bottom cloth off, you should be able to get a very good idea of the quality – is the frame hardwood or soft wood? What sort of webbing or springing has been used?'

PAT GIDDENS

Pat Giddens
68 Golborne Road
London W10 5PS
T/F: 020 8964 1185
pat@patgiddens.co.uk
www.patgiddens.co.uk

Costs Reasonable. Cushions from £20 plus VAT, Roman blinds from £225. Wood slat Venetian for a standard sash window from £275. Curtains for a standard sash window from £225.
Travel Anywhere. Currently doing jobs in Cornwall, Gloucester and Nice, with a job coming up in Dubai. Has gone as far afield as Japan and Mustique, bearing suitcases full of curtains.
Travel Anywhere. Currently doing jobs in Cornwall, Gloucester and Nice with a job coming up in Dubai. Has gone afar afield as Japan and Mustique, bearing suitcases full of curtains.
Attitude Very humble for someone who is obviously the royal family of soft furnishings.

Pat Giddens is the doyenne of curtains. People in the business sigh when they mention her name. 'You could sleep in her curtains,' is how one client puts it. Pat is based in Notting Hill and has a star-studded clientele (so many celebrities it's not worth bothering with a list). The company was started by her great-grandfather Herbert Giddens in the early part of the 20th century (there are actually pictures of him with his pushcart loaded with fabrics and his dog perched on top). She now runs the business with her husband. They produce curtains, blinds (roman, roller, Venetian, wood), cushions, loose covers, beds, headboards, valances, covers and throws, plus fabrics, curtain poles and tracking. They offer a full fitting service and follow a project all the way through to ensure the finished product is perfect, often finishing BEFORE the deadline. Their seamstresses went to Central St Martins – that's how serious Giddens is.

Clients include everyone from Paul Smith (quirky, modern) to the National Trust (historical, traditional, antique) to most of the Notting Hill celebrity crowd.

What the clients say
'Best-ever curtains and soft furnishings.' Joanna Plant, designer

Helpful advice from Pat Giddens

1. When measuring windows, include the total area that you want to cover. This includes any area that you will want curtains or blinds to stack back into.

2. Measuring to conserve light may often be a factor as to how far curtains or blinds should stack back.

3. Silk fabrics need to be used with caution, particularly at south-facing or sunny windows.

4. Choosing good-quality linings and interlinings can enhance and protect even an average fabric.

5. Traditional heading and making-up styles are often the best – time-honoured and reliable.

6. There is no substitute for good-quality poles and tracking. Cheaper alternatives are usually cheaper for a reason; they are often not strong enough to take the weight of lined and interlined curtains.

7. You get what you pay for. For durability and long-lasting performance, it is worth investing in good-quality merchandise and a well-thought-out product.

B – G

Cameron Broom at The Curtain Clinic
The Courtyard
15 Bellevue Rd
London SW17 7EG
T: 020 8767 2241
F: 020 8767 5784
info@cameronbroom.com
www.cameronbroom.com

Costs Recently competed against John Lewis on a big job and came in £1 under.
Travel Would go anywhere a client required them to.
Size of job From £15 to repair a roller blind to £240K if you want them to do what they did in the Concorde lounges.
Attitude Clinical efficiency

Penny Patterson is one of the top people in the business who came recommended by Olga Polizzi (she used The Curtain Clinic in her famous Tresanton Hotel, as did brother Rocco Forte). The smallest job they have ever been asked to do is make a cover for a budgie's cage. 'We get asked to do blinds for £50 all the time,' says Patterson, whose clientele is split down the middle between Mrs Bloggs in Wandsworth, who ordered one blind, and the great and the good (the Queen, Madonna and the Sultan of Brunei). All get exactly the same treatment.

Cameron Broom make curtains, blinds, upholstery, headboards, bedspreads, loose covers, lampshades, cushions, the whole gamut. They also supply a wide range of fabrics and wallpapers, as well as being the largest London suppliers of Swiss Silent Gliss products. They will come to a client's house or office and advise personally. Will also source fabrics. Four weeks delivery is typical.

What the clients say
'They're very good and very reasonable.'
Olga Polizzi, Tresanton Hotel

Downers Design Limited
4 Podmore Road
Wandsworth
London SW18 1AJ
T: 020 88770886
sales@downersdesign.co.uk

Costs Skeleton costs – fixed price for standard items.
Travel Do work abroad and would travel around the country, depending on the size of the job and what it involved.
Size of job Minimum of one room. Try not to take on more than 30 jobs at one time.
Attitude Know how to run a business.

Kelly Hoppen recommended Downers a while back. They make bespoke curtains and loose covers, and have eight full-time staff and six subcontractors working for them – predominantly women. 'We like to use unusual fabrics – some are made of grass – and often come up with new methods to incorporate different types of fabric,' says Shery Downer. Most of their work comes from designers and about 20 per cent comes from private client work, but that's mostly because no one knows about them outside of the industry.

Downers is run by two sisters, Shery and Kelly Downer. Shery worked as a textile fashion technologist at Marks and Spencer, and Kelly worked in fashion. 'Half of what we do is psychotherapy and logistics,' says Shery. 'The other half is making curtains and loose covers.' They are known for their standards: they will send a fabric back if flawed, even if it's gold-threaded and worth £3,000 a metre.

What the clients say
'They seem to know what you want and help you create it. There's a quality to the way they make their curtains. They come up with every possible design. They even help you come up with solutions to help cover nasty walls. Always do things to time and call you when fabric is late. They're extremely pro-active when it comes to time management.' Scott Maddux, designer

Edge Interiors
8 Clarendon Terrace
London W9 1BZ
T: 020 7289 1189
F: 020 7289 1389
info@edgeinteriors.co.uk
www.edgeinteriors.co.uk

Sasha Gibb
La Fosse
La Grande Route de Rozel
St Martin
Jersey
Channel Islands JE3 6AY
T: 01534 863 221
home@sashagibb.co.uk

Costs Over the last year the smallest job came in at about £500, the average job was between £5K and £25K, and quite a few got up to £50K.
Travel Will travel anywhere a client wants. Have worked in Holland (for the owner of Mexx clothing chain), in Paris on a hotel and on numerous homes in the Middle East.
Size of job Penthouses and hotels.
Attitude Utterly charming and professional.

Wayne Lipman takes the window treatment business very seriously (clients include virtually every modern architect and designer, including Philippe Starck, Seth Stein and Tara Bernerd). He started his company four years ago (after 15 years in the business) and now specializes in modern schemes: penthouses, for example, where the blinds go up and down automatically (they often collaborate with IT/AV companies). For one celebrity they painted the whole penthouse to match the curtains. He did all the upholstery for the Zetter Hotel and is presently trying to figure out how to replace buttons with fibre-optic lights for a bar (yet to be named).

What the clients say:
'Wayne cares deeply about his job. Everyone uses him.'
Tara Bernerd, designer

Costs Cushions from £60, throws from £250; she charges £60 an hour for consultations.
Travel Will travel to client for advisory service, but many commissions are done via photos.
Size of job Cushions, blankets, throws, etc.
Attitude Zen-like.

You would never know just how accomplished Sasha Gibb is from her calm zen-like exterior. She was the winner of the Royal Society of Art bursary for woven and printed textiles when still in her twenties. Then she was hired by John Lewis to design textiles. Then she set up a textile workshop in Africa where she learned weaving and dyeing techniques.

Her antique blankets and cushions used to appear in Browns and Egg, but now that she lives in Jersey, it's all done to commission. Many clients have never even seen the delicate work she produces; they merely heard about it from one of her stylist chums at *World of Interiors* magazine. Gibbs makes antique woollen blankets with satin trims, linen sheets that are felted and reformed into contemporary sheets, velvet cushions mixed with textiles. She can make entire curtains in this manner or take existing upholstery and give it something unique. She sews all the cushions herself.

Many of her clients are stylists and architects who admit they went overboard with the cement and stainless steel and want something 'that humanizes the place'. A typical commission might be a dozen cushions and five throws.

Gibb also offers an advisory service for those who need help finding things or just need some help with colour schemes, etc. 'I work for people who just don't know what they want or how to go about it,' she says. She doesn't have a website and prefers to send interested parties photographs of her work.

What the clients say
'Sasha is very talented with a very light touch. She's always slightly quirky.' Joan Heckterman, *World of Interiors* magazine

Phil Giddens
Unit 1
44 Mill Road
Lincoln LN1 3JJ
T: 01522 536 366
F: 01522 536236
info@philgiddens.co.uk

Costs Trade discounts. Pricey for Jo Average (though less so because not paying London prices).
Travel Ireland, Wiltshire, Devon, Cornwall and Geneva.
Size of job From a blind to curtains for several palaces worth of windows.
Attitude MI6 discretion.

Let's face it: no one expects an upholsterer to be funny. Ten minutes into the conversation and Giddens had me in stitches. 'When a woman starts decorating…' he says and out comes some great British humour. He comes from an upholstering dynasty four generations old (see Pat Giddens page 124, his sister).

Phil is the 'It' upholsterer, the end of the line. The best. Clients are so important that he is not even allowed to show his name on the van. He works mostly for designers: VERY BIG international designers who don't like sharing him. Having said that, he is happy to do a blind, make curtains or reupholster a sofa for anyone who cares to ask. He can put fabrics on walls and just about anywhere you need them. He has one of the biggest factories in the country.

What the clients say
'I wouldn't use anyone else.' Pat Giddens

Kirsten Hecktermann
1 Airey Cottage
Ferry Road
Fudbourne
Woodbridge
Suffolk IP12 2BQ
T: 01394 450 548 M: 07887 680672
kirstenhecktermann@btopenworld.com

Costs Cushions start from £60, bedspreads from £350. Depends on work involved.
Travel Will travel anywhere.
Size of job Cushions, curtains, bedspreads.
Attitude Old-world sensibilities.

Kirsten designed costumes for films before turning her eye to styling for *World of Interiors* magazine and making wonderful things with fabric. She doesn't make curtains, rather she painstakingly covers them with handmade and hand-sewn appliqués (made from antiques silks, velvet, dyed materials, found objects). Designer Annabel Grey recently commissioned a set of 8-foot curtains created around the idea of a butterfly and moth specimen box. Kirsten dyed eight 9-foot panels, then hand-embroidered and appliquéd the butterflies using antique silks and braiding. The lucky recipient was book dealer Simon Finch.

For Normandie Keith's meditation room, she made one of her famous bedspreads and 20 cushions. All of her work comes from commissions. She will make the cushions up herself, though the rest she sends off.

What the clients say
'I would go to Kirsten for any hand-dyeing, appliqué or embroidery job as she translates the brief so well.'
Annabel Grey, interior designer
'Kirsten has an incredibly sensitive feel for colour, shape and form. She has a subtle eye, with an example being the extraordinary buttons she finds for cushions. Everything is something completely original. She is a very special person.'
Francesca Mills, client

William Howard Contracts
Chris Hutchings Limited
Unit 1, Deltech Premises
Piperell Way, Haverhill
Suffolk CB9 8PH
T: 01440 709320 F: 01440 708932
chris@chrishutchings.co.uk
www.chrishutchings.co.uk

**Costs Reckon they are 50 per cent cheaper than John Lewis.
Four weeks turnaround.**
**Travel Comes to you and installs – anywhere (except
Middle East).**
Size of job Pelmets, headboards, chairs.
Attitude Mini John Lewis.

Chris Hutchings runs two parallel curtain and small
upholstery businesses. The first (Chris Hutchings) is
for trade – not just any trade, mind you. 'The most
expensive curtains we ever made cost £88,000,' he
says. 'They used gold-threaded fabrics.' Chris is known
in the business as the man to call when everyone else
fails. He owns a factory in which the tracks, curtains,
headboards, etc., and poles are made.

William Howard Ltd does the same thing but for
retail customers (in this case, normal people being the
Duke of Bedford plus, of course, the woman down
the lane). Chris is happy to advise and order fabrics:
he's been doing this for 30 years, so he knows where
to get the best deals. One client liked him so much that
he sent his Lear jet to pick him up and bring him to
Greece to measure up there. He used to be a designer
himself but when he couldn't find a decent curtain
maker, switched tack.

What the clients say
'Chris is very experienced and professional, patient… thinks for
you… helpful… fantastic finish. A lot cheaper (about 50 per
cent) than London curtain makers.' Carolyn Trevor, architect

John Lewis, Oxford Street
Peter Jones, Sloane Square
and branches nationwide.
For details of your nearest store,
call 08456 049049

No new discovery here, but just in case you didn't
know: John Lewis can do almost anything.

Their Furnishing Advisors offer free one-to-one
consultations in-store on anything from wooden flooring
to tailor-made curtains, shelving units to floor cushions,
ceiling lamps and table sets. The FAs will discuss the
proposed colour scheme with the client and analyse
the angle of light coming into the property – whether
it is a north- or south-facing room, for example. Once a
decision has been made and measurements taken, they
will coordinate all subsequent purchases and deliveries.

Premier Furnishing Advice Service
This involves home visits where measurements are
taken for curtains, carpets and wallpaper (or for tiling,
worktops, flooring, units and equipment if the room is
the kitchen). Style-board presentations are produced at
the customer's request. One of their people will be on
site to oversee the final delivery and fitting.
**Costs £200 refundable against the cost of the final furnishing
scheme, once charged and fitted.**

Tailor-made Compatibility Duvet
John Lewis can even make heart-shaped, circular,
hexagonal, 7-foot long, 6-foot wide, square or oval
fitted or flat sheets (as well as matching pillow cases)
on which you can place your couture duvet (which, of
course, they can also make). If you're super swish, you
can even have the Compatibility Duvet, i.e., each
member of the couple decides what tog rating he
wants on his half of the duvet! Prices start at £200 for
a double and go up to £800 for the doyenne of duvets:
the hand-plucked Siberian goose-down duvet.

Express Furnishings Service
The express made-to-measure service, available in-
store, can deliver curtains, valances, Roman blinds,
voiles, cushion covers and tie-backs within seven days.
Just provide the measurements.
**Costs From £85 for a one-width pair of curtains with a 100-cm
drop and pencil pleat (this includes fabric, lining and delivery).**

Services available at all branches nationwide.

K–S

Kings Road Upholstery
175 Stamford Brook Arches
Hammersmith
London W6 0TQ
T: 020 8741 3100
F: 020 87419699

Costs Middle.
Travel Local.
Size of job Will do small jobs if client brings goods to them.
Attitude Inject some glamour in this pretty serious world.

The charming Maltese Sancio De Carlo does all of Jane Churchill's and David Linley's upholstery. He will also gladly copy anything, working the old-fashioned way with timber frames, coiled springs). About 50 per cent of his work is to the public. Obviously it's much cheaper to have Sancio copy an existing chair you love than to go through all the mark-ups in the retail world. You will have to source your own fabric, though. It's a small office with a machinist and a delivery man.

What the clients say
'Sancio is consistent, efficient and, most importantly, the quality of his work is, in my opinion, excellent.' Tara Bernerd, designer

Powell Blinds
Sunblind House
Holmbush Potteries
Faygate, Horsham
West Sussex RH12 4SE
T: 01293 851 010 F: 01293 851 999
tim@powellblinds.com
www.powellblinds.com

Costs It normally works out at about £200 per square metre for a bespoke system. Can make anything up and loves a challenge.
Travel Will go anywhere in the world – has done jobs in Mexico, Santa Fe, Belgium, Paris, Amsterdam, etc.
Size of job Anything to do with windows that roll.
Attitude IBM.

Hello! magazine, eat your heart out. There isn't one famous person in the land that Tim Powell hasn't worked for. He is the man Nigella Lawson, Claudia Schiffer, Elton John, Gordon Ramsay and Anoushka Hempel call (as did the late Princess Diana) when they need Venetian, vertical, roller, Roman, pleated, wooden Venetian and conservatory blinds, as well as awnings and motorized awnings. Powell has his own factory in Wolverhampton, where he can make a huge variety of custom-made blinds, and also vast numbers of suppliers from whom he can source anything that he can't manufacture himself. Powell also services the architectural community: David Chipperfield, Richard Rogers, Norman Foster and John Pawson are also clients. Some budgets run as high as £250,000 (in one house in Ireland, Powell made the blinds out of artist's canvas, which was later painted by an artist). But Joe Bloggs is just as welcome to come into the showroom and order. Put it this way, Powell is a great businessman. That's why the list above gets bigger by the day.

To date Powell Blinds have covered in excess of one million windows worldwide.

What the clients say
'In my sort of work, the way light enters a space is critical. Tim instinctively understands what I am looking to achieve in a particular situation and will not settle for an approximation.'
John Pawson, architect

Jon Rhodes
Curtain Makers to the Trade
The Cockpens
Grange Farm
Felmingham
Norfolk NR28 0LT
T: 07860 839 853
jonrhodestrade@aol.com

Ian Sargent Reupholstery
(contact by phone only)
T: 020 8755 0324

Costs High end because all hand-made.
Travel Has been everywhere. From Kuwait to Singapore.
Size of job From one room to palaces and hotels.
Attitude Could he BE more friendly?

Costs Med/expensive.
Travel London.
Size of job From blinds upwards.
Attitude Charm not his forte.

Jon Rhodes originally planned to be an actor. 'I learned a lot about making costumes that way,' he says. The man is pure magic: he got a loan from the Prince's Trust and within a year was working for U2's bass guitarist Adam Clayton.

Years later, just like that, Michael Douglas and Catherine Zeta Jones noticed his window displays for Mulberry at Chelsea Harbour and the next thing you know he was off to Barbados. He still does a lot of work for Mulberry and interior designers such as Lavinia Dargie and Veronica Pascoe (and about 200 celebrities, including Natalie Imbruglia and Michael Crawford), though he's also open to the public. 'We always have time to make a few curtains,' he says.

Rhodes owns one the biggest factories in the country, where he makes curtains, draperies and soft furnishings of all kinds (tented ceilings, padded walls). He employs 24 people, so is in a position to take on projects for Bond Street (they supplied draperies and soft furnishings for Tiffany, Cartier and Asprey), palaces and hotels, but also the lady with one bedroom's worth of curtains. A charming man who goes out of his way to please clients (like Sir Cameron Mackintosh). He is known for his creativity and his ability to stick to budgets.

What the clients say
'Jon is brilliant. Can turn bog standard fabrics into something wonderful. Very creative.'
Victoria Murray, public relations executive

The modest Ian Sargent calls himself a 'quiet operative'. He started out as an engineer and a teacher before teaching himself the art of reupholstery (i.e., covering an existing piece of furniture). He won't make new furniture. He says it like it is: 'I'm not interested in being an interior designer. I do what the client asks me to do.' He will work with private clients, but they have to know what they want. 'I'm not a high-street retailer,' he says.

Sargent has a reputation for hard work: he does up to 16 estimates a day. As his men delivered a chair to me recently, they confessed that he works seven days a week. You can see why clients include Robert Kime, Nina Campbell and Colefax and Fowler. Much of what he does are small jobs.

What the clients say
'Ian's work is impeccable and he is completely straightforward. He will tell you exactly what can be done, how much it will cost, and when it will be ready. Accurately!'
Scott Maddux, designer

W - S -

Stefanou & Co
2a Camden Mews
London NW1 9DB
T: 020 7267 5557
stefanou@btconnect.com

Succession
84 Pimlico Road
London SW1W 8PL
T: 020 7259 9888
F: 020 7259 9777
info@succession.uk.com
www.succession.uk.com

Costs Medium. Cheaper than going through a retail operation.
Travel UK. Goes to New York and Palm Beach. 'Apparently my
prices are half of those in New York,' he says.
Size of job Sofas, curtains, beds.
Attitude Artist.

Costs From £460 for the Capone lamp (cheapest product); sofas
start at £1,800 plus fabric.
Travel Wherever the client needs them.
Size of job Lamps to sofas.
Attitude Hip and helpful.

You couldn't find a nicer upholsterer than this one. Greek Cypriot Neo Stefanou is elegant and precise, which is what people say about his work. He's not grand and not fancy, prefers to work with small designers than factories, as he puts it, and takes deep care to explain the differences between a proper hand-made sprung sofa with beech frame, soft edge, horsehair and down feathers, as opposed to what you buy on the New Kings Road.

He will cover, re-cover, line walls, make curtains or make beds. Neo prefers working with designers but is happy to assist a retail client who knows what he wants (and has some idea of the fabric). Sofas take eight to ten weeks to deliver (the Aga Khan has one).

What the clients say
'I use Neo because he is incredibly intelligent and because he can solve the most technical problems. He is very, very good.'
Tom Bartlett, designer

If you haven't discovered them already, then you're in for a treat. Everyone in Notting Hill (Succession has since moved to Pimlico Road) owns something of theirs: either a leather chair, a sofa, footstool, lamp. This is made to please: so if someone wants a sofa that fits the Real Madrid team, they can do it. We all support Succession, because it's home-grown talent.

Brothers Liam and John Foley and their mate Nick Plant all originally worked in the antiques business. They decided to start designing and producing new furniture as a reaction to the poor standards that were available. Over time they added lighting, storage and modular furniture as well as sofas, chairs, daybeds, etc. And the clients – Kate Moss, the Beckhams, Julianne Moore, Mathew Williamson – rolled in.

They use materials such as leather, solid oak and top-quality modern fabrics, which seem to scream 'luxury'. Every detail is attended to, such as a leather-covered lamp base. But apparently the real measure of the quality is what you don't see. There are up to 120 individual coil springs in a sofa, and only the best quality hessian webbing, white cotton felt and rubberized horsehair is used. They were the first to come up with the idea to cover pieces completely in leather, such as the Trinity coffee table, which is now copied by everyone.

The service is retail or bespoke: you can buy directly from the showroom or you can commission a piece tailored to your specific requirements. They also offer a follow-up service where they advise on cleaning and care, though, says Nick, they usually end up cleaning it themselves.

What the clients say
'A sofa from Succession is top of everyone I know's wish list, and mine is a constant source of envy and admiration.'
Kate Moss, model

Walnut
Hackwood Park
Near Basingstoke
Hampshire RG25 2J2
(by appointment only)
T: 01256 327 400 M: 07768 701 914
nicolefulton@walnutuk.com
www.walnutuk.com

Costs £350–£3K which includes sourcing if necessary, the cost of the piece of furniture, reupholstery, restoration if necessary, and often also fabric.
Travel Based in Hampshire but visits people all over the country. Would travel anywhere if the client requires it.
Size of job Chairs.
Attitude Supermotivated.

Nicole Fulton started life in the City and then decided to start an upholstery business from scratch. She now runs two: The Walnut Collection is a collection of chairs, designed by Nicole and handmade in the UK, 'inspired by the form, simplicity and comfort of earlier chairs'. Walnut Originals is a unique collection of antique chairs reupholstered in leather, suede and contemporary fabrics. She uses old-fashioned techniques such as a hammer and tacks instead of staples to maintain the integrity of a piece.

Anything is possible here: you can buy one of her chairs directly from her barn in Hampshire (she sold out at the launch event) or she can come to you to match something, make it up, source it or just plain re-cover it. Clients are people like Bruce Oldfield and interior designers. Harrods is now talking about taking her whole collection. She has also just finished a book called *New Upholstery*.

What the clients say
'I originally saw her furniture at an exhibition at the end of 2001, and loved what I saw. My first purchase was pretty straightforward: buying a pair of armchairs that she already had in stock. The only choice that needed to be made was for cushion covers. They frequently draw favourable comment from visitors, who invariably ask for Nicole's contact details! My second pair of armchairs were old carcasses, which I believe Nicole found in Belgium. She brought them to our doorstep to review, along with various hides. And then delivered them, fully upholstered, soon after. If ever I wanted more furniture, she would be my first call as she understands our needs, has great flair, is reasonably priced, and never disappoints!'
Robert J Markwick, banker

Howard J Harris at Lynn Westward
458 Chiswick High Road
London W4 5TT
T: 020 8742 8333
F: 020 8742 8444
info@lynnwestward.co.uk

Costs Reasonable. Middle end. Typical budget: £5K–£20K.
Travel Will travel throughout England.
Size of job No bottom end, but up to £60K.
Attitude Straight-talking businessman.

Thoughtful and very polite, South African Howard Harris offers a very personal service. The company make blinds, curtains, soft furnishings, upholstery and reupholstery for Mr Public, as well as Philippe Starck, George Michael and Ringo Starr. Many of their clients are designers and architects, though their bread and butter are people who need one room made up. They have workrooms in London and nine employees (plus people they use in Birmingham), so can move fast. They come to the client to advise.

What the clients say
'Howard was happy to wait as I debated whether or not I like the sexy mirrored blinds he installed in my bathroom (I did). Comes off as an accountant, very precise, not one to talk your ear off. Seems to really care.'
Helen Kirwan-Taylor, author, *Home UK*

William Fountain and Co
68a Cobden Rd
London E11 3PE
T: 020 8556 3463
info@williamfountain.com

Ed Wilson
T: 020 8518 0377
(No email, mobile or fax,
but he answers this number day and night)

Costs Reasonable for quality of work.
Travel Within M25, though they are presently working
in Norfolk.
Size of job The smallest job they've done is a cushion for
a piano stool.
Attitude Family firm.

This is a second generation East End upholstery and
curtain making firm with old-fashioned values, and
95 per cent of their work is for the public. In most
cases, one of the three Fountains (they're all related)
will arrive in person, meet the client, discuss materials,
etc., take them away and bring back the finished items
in two to three weeks. Very service-based and very
helpful. You don't have to be a style guru to use them.

What the client says
'They did a lovely job. Next winter, when I have finished my
book, I am going to get them to make me some loose covers for
the sofas.' Rachel Simhon, *Daily Telegraph*

Costs To re-cover a sofa you're looking at at least £500 plus
fabric; a new sofa is more like £3K but it will be fully hand-
sprung and last for ever. He is open to a bit of bartering with
regular customers.
Travel Mainly works in central London but has been all over
the world on jobs and will go anywhere a client requires.
Size of job Headboards to armchairs to sofas.
Attitude Life is fun.

Nicole Farhi, the White Company and the designer
Catherine Connolly have all used the highly amusing
Essex-based Ed Wilson, who works with his dad. He
recalls delivering some furniture to the late Freddy
Mercury's house. When he entered the room 'several
people scampered under the bed'.

He has used 'stuffed and stitched' methods, but
a stint at Percy Bass taught him everything he needed
to know about mass-produced furniture. Ed and his
dad can make anything from a modern headboard to
a traditionally reupholstered antique chair. They also
do rather accurate copies (for less) of the padded
chairs you see in magazines. They have the frames
made by a specialist company but they do everything
else themselves. Though Ed works mostly with
designers, he is happy to work with customers,
providing they have the necessary fabrics and so on.

What the clients say
'Ed learned the trade from his father, who worked for Charles
Hammond and Sibyl Colefax for years. Ed now employs him and
his stepmother. The father often sees pieces coming in that he
remembers making years ago and he is able to restore them.
Ed never takes on too much at a time, so if he says he will do
something in a week, it is always done in that time.'
Catherine Connolly, designer

LIFESTYLE IT APOLLO COMPU
ALAN STIRLING TECHNOLOG
ROBERT TAUSSIG MULTI RO
THINKING FISH LIMITED PJC
D&T ELECTRONICS THE LIS
SOUND IDEAS UK LTD GIBSO
DAWSONS HOME CINEMA PC
PC SERVICE LIMITED LIGHT IC
PATRICK SEYMOUR ROBERT T
PJC LIGHTING DESIGN THINK
MUSICAL IMAGES SOUNDT
GIBSON MUSIC LIMITED D
THE LISTENING ROOMS CINE

ERS LIMITED SOUNDTRACKS
LIMITED PATRICK SEYMOUR
OM **CONSULTANTS** IMAGES
GHTING DESIGN LIGHTPLAN
ENING ROOMS EMPORIUM
MUSIC LIMITED INFIDELITY
SERVICE LIMITED TUDORVALE
POLLO COMPUTERS LIMITED
USSIG MULTI ROOM LIGHT IQ
G FISH LIMITED LIFESTYLE IT
ACKS SOUND IDEAS UK LTD
&T ELECTRONICS PHASE III
A PHASE III DAWSONS HOME

CONSULTANTS

When was the last time you hit your computer? Or wanted to take a hammer to the TV because, although you have 257 channels, none of them work? Technology is moving at a rate that normal people simply can't follow. From mind-reading lights to refrigerators that speak to the oven, it's all gone mad. This explains why computer rage has now surpassed road rage. Normally, your architect or designer will suggest you call in a specialist technology firm because it's advisable to install equipment at the building stage (see Timeline, page 10). Changing TV points once the walls are plastered and decorated is very messy and very expensive.

Tech butlers

Tech butlers have emerged recently in response to the enormous growth in technology and home computing. Do you remember the days when you could program your own phone? Some people can; but many are too busy trying to figure out how to make their Blackberry speak to their Sony Viao laptop.

More than 12 million computers are now in use in British households. And 30 per cent of the workforce will work from home by the year 2006, says the Hamlyn Research Centre. This means no more dialling extension 12 and leaving the crisis in the IT department's hands. We're stuck. Tech butlers, or IT consultants as they call themselves, offer that service at home (most also install systems and program mobiles). Five years, ago they were trainspotter types, living in subterranean squalor somewhere in E19. Now they're professionals, like Bob Hundal and Ian Brown, who wear suits, carry briefcases, have famous clients and charge a lot. My advice is: get these guys in during the planning stage.

Home cinemas

Home cinemas took off in the late '80s. First, pop stars and footballers put plasma screens on top of the fireplace (this is now considered naff); more recently, celebrities have taken to building stand-alone home cinemas complete with leather movie seats and popcorn machines. Of course, they will also have a TV built into the base of the bed that pops up electronically on pressing ** 24 on the remote. They'll have a TV built into the bath, a TV in the laundry and surround-sound absolutely everywhere. It's not advisable to go there, though, unless you have an advanced degree in engineering. 'Technology should always be "aligned" with the clients' understanding and requirements,' says architect Patrick McInerney. 'It is nonsense to install something that comes with 20 owner's manuals or 10 hand controllers when a client may only want to watch *Newsnight*!'

But as the average Briton watches 27 hours of television a week, the reality is these rooms are constantly in use. Most audio visual (AV) consultants do more than simply advise on whether you should have a Loewe or a Sony: they wire up entire houses for music, television, phones, security – heck, you can probably fly a plane from your pad. This technology is constantly changing, so do not despair. What costs £100 now may well be yours for £20 in three years' time.

Lighting consultants

I once wrote an article on the art of lighting. It took me three weeks and I almost died. This is a whole new world/art form, where people talk about light-emitting diodes (LEDs), fibre optics and bluetooth technology the way I talk about shoes. It made my head spin and left me thoroughly exhausted. You should not have to have a PhD in order to turn on a light, which is why lighting consultants have now appeared on the scene. 'All clients really care about,' says Richard Aldridge of Lightplan, 'is the effect.'

The primary focus of lighting designers is to emphasize the existing architecture (indoors and outdoors). This is mostly done using smart lighting systems, such as Lutron and Leax, in addition to hundreds of others now flooding the market. The idea of these very high-tech systems is that everything is run from a central computer and can be programed to know your mood (lights dim themselves in the bedroom just in case). The technology is so high-tech that you can switch on the lights and raise your electronic blinds (as Philippe Starck does) from your mobile. The pioneer of the field in Britain is Arnold Chan of Isometrix, who came up with Colourwash, a system that allows individuals to create light effects on their walls using a rotary controller (it was first used in the St Martins Lane hotel). Chan expects to get a £200 version on the market by spring and I will be the first taker.

Points to bear in mind

- This field is heaven for unsolicited male advice syndrome. You do not need a plasma screen inside the fridge, even though you open it a hundred times a day. You do not need mood lighting in a broom cupboard.

- Make sure the company you use also offers a maintenance service. Most do, but check.

- It's extremely hard to know what these people are talking about half the time. Remember, they're salesmen.

- More is definitely not better.

- As many people hate computerized lighting (which is connected to the security system) as love it. Getting locked out of your house is a real possibility. It happened to Robbie Williams and it could happen to you.

- Halogen lighting is not the same as good old-fashioned bulbs. Make sure you have both.

- Do mention if you suffer from SAD (Seasonal Affective Disorder). This is something any lighting consultant should be able to help with.

- Make sure a mobile helpline is on offer. You do not want to have to consult the 2,000-page owner's manual written by graduates of MIT or translated from Chinese.

- Surround-sound can make you wish you'd never heard of it.

- Do not let your husband or partner take over the AV/music side of things. Remember: these are recreational toys, not necessities.

- If your budget doesn't stretch this far, you can put it all in later when you have more cash.

- Consider installing CAT5 cables, which are designed for multiple use.

- The more television and computer points you install, the better.

- Many colleges now offer computer lessons for morons. Most IT experts will train you but for a hefty fee.

LifestyleIT
106 High Street
Harrow-on-the-Hill
Middlesex HA1 3LP
T: 020 8423 2244
info@lifestyleit.com

Costs £120 plus VAT an hour (£90 plus VAT an hour for LifestyleIT Members) for home visits.
Travel Main service area is greater London, but have worked in Europe, and will travel worldwide, usually to relocate clients, or to connect international computers and systems into the client's London base.
Size of job From £800 a year for a single-user LifestyleIT Membership package in your home. Covers absolutely everything you need for your computers, including support. Equally skilled with PC and Mac systems.
Attitude Therapist.

Ian Brown and Bhobinder Hundal have had their share of late-night crises. If Kylie Minogue can't access her email at 2am while on tour, for example, Ian Brown will be on the other end speaking in a soothing voice until all is resolved. Brown has the skills of a therapist.

Brown got the bright idea to start the business in 1994. 'I had a client who asked me to train three daughters. I saw there was a gap in the market.' The first client was a Goldman Sachs banker, and soon many more were on his books. Brown joined up with Bob Hundal at JP Morgan to develop bank software, and now they work for everyone, from me to Nicola Formby, Charles Spencer, Sam Taylor Wood, Neil Fox and Nathalie Hambro, as well as a demanding host of international bankers and their families.

LifestyleIT does absolutely anything related to computer technology: they repair, train, upgrade and coach when absolutely nothing works. Their service extends from replacing a mouse to networking a whole house. Often they show up on the same day.

Their flagship product, annual LifestyleIT Membership, gives members secure broadband, firewall, personalized email and domain name, antivirus software, unlimited telephone support for the entire home computer technology, discount hardware and a reduced hourly rate for when site visits are needed. It effectively gives a family their own external IT department.

What the clients say

'LifestyleIT installed an excellent system in our new offices and have since given us excellent back-up support.'
Sam Taylor Wood, artist
'I can't be more complimentary. It's wonderful to have someone you can rely on who is always enthusiastic. I'm impatient and

Ian's energy is compatible with me. You can call him anytime and you know the problem will be sorted out. It's such freedom. My friends try to save money, but I think he's worth every penny. He has also advised me about what's on the market without taking mark-ups.' **Natalie Hambro, designer**
'I was in there early. They've grown quickly but they still provide a good service. Bob and Ian work extremely hard. Ian, in particular, never lets you now how stressed he is himself.'
Helen Kirwan-Taylor, author, *Home UK*

Dos and don'ts from Ian Brown of LifestyleIT

- Find a consultant you like and trust.
- If you're spending tens of thousand of pounds with a consultant, make sure you have their mobile number.
- Tread carefully with companies that offer IT and AV solutions from the same consultant – not many acoustic specialists are computer experts and vice versa.
- Ask your consultant what problems they anticipate and how they will deal with things if they go wrong.
- Don't be afraid to keep asking questions until you understand what is being explained to you.

For computer equipment and technology

- Always buy mid- to high-range equipment from a reputable manufacturer if you can afford it.
- Make sure your consultant can explain your system's security. You need to know if and how you will be protected from hackers, viruses and spy-ware.
- Plan to have your computer for two to three years, and spend accordingly. Then upgrade to a faster, more modern, cheaper computer.

Specific tips for redeveloping or building a property

- Make use of the opportunity to install the right cabling throughout the house that will support your technology now and in the next ten or so years.
- Decide on general room layouts in the very early stages so you can determine (as best you can) where all the outlets will go. These include telephone, computer, TV (including satellite and/or cable), security and door-entry systems outlets. They need to be added to the electrical schedule of the plans as soon as possible.
- Seriously consider modular-structured CAT5 cabling systems, which offer versatile points that can be used for telephones, faxes and computers.

A–D

Apollo Computers Limited
Eurolink Business Centre
Unit 63 Effra Road
London SW2 1BZ
T: 020 7924 0753
sales@apolloservice.co.uk

Cornflake.co.uk
37 Windmill Street
London W1T 2JU
T: 020 7631 0472
F: 020 7436 7165
information@cornflake.co.uk
www.cornflake.co.uk

Costs **£49 an hour.**
Travel **All of London and outside if clients require it.**
Size of job **Small companies and individuals.**
Attitude **Never give up.**

Costs **£500 – £500K.**
Travel **Worldwide.**
Size of job **CD player to a whole smart house.**
Attitude **We're going to make you love it, too.**

An Iraqi Kurd, Alan Taffamy started off as an academic studying biology, catering and computer science. In 1996 he set up a business bringing computer assistance to small companies that couldn't justify a full-time tech guy, and households that just needed help. Word quickly spread and by 2000 he was employing people to cope with the workload.

Even though they do PCs, Apollo's speciality is Apple, which accounts for about 90 per cent of business. Clients come from the world of design, music, publishing and architecture. Apart from small companies, he also finds himself working for writers and actors from their homes. 'There are three of us at Apollo at the moment,' Alan says, 'and we usually end up forming quite a relationship with our clients. I suppose this is why they keep recommending us to their friends.'

What the clients say
'He came to my rescue when my iMac went dead, and then when it got a virus he managed to retrieve a lot of the information I thought was lost for ever. Very impressive.'
Susana Raby, freelance writer

If they're good enough for Robbie Williams…

'Not only do I love music and films, but I love this industry because its always moving forward,' says Chris Adair, MD, co-founder of Cornflake and an 18-year veteran of the business. 'My partner and I considered opening a café as well.' (Hence the shop's unusual name.) Around 70 per cent of business is now custom installation, which tends to be done in conjunction with architects and interior designers while the builders are in. But this is a welcome-everyone kind of firm: clients range from Lord Rothschild to the couple who need a CD player (a top-of-the-line CD player, that is).

Cornflake offers as much service as you need. You can either come into the shop and browse or they will come to you and install anything from a home cinema to a fully automated house with phone, security and heating systems. Installation, care and maintenance are all part of the package. 'We like to make everything accessible, too. So it's not just the kids who can work out how to use it,' says Adair. What clients like most is the fact that they care enough to work late hours, even weekends.

What the clients say
'The two things that I feel set Cornflake apart are knowledge and enthusiasm. This is a company that seems to exist because everyone in the company is excited about what they do. This enthusiasm links directly to the fact that they have a very broad range of knowledge and experience in audio-visual as well as home automation. There is no "hard sell" approach – rather they work with you to achieve the best solution. From initial meetings and design discussions through to installation, everything is carried out with promptness and professionalism.'
Geoffrey Makstutis, architect
'They don't let you down and will come round on a Sunday night.'
Mike Rundell, architect

D&T Electronics
Unit 9a Cranbourne Industrial Estate, Cranbourne Road,
Potters Bar, Middlesex EN6 3JN
T: 0870 241 5891 F: 01707 653570 www.dandt.co.uk

Woodfield House, Woodfield Road
Altrincham WA14 4EU
T: 0870 444 5929 F: 0870 444 5945

Costs £10K–half a million.
Travel Whole of UK and some work abroad.
Size of job Small home cinema to complete household
techno-fest.
Attitude The Firm.

When D & T was founded back in 1979, most of its
business involved exporting hi-fi equipment to the
Middle East and West Africa. Now they're a high-level
home entertainment retailer dealing in brands you
wouldn't see in the high street, such as Lynn, Arcam
and Meridian. Customers are people like the late Paul
Getty, Catherine Ford II, Lord and Lady Young and the
Kuwaiti royal family and bankers, but also nice normal
people with limited budgets and big hopes. D&T is
now so exclusive that they don't have a shop anymore.
'We're essentially a consultancy that retails,' says Paul
Hellier, the delightful MD. A keen observer of domestic
life, he says: 'We'll go and see the client and work out
the best system based on their needs. We're very
lucky in that if a new client wants to test-drive some
equipment, we have old clients who will let us into their
homes so we can display our work and systems.' They
have two offices and a team of 20 experts, including
technicians, administrators, fitters, salespeople and
designers. They mostly do home audio and home
cinemas, but can also install lighting controls and
home security. Another service is rentals for exhibitions,
and they offer maintenance contracts, where they will
lend clients a set until theirs is repaired.

What the clients say
'We've worked with him on purpose-built private cinemas and
controlled lighting, amongst other things. He's always available
to talk and discuss matters and he responds very well. The quality
of the finished product has always been very good and the
process of getting there has been a very pleasant experience.'
Yves Allier, Michael Edwards Associates
'Paul and D&T have proved to be friendly, knowledgeable,
innovative and very efficient in the design, detailing and supply
of all of our audio-visual equipment requirements. It has also
been a pleasure to work with their site staff during the
installation and commissioning process… and we continue
to work with them as a result.'
Graham Massey, Creativemass and Brybuild

Dawsons Home Cinema
74 Poole Road
Westbourne
Bournemouth
Dorset BH4 9DZ
T: 01202 764 965 F: 01202 763 622
mark@dhcav.co.uk
www.dhcav.co.uk

Costs £3K–£750K.
Travel Whole of Europe.
Size of job From a Bang & Olufsen telephone to a fully
automated house.
Attitude We know what we're talking about.

Kevin Dawson's grandfather opened a shop in
Bournemouth 75 years ago, selling the latest in radios
and record players. In 1964, Dawsons started stocking
equipment by an unknown Danish Company called
Bang & Olufsen. They are now the longest-serving
B&O dealer in the country and employ about 20 people.
They have two shops, one behind the other.
    Kevin now runs the B&O side and Mark Buckfield
deals in home cinemas for people like Anthea Turner
and Harry Redknapp. They also supply furniture,
design, lighting, heating or cinema equipment for
property developers. Service is their schtick. 'We're
very fastidious,' they claim, and it is clear that they
take home cinema very seriously from the 20-seat
demo movie theatre in their basement and the fact
that, 'If all you wanted was a plasma screen, we'd
probably direct you to Comet.' No doubt it is this
dedication to the culture of home cinema that has
secured them their loyal client base.

What the clients say
'Dawsons give a very personal service. They know what they're
talking about. They take you from cradle to grave so to speak'.
Frank Mountain, racing car driver and property developer
'I've been working with Dawsons for seven years. They
designed my home cinema and did all the audiovisuals in my
office. They did a very good job.
Grant Bovey, entrepreneur

G–L

Gibson Music Limited
Unit 8
The Broom House
50 Sullivan Road
London SW6 3DX
T: 020 7384 2270
sales@gibson-music.com
www.gibson-music.com

Costs **£25K (small); £40K (average); £80K–£150K (large).**
Travel **UK, Europe and USA.**
Size of job **From family homes to completely centralized systems.**
Attitude **Won't sell you the kitchen sink.**

Angus Gibson is one of the most popular of this bunch: he has fancy clients like Dustin Hoffman and Elton John, but also young families in Clapham.

Angus Gibson founded the company in 1985 (it was recently acquired by Holloway, Allom and White, although still trades under his name), and has witnessed the home entertainment revolution firsthand. In the past one would need a retailer, an electrician, a BT engineer and other guys in boiler suits to equip and install your house. Now the serious money has a bespoke design house like Gibson's take care of the whole job. Today, this means a centralized system where your lights, music, TV, phones and security are housed all together and controlled by smart pads throughout your house. People call Angus in when they are refurbishing their house, and he wires them with a view to the future. Putting enough CAT5 cable in your walls will mean that you won't have to run extra cable through your house for a long, long time – no matter what the future brings. It will feed your home cinema, your music into every room, your home disco, your broadband and, in the future, your streaming AV and any other new developments.

Angus prides himself on providing a complete service for the present and future. He'll supply you with everything you need for your home, design its installation and even buy you a record collection if you don't have one already. He now employs 22 people.

What the clients say
'Takes all the stresses and strains out of the area of audio-visual. He's absolutely brilliant, charm personified and very sympathetic to his customers requirements.'
Joanna Wood, Joanna Trading Ltd
'He's the darling of the hi-fi set. He's tactile and friendly. He makes you feel at home within minutes of sitting down next to him, and doesn't seem like a salesman. Hugely knowledgeable. He won't try and sell you a system immediately – he will wait for the latest models.' Peter Grabham, project manager

Infidelity
9 High Street
Hampton Wick
Kingston-upon-Thames
Surrey KT1 4DA
T: 020 8943 3530 F: 020 8943 4509
info@infidelity.co.uk
www.infidelity.co.uk

Costs **£200–£150K.**
Travel **London and Surrey.**
Size of job **CD player to full-house custom installation.**
Attitude **The Specialist.**

Simon Byles opened Infidelity in Kingston-upon-Thames 14 years ago. 'Even though we do large-scale domestic installations as well as retailing hi-fi and home cinema, we're more interested in the quality of the sound than the convenience. We're unlikely to appeal to the gizmologists!' he says. First and foremost, Byles is running a specialist hi-fi shop with the best equipment and expertise, for those who really care about their apparatus. They also take pride in staying ahead of the times. 'We make a point of learning as much about new technology as possible and incorporating it into what we do.' Complete home entertainment systems now account for about 50 per cent of their business. This includes the design and installation of home cinema and top-quality sound distributed throughout the house, as well as managing the installation of alarms, phones and lighting. A fully comprehensive service for those who've decided to have the best – or as Byles puts it, more succinctly, 'Once we make a customer, we keep a customer.'

What the clients say
'Excellent service. They listen to what you say and are willing to do as many different viewings of different products as you want, until you're happy that the final result is what you want, rather than what they want you to buy.' Simon Taylor, client
'Very good, very friendly, very helpful. He spent hours with us, making sure we had what we were after, and then brought it round and spent hours fitting it all. In terms of after-sales service, I'd also highly recommend him.'
Brian and Pippa Cooper, clients

Musical Images (Covent Garden and branches)
18 Monmouth Street
London WC2H 9HB
T: 020 7497 1346
information@musical-images.co.uk
www.musical-images.co.uk

Costs £1K–£200K and above.
Travel Nationwide and worldwide.
Size of job From a CD player to a full home automation system
Attitude Everyone welcome.

Andrew Butler, operations director of Musical Images, is keen to point out that they don't cut off low spenders. 'We want to deal with them in the same way as the big spenders. Come in, browse and enjoy the "wow" factor!' he says 'We make a point of keeping our three stores, particularly Covent Garden, on the cutting edge when it comes to home cinema and hi-fi. We like people to come in just to experience what is out there, and in so doing, educating and inspiring them with what is possible.'

True to its word, you can either walk into the shop and browse, buy the latest in audio and home cinema, or have them come to you, as the Beckhams did, and install everything. That 'everything' may include full home automation: heating, lights, gates, security, home entertainment and as much control as you want – from touch pads on the wall or via the internet. They can even furnish you with a huge home cinema.

Butler prefers to give clients what suits them, rather than shove brands down their throat. He is also very concerned with customer care and provides a one-year warrantee on all installations, as well as replacing anything that has to be taken away to be repaired.

What the clients say
'So far, so good. Though we are only at installation stage and I have no end result to report, all my dealings with them have been great. They have been very efficient and give a high level of personal attention. Definitely service with a smile.'
Joanna Plant, designer
'They installed a living control system, incorporating plasma screens and hidden speakers, at my London apartment. I found them to be absolutely excellent. They liaised with the contractors, and came in at every stage of the build that they needed to. Andy was very much in control and extremely knowledgeable. He helped me throughout. I've recently finished another property, which I also used them on. They were very good, as were all their engineers and staff. It is very difficult to fault them.'
Bill Heasman, MD, Westland Estates

Light IQ
Carpenters Yard
27 Gironde Road
London SW6 7DY
T: 020 7386 3949
F: 020 7386 3950
www.lightiq.com

Costs £10K–£15K for an average job.
Travel Has completed jobs in USA and Europe but most are in London and south-east England.
Size of job From a kitchen to a stately home.
Attitude Behind-the-scenes wizardry.

Rebecca Weir discovered her passion for lighting at the KLC School of Design. She has been booked solid since starting Light IQ three years ago, after leaving John Cullen as senior designer and being protégé to Sally Storey. Her projects include Barnsley House in Gloucestershire, where Elizabeth Hurley and friends stay while her nearby house is being done up. Tarquin Gorst, restaurant and gastro-pub owner, has involved Weir in some of his commercial projects as well as his own London home. Lighting up Glyndebourne is next on her list.

Weir prefers her effects to be almost unnoticed, and the hand of Light IQ to be invisible. 'People should notice the ambience, not the fittings. Each project is so unique there is no room for a house style,' she says. Weir does not manufacture, and will trawl the industry for the perfect pieces, including retro and period.

What the clients say
'She is very professional and had great ideas and a good eye. She enhanced the features of some old premises using modern contemporary pieces and clever lighting.'
Rupert Pender, co-owner of Barnsley House
'Rebecca was thoroughly organized, efficient and always up to date with what is current in lighting. She was always prepared to drop things and come over. She also offered useful advice and opinions on the project as a whole. I've used her three times, and will be asking her to work on my next project.'
Tarquin Gorst, restaurateur

Lightplan

2a Cromwell Place
South Kensington
London SW7 2JE
T: 020 7584 1240
office@lightplan.org
www.lightplan.org

The Listening Rooms

161 Old Brompton Road
London SW5 0LJ
T: 020 7244 7750
F: 020 7370 0192
info@thelisteningrooms.com
www.thelisteningrooms.com

Costs Not cheap. Richard charges £1,000–£1,200 a day for consultation, £600 a day for project management.
Travel Worldwide.
Size of job Projects range from £5K–£500K.
Attitude Puts some funk into technology.

John Aldridge was a singer before he turned his eye to lighting. He first specialized in fine art and now consults for private clients as well as the Fine Art Society, 10 Downing Street and Hampton Court. He is a consultant for Lightplan, which is owned by John Robert, also a lighting consultant.

Clients, such as PR guru Alan Parker and film director Ridley Scott (whose house Aldridge did in France), are very high profile. Intense but also quite funny, he not only designs but also project manages his jobs. 'When you're dealing with circuits that are attributed to certain spaces, you really should be on site.' He uses a range of lighting (did you know there are hundreds to choose from and then sub-categories of each?), from LEDs to fibre optics to fluorescents, whatever is appropriate – though maintenance is always key. 'This is the most important aspect. It's the top issue.' That's what the client cares about as well as the effects. He doesn't bore them with technology. Lightplan also do AV (home cinemas) on a minor scale.

What the clients say
'The final effects of his lighting are extremely subtle. See his work in the V&A furniture rooms setting. We collaborate regularly.' Chester Jones, interior designer

Costs: £2K–£150K.
Travel Have travelled all over Europe for their customers.
Size of job From a single room to a whole estate.
Attitude Help us to help you.

When John Oliver and Paul Tam started their company in 1989, they were very conscious of new technology and saw that there was a future in high-end audio and installation. 'Back then, 90 per cent of the business was high-powered hi-fi's,' says Tam. 'Now 80 per cent of our business is "audio central heating" with an element of home cinema, and 20 per cent is pure home cinema. So I guess we were right!'

'Audio central heating' is Paul's way of describing the fact that people now have whole music collections saved to a central location, and then wire up their house so they can access and hear it from any room. 'There is still a market for superb two-channel sound [i.e., a stereo], but this is very much for the aficionados. The high-end market has become much less selfish and more family orientated,' he says. Clients are bankers and financial types. However, The Listening Rooms still insist that whether they're supplying lighting control systems, home cinema or just a superb sound set-up, their most valuable product still comes for free: informed advice.

What the clients say
'I thought they were complete professionals. They come when they say they're going to come. Paul Tam is a genius – he can figure absolutely anything out. I am using them again at the moment.' Diane Kordas, client
'They are technical, artistic and efficient. I have used them for my office and my home, and recommend them to many of my patients. I have very high standards, I should add, and insist things be done well.' Dr Georges Kaye, consultant physician

PC Service Limited
22 Hans Place
London SW1X OEP
T: 0800 956 1047
www.pcservice-net.co.uk

PJC Lighting Design
72 Beechcroft Road,
London SW17 7DA
T: 020 8772 4122
M: 07931 997 696
phil@pjclighting.co.uk

Costs **£30 an hour plus VAT.**
Travel **London.**
Size of job **From helping you choose your machine to setting up a whole wireless network.**
Attitude **How can I help?**

Costs **Charges a fixed fee, so no surprises; alternatively £70 per hour. Can come in after the fact, too.**
Travel **Nationwide and abroad.**
Size of job **Often works on an horly basis, £50 – 60 for small jobs.**
Attitude **Doesn't cut corners or wow you with science.**

Polish-born managing director Tom Breza's love for computers started when he was ten. Seeing how badly customers were treated in Britain, he decided to start his own IT company. 'I was working at a London computer shop and was amazed by how everyone behaved – shouting and never returning calls. So I decided to do things my way. Six years ago I started out on my own with £200 and a beat-up PC.' Pretty soon he had the advantage. 'Most of our competitors are cowboys,' he says, 'so when a customer hires us to look after their computer, we like to explain everything to them, so they don't feel they're being taken advantage of.' He now employs 15 people at his offices in Kensington, and expects that number to double by 2005. 'We have an 0800 hotline that we hope will eventually be open 24 hours a day, but I find that trying to talk someone through it on the phone can be a nightmare for all involved, unless the client is quite savvy,' says Tom. PC charge only for the time they're with a client, so Breza would rather send a qualified engineer to the home. 'My main concern is that the customer is relaxed and happy,' he says. Clients are normal people with children and bills to pay.

After leaving lighting and design company Isometrix, Philip Caton's first job was on Stella McCartney's design studio. Almost 60 per cent of his work now comes from architects such as Nick Lee, who know that architecture benefits from good lighting (don't we all?). Caton is also a product designer with a Masters from the Bartlett. He is slow-speaking and clearly very methodical, which is what you want from someone who puts his fingers in circuits for a living.

He mainly uses Lutron for residential projects (along with other companies) but is careful to keep things simple. 'Some techno junkies want the whole thing – they want to be able to turn on the fridge from the phone – but most of my clients just want the minimum fuss. This means putting in normal switches and normal lights that work with isolated pieces of furniture.' It's best to get Caton in on the early stages, when he can pay attention to architectural features. The decorative side of things comes after that.

What the clients say
'They've been very good to us. Tom and his wife are both charming. They seem to employ quite a few Polish people who really understand computers.'
Mr Greenwood, client

What the clients say
'Greenway and Lee have worked with Phil Caton on a wide variety of projects, ranging from a 15-shop roll-out retail programme to private residential and commercial work. We have found that he has a great understanding as to the design needs of the architect and never fails to introduce fresh ideas and new technology into the creative equation. His input is now regarded as an integral part of the design process, which we would recommend the client takes on board.'
Nick Lee, architect

P–S

Patrick Seymour
42 Chertsey Street
London SW17 8LG
M: 07775 795 342
F: 0871 733 5702
info@seymour-it.co.uk
www.seymour-it.co.uk

Phase III
215 Tarring Road
Worthing
West Sussex BN11 4HW
T: 01903 245577
F: 01903 505824
sales@phase3hifi.com
www.phase3hifi.com

Costs On-site call-outs, £85 an hour; telephone support, £130 a month.
Travel Just London.
Size of job Can set up IT for a whole office of 180 terminals, or will come over just to set up your console.
Attitude Thinking big but still small.

For the past 15 years, Patrick Seymour has mainly worked for architects (such as Eva Jiricna and Richard Rogers) and interior designers who can't justify a full-time IT person. He was asked by Allies and Morrison, an architectural firm of 180, to get their systems up and running when they moved offices, so he's pretty knowledgeable and flexible.

'I do everything from blowing dust out of their floppy drive to teaching CAD programs,' he says. A CAD expert, Seymour even got himself a building qualification so that he could offer a fuller service to clients. Clients pay him a retainer so they can call when they have problems. He's ideal for those running a small business from home.

What the clients say
'We're very happy with him, that's why we've stuck with him since he started his own business more than ten years ago. He's a very clever man and very pleasant to deal with.'
Gillian Gould, Eva Jiricna Architects

Costs No standard charge; varies depending on your needs.
Travel Nationwide, although CCR installs systems globally.
Size of job From a DVD player to completely mechanizing an estate.
Attitude An old classic.

Phase III have put cinemas on yachts. They could put one on the moon, that's how experienced they are. Their clients are people you ogle at in the pages of *Hello!*. Their business is being the best at anything to do with hi-fi, home cinema and everything in between. Despite their south-east location, they have a huge customer base spanning the entire south coast and continuing north of London.

First and foremost, Phase III see themselves as consultants. 'We provide solutions first, brands second,' says owner Gerry Heely. His shop is set out as living-room sets, where customers can play around with the remotes. They also have a sister company called CCR that deals in high-end specialist installations for everything from British stately homes to yachts in the Caribbean. Phase III's service extends to lighting systems, control systems and anything else you may want to make your home a completely electronic environment. This is a customer-led business, and Phase III is the brand they are selling – not Sony or Bang & Olufsen.

What the clients say
'Phase III were good at interpreting our wishes and at all times good to deal with. They know their stuff and I'd recommend them to anyone.' Piers Gibson, client

Sound Ideas UK Ltd
The Oast, Perry Court
London Road
Faversham
Kent ME13 8RY
T: 01795 591991 F: 01795 591995
info@soundideas.co.uk
www.soundideas.co.uk

Costs **£200K–£1.5 million.**
Travel **Worldwide.**
Size of job **Big projects.**
Attitude **Crème de la crème.**

Need your Boeing equipped with the latest in home cinema technology? Have a couple of kingdoms that could use music systems? Sound Ideas, founded 20 years ago by Kevin Andrews and Steve Godalman, is your best bet.

This Kent-based company has 37 staff, which means they can do really big jobs for really big clients: their books read like a *Who's Who*, including director David Putnam and so many celebrities and royals this entry would read like *Hello!*. But top interior designers David Mlinaric and Collett-Zarzycki seldom use anyone else.

The minimum spend here tends to be around £200K (budgets go as high as £1 million). Sound Ideas may not be for you unless you recently won the lottery or a huge City bonus. But if you have, Sound Ideas provide service plus. 'We will even change light bulbs for our clients,' says Kevin Andrews, who prides himself on never losing staff.

They have no retail space but occupy an office of 8,500 square feet. A class act, even their brochure is leather-bound and comes in a box. Every project gets its own designer, a project manager, a project engineer and an installation team. 'Everything we do is custom-designed,' says Andrews. 'We just finished a wine cellar that is hydraulically revealed under a billiard table in a Scottish castle.'

What the clients say
'They are efficient and thorough, and what's good about their approach is that they are not pushy. You won't feel intimidated because you're not spending half a million on a sound system.' Anthony Collett, designer

Soundtracks
PO Box 144
Cirencester
Gloucestershire
GL7 3YY
T: 01367 850 151
M: 07790 833721
the.baskins@virgin.net

Costs **£35 to £35K.**
Travel **Will go anywhere, but primarily Gloucestershire or London.**
Size of job **From buying a CD player to wiring an entire house.**
Attitude **Thank you for the music…**

'Music plays a critical role in our lives. It inspires, it consoles and it communicates on all levels. Sadly, most of the time sound is pushed in our ears like a harsh artificial light being shone in our eyes. It should be like well-directed natural daylight, which can illuminate clearly without tiring or irritating us.' This is why Jules Baskin, a 20-year veteran of the media business, set up Soundtracks three years ago.

'My primary interest is good hi-fi,' says Baskin. 'Giving it to people at a reasonable price is what I do.' However, it turns out he does quite a bit more than that. Although he can calculate your home's acoustics and provide you with a fully integrated entertainment system streaming into every room, he has a policy of being 'careful not to spread myself too thin'. He also provides a consultancy service where he will go through the quotes you've got from other home entertainment providers and help you pick the right one. 'I end up saving clients a lot of money because most people's eyes have glazed over within seconds of starting a conversation with a hi-fi dealer.'

Bottom line: Jules is a music lover who wants others to enjoy music as it was meant to be enjoyed, and also has a penchant for demystifying the greyer areas of the hi-fi market to his customers. Or, as he puts it: 'Giving them a hi-fi that allows them to hear the music rather than the sound of poor equipment getting in its way.'

What the clients say
'The best, most reliable, most efficient, most helpful, most comprehensive and imaginative service we could imagine. Jules Baskin is a joy to deal with and has revolutionized the way we listen to music.' Richard Curtis and Emma Freud
'He's great. I wanted to move to widescreen and put a sound system into my chalet in Switzerland. Jules explained it in layman's language so I could understand why I was buying what I was buying. I think he did brilliantly.' Bob Burnett, client

Alan Stirling Technology Limited
135 Lisson Grove
London NW1 6UP
T: 020 7724 2456
F: 020 7724 8788
info@ast.fm
www.ast.fm

Robert Taussig Multi Room Emporium
39 Blanford Street
London W1U 7HD
T: 020 7487 3455
F: 020 7487 3475
sales@roberttaussig.co.uk

Costs **Between £70 and £120 an hour, depending on what's involved and the technician.**
Travel **Within the M25.**
Size of job **A family home to a national company.**
Attitude **What you had at the office, at home.**

Costs **Start at £5K and the sky's the limit.**
Travel **UK, USA, Europe, will go anywhere.**
Size of job **Big projects.**
Attitude **Super smooth and very good.**

Alan Stirling used to win awards for customer service when he owned an Apple dealership, so when he sold his franchise after 14 years, the obvious thing to do was put his skills into practice. Installing them wasn't enough. 'I realized pretty quickly that I couldn't just set people's computers up and then leave them,' he says. 'If I was to be relied upon, I had to offer them a full support service.' His customers on the corporate side range from small studios to large companies, but he also supports, trains and advises normal people. 'Most are professionals who have come across us in the business sector,' he says. He's a Mac specialist (though he will also do PCs) with a team of five technicians. 'I try to be as available as I can. Most of my customers know my mobile number.'

What the clients say
'His technical skills are outstanding and his ability to find the solution to even the most sophisticated problem is quite exceptional.' Rory Bergen, HTA Architects

Robert Taussig is the Mr Big of home cinema. His clients include Eric Clapton, Liam Gallagher, Charles Saatchi and the Duchess of York, to name a few. He founded his company in 1984 and now employs 12 people to guide you through AV, cinema, light and control, audio, satellite TV, security, phones and data. He is used to big budgets – clients with limited funds might feel intimidated.

What the clients say
'Robert's great. His speciality is top-end integrated systems with audio and visual. He can pretty much do anything, so it's no surprise he has such an interesting client list.' Richard Paxton, client

Thinking Fish Limited
Trafalgar House
Grenville Place
London NW7 3SA
T: 0800 458 5883
www.thinkingfish.com

Tudorvale
212 Piccadilly
London W1J 9HG
T: 020 7917 6230
info@tudorvale.com
www.tudorvale.com

Costs £80 an hour, plus competitively priced products and services.
Travel Anywhere within the M25 and some destinations along the M1 (Leeds, Manchester, Birmingham).
Size of job From installing a Netnanny on your PC to fully automating your mansion.
Attitude The only one you'll ever need.

Costs £120–£20K.
Travel Nationwide, Paris and New York, but domestic service is focused on London.
Size of job From installing a phone to wiring up a five-floor house with computers, phones and wireless access.
Attitude We're all you need to get by.

In the future, all service companies will be like Thinking Fish. They offer four services: Telephony, where they will be your phone company, providing you with low cost calls; Internet Service, providing you with Internet access and being your service provider; IT, including helping you choose a computer, buy a computer and install it; and consultancy, adding value to all the other products and services they provide. 'We're 100 per cent customer-focused, rather than product-focused,' says Andrew Lobel, the 25-year-old MD and co-founder, who spent years analysing business models. 'And although we can sell you just about any product you want, the point is that we're here to help our customers get what they need.' This is not just an empty pledge. Despite all the products and services they provide, they still dedicate about 80 per cent of the 40-strong company's manhours to consulting with their clients – be it getting phones for your kids, acquiring security equipment for your house, teaching you how to stop that annoying noise on your computer, making your central-heating controllable over the Internet or sourcing a particular gadget. Thinking Fish also offer a 24-hour helpline and source products for customers that are unavailable in the UK. Contented clients range from footballers to ambassadors to concierge services.

And in case you have a technological disaster, Thinking Fish has six on-site engineers driving around London: talk about being well prepared.

What the clients say
'I work for a textile company previously based in Mill Hill, London. When we decided to move our business to our home address, a friend recommended Thinking Fish. They helped us through the entire process, moving computers and setting them up again, organizing email and hosting, reliably and promptly.'
Debra Isbitt, LS International

Andrew Jones founded Tudorvale four years ago to provide IT support to the art and antiques trade. As time passed, things changed and now he looks after various large corporate clients as well as the private sector – everyone from the British aristocracy to families buying their first PC. Tudorvale will help you buy a computer, give you advice on networks, install your machines and provide support. 'It's a full hand-holding service,' says Jones. 'A lot of our domestic clients know nothing about computers. I like to get involved myself, get to know the customer and help them understand.'

His ability to demystify and explain the rudiments of computing in plain English is something clients love him for. Whether you're buying your computer ('because we sell into corporations and have a high turnover of stock, we can pass these savings on to our domestic clients'); using your computer ('If you can't get through to me, you'll reach our fully manned hotline'); or avoiding your computer ('we'll remember to update your anti-virus software, so you don't have to'); Tudorvale can do it.

Clients have said that he's got very busy lately.

What the clients say
'My son's girlfriend recommended him. I had never been on a computer before, so I went direct to Andrew Jones and he taught me how to use the Internet and everything else I needed. He did it very quickly and very patiently. Not only did he teach me how to do it, but he showed me how easy it actually is. A lot of teachers overdo it, which I feel just complicates matters. What you need is to be set on your way and then have help when you get stuck. If I can't get through to Andrew, then the people in his office are extremely good. If there's something they can't talk you through, they'll be over within the day to sort it out. Overall, very patient, a very nice manner, very efficient and very helpful.'
Lord Stevens of Ludgate

TRUE TO THE GAME ROBERT
MARK GOWMAN TIMOROUS
CHARLOTTE INGLE PAUL COC
PATRICE BUTLER URBAN GL
JENNIFER MERREDEW MAR
ORNAMENTA BECHER JOINE
SCOTT HYDE PAGE LACQUE
HARRY BERGER COLIN CLARK
CENTRE FOR ADVANCED TE
THE EDWARD BARNSLEY WC
SENIOR AND CARMICHAEL R
PAUL CLIFFORD SUSY KENN
RICHARD CULLINAN JOINER

AGAARD & CO PAUL BELVOIR
EASTIES MARSHALL PHILLIPS
SEDGE CALMELS DESIGN LTD
SS WORKS MARK STEPHENS
GOWMAN PAULO DUCASSE
LTD JOHN JONES FRAMING
JENNIFER MERREDEW DKT
URNITURE NICKY CORNWALL
ILES INSIDESPACE TIM HINE
KSHOP CARTER MCARTHUR
OKS BOOKS **MADE TO ORDER**
RD PAUL BELVOIR JOE SMITH
YOON HEE AHN WILKINSON

MADE TO ORDER

The builders have moved out, the curtains are up, but it still doesn't feel like home. Nothing about your house screams out 'me'. For years this 'me' has been lost in the homogenization of modernism: everyone now owns exactly the same Arco light by Castiglione, the same B&B Charles sofa, the same stainless steel kitchen. The sameness applies just as much to those who favour the school of floppy George Smith sofas and muted double-lined Colefax and Fowler curtains. It all starts to look really boring, particularly since developers and hotels have also jumped on the same bandwagon. How many times have you opened a style supplement and seen anything really new?

Having something made just for you is an extremely gratifying experience. 1) You get to pretend you're a bit of an artist yourself because it is a highly collaborative process. 2) You get exactly what you and the space demands. Yes, the high street offers hundreds of desks, cabinets, lights and sofas, but do they match your room? Store owners always say: 'We can do anything' – but, as a veteran of the business, I tell you they can't. Most high-street products are made in factories and follow a grid: you can only have a sofa or kitchen that fits around an odd corner if it's made for you by hand.

The sky's the limit
We have found light artists, artisans, cabinet makers, joiners, gilders, paint finishers, chandelier designers, wallpaper designers, bespoke framers, duck carvers – we even found a sign writer for you. Want to be like Matthew Williamson and have graffiti splashed across your bedroom wall? That's what A. Dee does. Mr Ronald Sitch of William Sitch, the lighting specialists, is Kelly Hoppen's favourite. He's big on collaboration to make sure, in his own words, that the final product looks neither like a pimple or a boil. Some craftsmen are up and coming, some are stars already – but they all want your business. We've also sourced blacksmiths who can do for you what they already do for Tom Dixon.

Where to start?
Many of those included in this section can be called upon at any time to put together a dining-room table or paint a ceiling around a theme. However, joiners, light artists, blacksmiths and even chandelier makers like Patrice Butler need to be brought in early (i.e., at first fix). If you plan to commission one of Dominic Berning's light artists, you will need heavy-duty electrical cabling. Chandeliers are very heavy: large amounts of Murano glass plunging down on the heads of your guests would be a social faux pas, not to

mention a lawsuit in the making. Commissioning does not need to be expensive. Most of those included are artists: they care more about their work than their wallets.

Dos and don'ts
- Do get to know the artist's work. If he has never made a sleek, modern, highly glossed, black-lacquered cabinet, but makes wonderful traditional pieces instead, don't be surprised if the designs offered fall short of your expectations.

- Do visit the workshop. If this is not possible, many artists have websites or can send you brochures or CDs.

- Do get to know the artist. He relies on your imagination as much as you do his.

- Don't sit silently baffled because you don't understand the design on paper. Speak up – you will not be judged an idiot or artistically challenged. (Many designers know their clients do not understand drawings and will, in the case of cabinet makers, for example, often make maquettes (miniature models).

- Do state how much you can afford from the very beginning.

- Do remember artists, such as stained-glass man John Reynteins, are passionate about their art.

- Don't nickel and dime: most artists don't get up in the morning to rip you off – there is a balance to be drawn.

- Do be nice. Nothing shrivels up the creative juices faster than animosity.

- Do remember what the artist's materials cost. Gold leaf is expensive before the artist even starts using it.

- Do ask if they will install the work.

Lexicon (There is a lot of overlap in the business and titles get confusing.)

A **joiner** (such as Richard Becher) makes fixed fittings such as fitted kitchens, fitted cabinets, fitted dressing rooms, stairs and doors.

A **cabinet maker** (such as Mark Stephens) tends to make free-standing one-off pieces. Others such as Paul Belvoir have the skills of cabinet makers as well as the aesthetics of an interior designer. They call themselves **interior architects**, and will design doors with intricate metal work and wood-panelled libraries.

Paint finishers vary in the services they provide. Some (Renee Kopac) will do dragging and marbling, some (Paul Czainski) specialize in trompe l'œil and murals, others do architectural gilding, but they are not to be confused with gilders.

Gilders (such as Rupert Bevan) have their own unique craft, which includes gilding in a variety of metals, in a variety of finishes, on a variety of products (including glass).

Colour consultants are also a mixed bag. Gail Arnold specializes not just in paint for the walls, but will also advise on fabrics, while Charlotte Ingle does only paint.

Finally… these people are very hard to find
We didn't find these names in the *Yellow Pages*. Included are some of the most talented and exclusive craftsmen in the country, who hardly ever receive press coverage (though their clients certainly do). Talk about a Servant's Heart: we found no big egos here, just a desire to please. Many craftsmen such as Rupert Bevan (whose referee is the Hon. Simon Howard of Castle Howard no less), called us again and again to make sure all was OK. They told us about their friends and pretty soon we were inundated with talent.

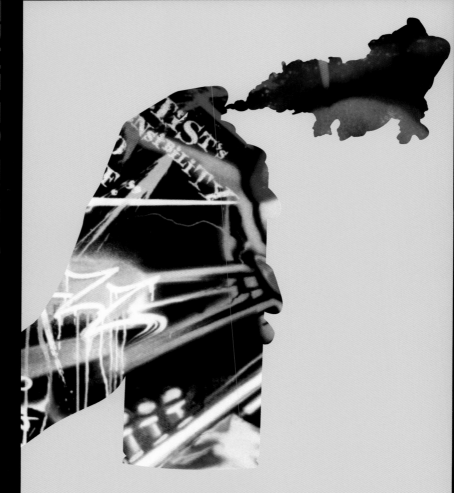

True To The Game – A Dee
Studio 83
Culvert Court
105 Culvert Road
London SW11 5AU
T: 07734 113 264
psyVi@aol.com
www.skil-urbanarts.com

Costs **Depends on the medium. Canvas, £1K and up.**
Workshops, £35 to £50 an hour. Other projects, £500 a day upwards.
Travel **Worldwide.**
Size of job **From statues to large installations.**
Attitude **Visual music for thinkers.**

We chose the graffiti artist A Dee (The Artful Dodger) as our pin-up because, quite frankly, no one else does anything like this. He is also a very nice man (aged 29), who spent hours with my children going through his previous illustrations (I want them each to have an A Dee of their own). Some of them look cartoon-like, until he starts to explain the narrative. A thoughtful man, he gives his time to the community as much as he does private clients.

A Dee is a self-taught artist/psycho-visualist who works with a variety of media, which includes computer graphics. He was inspired by jazz music and the Aerosol (art) Culture movement in New York (including 'writers' like Phase II, Dondi, Futura 2000, Lee, Doze and Seen). This was street art at its best, the visual equivalent of rap and jazz.

He started his artistic career with calligraphy in the mid- '80s and was soon being called up by advertising agencies for their print campaigns. He has also managed to capture the imagination of merchant bankers and stockbrokers in the City, securing a number of commissioned canvases in the process. A Dee could have followed a strictly commercial route but instead he started setting up workshops (for ages 6–60) in diverse places such as Barcelona, the south of France (Montpellier), Wales, Dover, as well as London and the south of England. One of his mural projects on 'drugs awareness', held on South London's Aylesbury Estate in 1992, won an award from the late Princess of Wales. He also designs logos and websites.

Commissions are highly personal. He listens carefully to what the client wants, then he sends a sketch, then he gets down to work. He always writes a page of text to accompany the more conceptual artwork so the client can understand all the symbolism. A few clients have been taken aback when they read his interpretation. A Dee is very perceptive and can read between the lines.

What the clients say
'If you only see this type of art as being limited to "street" style graphics, then you are looking at your *own* limitations, not his!'
Susan Shaw, producer, *The South Bank Show*

A few tips from A Dee
- Listening to the client and 'seeing' things through their eyes is of the utmost importance in order to properly serve their vision. For this to happen I normally suggest meeting in the space that the work is to be displayed and then hearing what the client thinks the work should be about or put across.

- The greater the chemistry, the greater the vision.

- Once both are clear as to what's expected, then terms (i.e., the contract, including staged payments, deadlines and delivery) should be discussed.

- I suggest bringing a work-in-progress for the client to see and discuss.

- Open and clear communication throughout the process is very important, so that any questions and queries can be dealt with before completion.

- Lastly, just because the job is over doesn't mean that the lines of communication should be. I usually keep clients updated with new works and projects, and ask them for feedback from others that have seen the work.

A – B

Robert Aagaard & Co
Frogmire House
Stockwell Road
Knaresborough
North Yorkshire HG5 0JP
T: 01423 864 805 F: 01423 869 356
robertaagaardco@btinternet.com
www.robertaagaard.co.uk

Costs **£2,500 upwards**
Travel **London, Scotland, Cheshire and the north-east.**
Supplies **south-west only.**
Size of job **Restoration to reproduction.**
Attitude **We believe in old and new.**

Robert Aagaard has more than 40 years' experience in antique fireplaces. They not only stock a large selection of antique grates, chimney pieces in a variety of woods, marbles and stone, as well as the surrounds for hearths – they also have a bespoke service manufacturing, and restore period fireplaces. Everything is done by hand from the carvers, from replacing and restoring damaged surrounds (even if it is the replacement of a missing floret), to masons and fitters. Such hand-craftmanship might seem slightly old worldy, but the attention to detail means that they get large contracts restoring for The National Trust and The Landmark Trust. They can even reproduce fireplaces from old photos. Do not call them for contemporary fireplaces – this is not their area, it is purely Georgian to Victorian. They have a dedicated team of nine.

What the clients say
'We had a fireplace removed, replaced by a new one, and one fireplace restored. What I like about Robert Aagaard is the personal touch and the efficiency. There was no hard sell. We are delighted with our fireplaces.' Mrs Cundall, client

Yoon Hee Ahn
90 Elmore Street
London N1 3AL
M: 07932 003 041
yuniahn3@yahoo.com

Costs **£300–£500 a day.**
Travel **Worldwide.**
Size of job **Lamps, screens, wall coverings.**
Attitude **'Let me show you what I can do.'**

Yoon Hee was in her third year, studying fashion design and print at Central St Martins, when she was talent spotted by Stella McCartney. Stella offered her a permanent placement; Yoon Hee took it and has never looked back. Since then she has designed all the interiors of Stella's shops from New York to London. Her style falls between interior design and *haute couture*. Very hands-on, Yoon Hee likes to take vintage materials, such as antique lace from the '30s, to create modern, off-beat wall coverings such as those found in Sketch, London. The room has a 1920s feel, but upon closer inspection you will notice that walls are covered in figures of pole dancers and b-boys made out of crystal and lace. Her skills are all-encompassing; she creates lamps and screens, as well as designing textiles for a couture collection. Currently the darling of the commercial interior world, she would love to get her hands on private residential properties.

What the clients say
**'Yoon Hee is more of an artist than a designer. What she did for Sketch is romantic and sexy. I asked her to give the space some feeling, which she did. She approached Swarovski for the crystals herself. What I like is that the space is completely bespoke. No one can have anything like it.'
Mourad Mazouz, Sketch**

Gail Arnold
1 Tynemouth Street
London SW6 2QS
T: 020 7731 6355
F: 020 7792 1292

The Edward Barnsley Workshop
Cockshott Lane
Froxfield, Petersfield
Hampshire GU32 1BB
T: 01730 827233 F: 01730 827159
enquiries@barnsley-furniture.co.uk
www.barnsley-furniture.co.uk

Costs Chrages £60 per hour for consultation. £300 for painting per day.
Travel Worldwide
Size of job One wall upwards.
Attitude Takes the hassle out of repainting your rooms.

Prince al-Faisal, Andrew Lloyd Webber and King Hussein have all used Gail Arnold's skill as a colour consultant to spruce up their pads with new colour schemes – not to mention her recent overhaul of Clarence House, having previously worked at Highgrove and St James's Palace. Gail provides a niche role, especially where a client may not want to use an interior designer, but needs help on colour. Having trained as a specialist paint finisher, Gail is well qualified and will mix up paints to provide a large range of colours. First, she will visit the client's house to get a feel of 'what's going on in the room', such as the style of furniture, before supplying samples and colour boards. She has an amazing eye, and works mostly word-of-mouth. She also has a shop in Notting Hill called Hand at 11 Colville Mews. Stop by and check out the eclectic range of hand-made goods, from home-ware and furniture to bags and jewellery.

What the clients say
'Incredibly, amazingly talented. She has done lots of work for us over the years.' Karen Killik, client

Costs Breadboards, £35; dining tables, £60K.
Travel All over the world.
Size of job Jewellery box to whole room's worth of furniture.
Attitude Service as it used to be.

The Edward Barnsley workshop is a bespoke cabinet makers with an illustrious past. Established in 1923, they originally contributed designs to the Arts and Crafts movement. Now, retaining the traditional skills, they design one-off, free-standing pieces that are created to accommodate our needs of today, such as cabinets that incorporate televisions and hi-fi systems, and desks with computer systems (each piece is still beautifully crafted), as well as more traditional pieces. Native timbers are predominantly used in the designs, and they have access to more exotic timbers (bought over 40 years ago and stored) for inlays. When commissioning, they provide a design consultation and visit the client's home. They will then design the piece, often producing a beautiful watercolour of the proposed design. Clients are encouraged to watch the piece being made. Private collectors buy most of their work. A two-year-old piece sold at Phillips this year went for £10,500, an indication that Barnsley work retains its value.

What the clients say
'The pleasure of commissioning a piece of furniture from Barnsley is akin to the establishment of a lasting friendship. The first meeting occurs in the most romantic setting of the Barnsley Workshop perched on the edge of a Hampshire hanger, looking over Petersfield plains towards the Sussex Downs. To be part of the design process is the greatest fun and privilege, and to watch the piece during its construction by a single craftsman in the Barnsley team is a singular pleasure. Once in your ownership, the piece matures like an old friend, and the pleasure of its company is enhanced by the memories of its creation.' Michael Campbell, client
'I have used them for the past four years. They have made a total of four pieces for me. Extremely good service, wonderful designer. I would recommend them.' John Leeson, client
'They make the most beautiful, astounding furniture.' Duncan O'Kelly, architect

Becher Joinery Ltd
7 Worton Hall Industrial Estate
Worton Road, Isleworth
Middlesex TW7 6ER
T: 020 8568 9488 F: 020 8568 9311
M: 07711 009 165
richard@becherjoinery.com
www.becherjoinery.com

Costs **Commission based.**
Travel **He will travel to wherever you are.**
Size of job **Budgets of £10K–£100K.**
Attitude **Helpful at all times.**

Becher Joinery is at the top-end of the market. They
do mainly highly polished shop and restaurant fittings,
with clients such as Theo Fennell, Gucci, Hakkasan,
Yauatcha and the private gym KX. Don't ignore them
if you are a private client. Masters of the contemporary
bathroom and wardrobe, as well as sleek, urban,
high black-gloss lacquered pieces, they can do quite
traditional looks, such as panelled doors or large
curved windows. Most clients come to them with
their architect or interior designer, but Richard is happy
to interpret a client's needs if they have a design of
something they like the look of on a piece of paper.
Richard sees his firm as falling in the middle between
joiners and cabinet makers, as he covers built-in
furniture as well as free-standing pieces. The quality
is superb, and if he needs to combine the wood with
another material, such as leather or steel, he has
contacts to all the best specialists in these areas as
well. He has made the most expensive dressing room
in London (his and hers): a mere £80 grand.

What the clients say
'Richard is very artistic. He can take a brief and interpret it
where most require a specific set of drawings. He has a great
eye.' James Thorp, Thorp Design

Paul Belvoir at
Gordon Watson Ltd
50 Fulham Road
London SW3 6HH
T: 020 7589 3108
F: 020 7584 6328
gordonwatson@btinternet.com

Costs **High. A desk will set you back £10K.**
Travel **Worldwide.**
Size of job **Furniture to a whole room.**
Attitude **We're good.**

The artist and his mentor come highly recommended
by every serious interior designer in town, from
Todhunter Earle to David Mlinaric – not to mention
the odd visit by Madonna. Paul and Gordon have the
perfect symbiotic partnership. While Gordon is an
antique dealer by trade, specializing in Art Deco to
the 1940s period, Paul is the creative genius behind the
bespoke designs commissioned through Gordon's
shop. Paul's eye and sense of aesthetics are the source
of much envy in the design community. He can turn
his hand to any medium: silversmithing, jewellery,
metalwork or furniture design. If you have a beautiful
1920s house and want furniture that fits the period but
cannot find that Art Deco look in Gordon's shop, Paul
will create a sympathetic design that blends effortlessly
with the house. He will even design the door hinges.
The pair of them are capable of creating a dining room
à la Jean Michel Frank, pear-wood-panelled rooms,
plaster work or intricate carved railings – in fact,
whole interior designs (but they are not to be confused
with interior designers). The firm has ten craftsmen
specializing in different areas. Quality speaks for itself.

What the clients say
'It's about the workmanship. It is the best I've ever come across.
Paul made a plaster chandelier for me from a photograph. He
studied the picture for a month. The chandelier was extremely
detailed, and he got every detail right. He's a perfectionist.
When Paul makes something it is even better than I could have
imagined.' Janet de Botton, client
'I think he really is a genius, an amazing designer; very creative
with a wonderful sense of proportion. He has knowledge in
many different mediums.' Emily Todhunter, Todhunter Earle

Harry Berger
25 Station Road
Cheadle Hulme
Cheshire SK8 5AF
T: 0161 485 3421
F: 0161 282 2860
harryberger@emailx.co.uk
www.harryberger.com

Dominic Berning
1 Hoxton Street
London N1 6NL
T: 020 7739 4222
F: 020 7739 2130
mail@dominicberning.com
www.dominicberning.com

Costs Dyeing services only: curtains, approx. £12 per square metre; blankets, £65; bedcovers, £36 single; £49 double; flexible and stiff backed floor/wall rugs by quotation, starting from £78.
Travel UK.
Size of job (See above.)
Attitude One of a kind, friendly and helpful.

Costs Depends on the commission.
Travel Worldwide.
Size of job What can you can afford?
Attitude There are infinite possibilities.

Domestic dyers are a rarity these days, so the name Harry Berger is one to remember. The Berger family have been in the dyeing and specialist cleaning business since 1912. Outlasting their competitors, they are now unofficially recognized as the last domestic dyers in the UK. Clients flock to them from all over the country for their expertise on textiles. They will tackle soft furnishings such as blankets, as well as loose covers for sofas and cushion covers. As specialist cleaners, they have unparalleled knowledge on stain removal, especially with antique materials such as christening gowns that have seen service over generations. They also handle oriental rugs, for which they have a dedicated depot. Some items they will clean by hand. This is one secret that should be let out of the bag: the Macclesfield Silk Museum uses them to clean all their stock.

Dominic Berning is an artists' agent representing artists who work with light. Often working at the cutting edge of light technology, the artists' work ranges from sculptures that incorporate light as part of the design to swimming pools bathed in subtle hues to whole façades of buildings clad in an iridescent glow. Dominic represents high-profile artists such as Martin Richman, Jane Watt, Jane Mulfinger and LEO, to name a few. The size of their work can be as small as a book to a whole power station clad in light. You've probably seen Richman's work on the street. He created the luminescent books at the Women's Library, Whitechapel, as well as the futuristic-looking light installation on the west colonade of Canary Wharf. Dominic provides a complete service, working as the interface between client and artist; he is very much involved from the production of the artwork to its installation. He provides the technicians, electricians and builders to install the final product. There is no limit.

What the clients say
'Harry Berger is a great find. I am really pleased. We had two settees' loose covers done. One set dyed to the original colour, and the other was dyed in a new colour. Mr Berger kept us informed the whole time. The covers were delivered beautifully.'
Liz Sargent, client

What the clients say
'The light emanating from Martin Richman's set of three window lights in our kitchen is deliciously warm and atmospheric, changing with the time of day.' Lucy Morris, client

B–C

Rupert Bevan
40 Fulham High Street
London SW6 3LQ
T/F: 020 7731 1919
info@rbevanconservation.com

Golden-Section Design Ltd
Church Farm Studios, Stanton Lacy
Shropshire SY8 2AE
T/F: 01584 856 699
enquiries@golden-section-design.com
www.golden-section-design.com

Costs **Commission based.**
Travel **Worldwide.**
Size of job **Picture frames to furniture.**
Attitude **'We are interior architects.'**

Furniture maker Paul Belvoir considers Rupert Bevan to be 'the best in his field' as a master gilder. He works in a variety of metals: copper, silver, gold, even aluminium (he did the aluminium leafing at the Savoy Theatre), which he applies to a variety of surfaces. Finishes are his speciality. He can achieve for you Art Deco-style aluminium to an old gold that seems like it has been on your picture frames for years. Gilding is not his only talent. Having worked on numerous restoration projects (including Windsor Castle), and asked to make up tables, chairs, etc., he branched out with his own design company Golden-Section, with business partner Adam Hely-Hutchinson. Their name has spread: the Sultan of Oman, St James's Palace, Castle Howard and the Duke of Richmond have all used his services. Their products are diverse in style, from medieval-looking doors with intricate iron work to glass staircases, and a mahogany library – the idea is for people to commission one-off pieces. Rupert says: 'We try to give the client what they want,' combined with quality and craftsmanship.

What the clients say
'Rupert is very conscientious, and researches the project before starting. He discusses all aspects of restoration with the client, producing documents and photographs to support his finds, which are nice to have for the archives.'
The Hon. Simon Howard, client

Tord Boontje
info@tordboontje.com
www.tordboontje.com

Costs **Commission based.**
Travel **Worldwide.**
Size of job **Textile commissions to chandeliers.**
Attitude **Huge talent, modest ego.**

There is probably no one more fashionable in the design community at the moment than Tord Boontje. He won Designer of the Year in 2003.
    A former student of the Design Academy, Eindhoven, and the Royal College of Art, Tord is an established name among the design world. As well as bespoke furniture, he is famous for his lighting designs: look for his big metal flower garland on Kean Street, London, as well as his permanent piece in British Airways First Class lounge, Terminal 1. Inspired by the 18th and 19th centuries, his lights take on a fairytale romantic quality. He uses a mixture of handmade crafts, such as embroidery and lace, to create chandeliers that look like paper filigree, giving them an ethereal quality. Tord likes to work in a very fluid way. Once commissioned, he will make up some drawings, before commencing with the work in different stages. Last year he collaborated with Alexander McQueen to make the V&A's 'Crystmas Tree'; he's also created works for Ian Schrager and two large chandeliers for Swarvoski. But most of us know him through his Garland Lights for Habitat, which they find impossible to keep in stock.

What the clients say
'I think that Tord's work is beautiful: it's feminine, playful and it has impeccable craftsmanship.' Lauren Booth, client

Patrice Butler
T: 020 7609 5630
F: 020 7609 5630
patrice@patricebutler.com
www.patricebutler.com

CA1
45 Stanley Road
Whitstable
Kent CT5 4NQ
T: 01227 264 133
M: 07775 686 267
www.ca1.co.uk

Costs **Approx £5K upwards; larger pieces can cost up to £30K.**
Travel **Worldwide.**
Size of job **Chandeliers only.**
Attitude **Takes it seriously enough to have studied at the Architectural Association.**

When it comes to chandelier design, Patrice Butler outshines all others. From the jet-set to the Eurocrats, his work appears across the globe. Clients include Princess Gloria von Thurn and Taxis, The Duke and Duchess of Westminster, Mick Jagger, Valerie Wade, Michelle Yeoh, The Groucho Club, Browns, Dr Stanley Ho (Macau casino magnate), Janet Street-Porter, and that's even before we start on the interior designers such as David Mlinaric and John Stefanidis, as well as collaborating with milliner Philip Treacy. Trained as an architect at the AA, he now focuses predominantly on chandelier design. His style has been called Baroque, as his chandeliers drip with crystal pendants, gem-colour Murano glass beads and semi-precious stones. As well as collaborating with well-established, quality-producing glass manufacturers such as Swarvoski and Baccarat, he is very much craft based. He has a team of craftsmen – metalworkers, gilders to glass-blowers – across Europe making specialist parts for his chandeliers. Many of the glass components are hand-blown, such as the chandeliers recently made for Browns and The Groucho Club. Patrice has also worked with glass specialist Simon Moore, who is the glass tutor at the Royal College of Art. Patrice makes only large chandeliers, which he often assembles on site. When it comes to commissioning, he likes to visit his client's residence. If this is not possible, then the client can send him drawings, photos and, most importantly, the measurements of the room where the chandelier will hang. This will help Patrice with the dimension of the chandelier. If you are restoring your house, he likes to get involved early on, as he can then advise on weight and electrical requirements.

What the clients say
'Patrice is fantastic; he's great; he's a chandelier genius. He's always experimenting. He is very easy to work with and has no prima donna manners.' Martin Brudnizki, client

Costs **Mid-range.**
Travel **London and the South East, but will go all over the UK.**
Size of job **From a cupboard to a kitchen.**
Attitude **Italian style at half the price.**

Ben Mather of CA1 works in the more specialist area of the joinery trade. He has the eye of a designer with the skills of a cabinet maker. If you want a modern-looking cupboard with a white, lacquered veneer, he will design and make this for you. Likewise, if your style is influenced by the East, he will make beautiful oriental-style sliding doors in American walnut. CA1 burst on the scene a few years ago. Previously, anyone wishing for contemporary cabinets and beds would have had to order from Cappellini or B&B Italia.

From in-built cupboards to bespoke kitchens, whatever the size of the job, Ben will turn your ideas into a reality. When commissioning, he will visit the client's house and measure up before providing detailed drawings of the final product. He will then install the work. Impressed clients have asked him to do complete interiors. He has worked on furniture ranges for Habitat and M&S.

What the clients say
'Ben built a fantastic home office for us. You would never guess that behind the glass-panelled sliding doors, there is a computer, scanner, fax, etc. The doors are as much a feature of the room as the furniture.' Rachel Boser, writer

Calmels Design Ltd
3 Southville
London SW8 2PR
T: 020 7622 6181
F: 020 7498 2889
louis@calmels.co.uk
www.calmels.co.uk

Carter McArthur
6 Folly View Road
Faringdon
Oxon SN7 7DH
T: 01367 820 487
F: 01367 820 126

Costs Commission based.
Travel Yes, if the job is big enough.
Size of job Furniture to architectural work.
Attitude A family affair.

Calmels are blacksmiths who can create almost anything (for the likes of Tom Dixon, Nigel Coates and Mark Brazier-Jones) from furniture to props for the theatre trade to architectural work. They work with aluminium, copper, stainless steel, bronze – in fact, any metal except zinc – to create bespoke tables, chairs, benches, gates, banisters, whatever your needs, for either your house or garden. They're not designers but they can re-create furniture from pictures and build them to your precise requirements, but note they work purely with metal and do not combine materials such as metal and marble. Clients include The Royal Opera House and the National Theatre.

What the clients say
'The type of customers we deal with demand high quality. We expect the best and Calmels deliver it.'
Shaun Futter, Marston & Langinger
'There are very few companies like this left in Britain. They are prepared to take on very complex designs.'
Tom Dixon, designer

Costs Up to £1K for an English or European oak door.
Travel Generally within a 150-mile radius. Will travel further for a big job.
Size of job Windows, staircases, kitchens.
Attitude Takes the time to tell you about the beautiful.

Carter McArthur is a high-quality joiners firm. If you are converting an old chapel and need new windows, they can make them to fit your requirements. The same applies to doors, staircases, balustrades – whatever your needs. They made an amazing staircase for Alex James of Blur.

They will make the product in a wood of your choice, advising the best material for the job. Immensely adaptable, the same approach applies to the style – they can make anything from a Gothic oak door to the grand classic French doors found in stately homes. From in-built wardrobes to kitchens, these guys are considered some of the best joiners in the White Horse area. When commissioned, they will meet the client, discuss the brief and come up with some drawings. They have been established since 1972, but have never advertised as their work is purely word of mouth.

What the clients say
'We were 100 per cent absolutely delighted with them. Couldn't recommend them highly enough. They are individual, old-fashioned craftsmen. They made our entire wooden timber-framed house as well all the furnishings.'
Mr & Mrs Topless, clients

Centre for Advanced Textiles (CAT)
Foulis Building
158 Renfrew Street
Glasgow G3 6RS
T: 0141 353 4742
F: 0141 353 4745
cat@gsa.ac.uk
www.catdigital.co.uk

Costs **Approx £35–£65 a metre, depending on the complexity of the print.**
Travel **No need. Download your image, send it to them and they return the fabric by Fedex.**
Size of job **Minimum half a metre.**
Attitude **From a prototype to a large print run, we have the capacity to print whatever image you want onto fabric.**

Gucci, Sadie Frost, Tristan Webber, Jonathan Saunders, Giles Deacon, even Formula One Racing, have discovered the joys of digitally printing designs onto fabrics. With a super-fast turn-around, Lyndsay Taylor and Alan Shaw at the Centre for Advanced Textiles can take any image and reproduce it in any colour, any size and any amount of repeat. The smallest print run they do is half-a-metre. Before sending them a photo of granny in the hopes they will turn her into a Warhol-style pop-art image, give them a call – too often they receive files they cannot open or poor-quality photos. All images are printed on natural fibres: they can't print onto man-made materials. This is a great way to have your own-designed material, which you can turn into cushions, curtains, seat covers, etc. They are currently working with Lucienne Day, reproducing her classic '50s and '60s designs, which have grabbed the attention of Converse, the All Star sneaker manufacturers.

What the clients say
'As a small Scottish textile company with a UK and international customer base, we've benefited from the short-run service CAT provides, significantly reducing costs. Maintaining a competitive edge is a concern for any small business and in textiles the timescale from design to production is a key competitive issue. The digital print process provides increased scope for creating both complex and subtle designs, while the rapid turnaround time means that reordering can be based on demand, without the need to carry costly stock.' Paul Simmons, Timorous Beasties
'Having established British Design in 2002, on graduating from the RCA, I continued to explore the digital aesthetic for interior printed textiles. Through collaboration with CAT, I have pioneered the digital printing of leather to develop a product range suitable for both walls and seating. I will also be launching a range of digitally printed lighting, which has also been prototyped at CAT.'
Helena Britt, British Design

Colin Clark Furniture
The Old Forge
Hampton Street
Tetbury
Gloucestershire GL8 8JN
T: 01666 504 838 F: 01666 503 079
clarkfurniture48@aol.com

Costs **Solid oak dresser, approx £4K; table, £1,200 upwards; beds, £1K upwards.**
Travel **Delivers all over the UK.**
Size of job **Traditional furniture.**
Attitude **Quality, traditional craftsmanship.**

Established in 1977, Colin Clark is a traditional furniture maker and restorer who still cuts his dove-tail joints by hand. He works purely in solid hard woods – no veneers here – turning his lathe to book cases, oak panelling, tables, chairs, etc. He is very good at marrying up pieces of furniture; for example, if you have a chest with some carving on and would like a chair made in a similar style, Colin will reproduce the carving and work it into the design of the new chair. As a restorer, he has all the skills at his fingertips, from matching up colours to replacing joints. He will even do a bit of inlay.

What the clients say
'Over the past 20 years he's done various jobs for us… doors, wardrobes, chairs. His workmanship is excellent. He is a very nice person, which makes all the difference. His work is absolutely top class.' Tony Bond, client
'Please let me recommend Colin Clark, a fantastic furniture maker just down the road.'
Simon Dodson, French polisher and restorer

Paul Clifford
Arch 3
Miles Street
London SW8 1RZ
T: 020 7819 9619
F: 020 7819 9719
M: 07956 580 812

Paul Cocksedge
2A Brenthouse Road
London E9 6QG
T/F: 020 8985 0907
M: 07966 790 998
info@paulcocksedge.co.uk
www.paulcocksedge.co.uk

Costs Reasonable. Commissions from £150 upwards.
Travel Worldwide.
Size of job From a cabinet to a floor.
Attitude Relaxed, friendly professionalism.

Paul was working in the lucrative business of lettering head stones before he started to experiment with glass. Somehow or other, he moved into making sandblasted and plain glass cabinets, glass floors, as well as stone cabinets – anything that took the client's and, more important, the designer's fancy. The beauty of sandblasting, explains Paul, is that it produces a very deep carving. What's carved is between you and the very affable Paul.

He now gets commissioned by John Stefanidis. He has recently been picked up by Pearl Lam, one of Hong Kong's leading fine art collectors. She is spreading the word on Paul at her gallery, Contrasts.

What the clients say
'We love him.' Tony Collett, Collett-Zarzycki architects
'I think very highly of Paul. I like him as a person. He is very creative and efficient, and really quite impressive. I'd recommend him for any project of any size. He's the best I've ever worked with.' Iada Hersham, client

Costs One-off commissions are individually priced.
Travel Worldwide.
Size of job Sculptures start from £140; lampshades, £495–£625; vase, £340.
Attitude The next Ingo Maurer.

Twenty-six-year-old British light designer Paul Cocksedge hadn't even graduated from the Royal College of Art when Issey Miyake called on him. When he did graduate in 2002 (Ron Arad was his mentor), he was introduced to the legendary lighting designer Ingo Maurer (this is like being introduced to Stephen Spielberg after finishing at Juilliard). Cocksedge presented his lighting collection alongside Maurer's at the Milan Furniture Fair in 2003. Now, art collectors and museum curators are knocking at (more like knocking down) his door. What makes him so special? His ability to create new lighting formats such as Bulb: place a daisy in one of his vases and the flower lights up, and will stay alight until it dies. He has a range of four products, as well as selling one-off, commissioned pieces. For a closer look at his work, visit Mint in Wigmore Street, London.

What the clients say
'Paul Cocksedge brings a technological maturity to his fascination with the lyrical possibilities of light. His work returns us to the first principle of design: the unity of nature, art and science. These are objects that are not only beautiful, but inculcate a sense of wonder.' Jane Pavitt, senior research fellow, V&A Museum and University of Brighton

Nicky Cornwall
8 Higham Street
Totterdown
Bristol BS4 2BJ
T: 0117 971 1243
nicky@bowerbird.freeserve.co.uk
www.bowerbird.co.uk

Costs **Medium/high. Commission based.**
Travel **Worldwide.**
Size of job **Walls upwards.**
Attitude **Self-effacing but determined.**

Nicky Cornwall is a specialist painter with a natural flair for design. An all-rounder with the paint brush, she can create whatever you ask from trompe l'œil images to an Art Deco-look to geometric designs. She was trained in illustration and graphics, so her work is very good on detail, which, combined with her ability for freehand drawing, means she can draw straight onto the wall (she's recently painted a Romany caravan). She has worked predominantly with paint specialist Ian Cairnie, who describes Nicky as 'a great team player'. Her work can be seen at the Ritz's casino and on Queen Mary II. Nicky is a sophisticated mural painter – no graining or marbling here, please.

What the clients say
'She's just wonderful and incredibly flexible. I find most people who do trompe l'œil tend to be rather naff, but Nicky has style whatever she's doing. She just does exquisite work.'
Gail Arnold, colour consultant

Paul Crudge
The Workshop
Great Holt Farm, Bodsham
Ashford
Kent TN25 5JG
M: 07881 467 774
info@paulcrudge.com
www.paulcrudge.com

Costs **12-seater dining table, approx £5K–6K; coffee table £1K.**
Travel **Worldwide.**
Size of job **Furniture.**
Attitude **Conscientious.**

Trained by famous furniture designer John Makepeace, Paul makes contemporary and one-off pieces of furniture to the client's specification. Unfazed by the size of a project, he has produced everything from a 22-foot, English elm dining table to a display cabinet in American walnut and cherry – you name it, he'll make it. Paul likes to make sure the whole piece looks good, from the top to the unseen underside. Working closely with the client, he will first produce a miniature model of the commission. The final piece is often clean-lined and unadorned because, as Paul says: 'I let the wood do the speaking.'

What the clients say
'Paul works by commission, creating beautiful works of art in the form of tables, desks, etc.' Nicole Fulton, Walnut

C–D

Richard Cullinan Joinery
8 Ferrier Street
Wandsworth
London SW18 1SW
T: 020 8871 0029
F: 020 8871 0020
richard@rcjoinery.co.uk
www.rcjoinery.co.uk

Costs The average order falls between £5K and £10K.
Travel Generally he works within M25, but is happy to travel all over the UK.
Size of job Bookcases upwards.
Attitude Very helpful chap.

A bespoke joiner, Richard Cullinan specializes in built-in bookcases, libraries, wardrobes, radiator cases and home work/office areas. He is sympathetic towards design, and can create any period style, such as a Georgian bookshelf to a TV cabinet that can slip discreetly into a minimalist loft conversion. He will turn his eye more or less to anything you want – however, he does not do kitchens. He works with a number of designers and decorators, but is very happy to take on private clients. He is predominantly word-of-mouth, and 70 per cent of his business is from returning clients.

What the clients say
'I couldn't recommend Richard highly enough. I have been working with him for 15 years on very illustrious jobs down to very small jobs. On every occasion he is totally professional, always gives a rapid response, his costs have never been over the estimation (unless he's informed me at an early stage). He has an excellent workshop and keeps all the messy work off site. He is always on time and has great communication skills.'
Katherine Tawell, client
'You get the quality you are hoping for. He talks the same language as you; he really makes sure he knows what you want. And it's done beautifully. It's great.'
Mrs Diana Henderson, client
'He had so many great ideas. We parted ways with our builder and he took over. He made things perfectly and was always on time. He is charming and polite and has a proper workshop.'
Caroline Amrolia, solicitor

Paul Czainski
Old Oats Royd
Oats Royd
Luddenden
Halifax HX2 6RF
T/F: 01422 884607
oatsroyd@btopenworld.com
www.czainski.co.uk

Costs Commission based.
Travel Worldwide.
Size of job Wall-sized.
Attitude Renaissance man.

Paul Czainski has worked for some of the biggest names: Lord Snowdon, Lord Sainsbury, Ringo Starr, Mick Jagger, Prince Amyn Aga Khan, the Earl and Countess of Verulam, which makes his client list read like an A-celeb party roll-call (not to mention the designers such as Nicky Haslam and David Mlinaric, Colefax and Fowler and Designers Guild). Trained in fine art at the Jacob Kramer School in Leeds and Goldsmiths College, Paul turned his talents to specializing in trompe l'œil, grisaille (friezes), as well as gilding, marbling and graining. His work looks so real, you have to touch it to believe that it's faux. He is good at interpreting what the client wants, while giving them something a bit different – a mural's Rococo frame may have, upon closer inspection, intricate nautical details rather than curlicues. These are not the only talents at the tip of his paint brush. As an artist, he paints very detailed still-life, echoing the Dutch tradition, while his off-beat sense of humour leads to rather quirky doodles. Visit Gallery Iris (Paul's own gallery), Todmorden, Yorkshire, to see his work.

What the clients say
'Paul is a genius, who knows he's a genius, but doesn't parade it. He is modest and brilliant at the same time. He knows how to translate ideas into something tangible. He has an enormous knowledge of the history of art. If you want something Egyptian, he knows exactly how to create it. He spoils one for anyone else. He is the best, the most skilled and the most inventive of anybody.' Nicky Haslam, designer

DKT – Specialist Decorators
3 Charterhouse Works
Eltringham Street
London SW18 1TD
T: 020 8874 3565
F: 020 8874 2058
info@dkt.co.uk
www.dkt.co.uk

Costs **£1K–£350K.**
Travel **Worldwide.**
Size of job **From one room to a palace.**
Attitude **Quiet professionalism.**

DKT are specialist decorators, not to be confused with specialist painters. Although they do murals and trompe l'œil, what makes them different is that they also do bas-relief and moulded art-works, such as cornicing. An in-house team of 20 means they can do sizeable jobs. Most of their jobs are commissioned through designers and have included large projects such as the Queen Mary II, the Dorchester Hotel and Alfred Dunhill. Their skills are just as easily translated to the private sector. Deciding which service you require is made easy by their extensive library of finishes.

What the clients say
'DKT's work is absolutely amazing. Everything they do is incredible. I have done loads of work with them and I can most highly recommend them.'
Charles Bateson, Charles Bateson Design Consultants
'We have used them on various projects and they are always very professional and accommodating.'
Leslie Bond, Private Lives Interiors

James Denison-Pender
Glenbrook House
Balerno
Midlothian
Scotland EH14 7BQ
T: 0131 449 4116
F: 0131 449 2506
www.glassengrave.co.uk

Costs **Approx £2,500.**
Travel **Worldwide.**
Size of job **From a goblet to a glass wall.**
Attitude **Hibernian gentleman with rare talents.**

As a specialized glass engraver, James Denison-Pender's work has found itself into the homes of US philanthropists the Mellon family, Charles Price, former US ambassador to the UK, as well as the late Princess Diana. The technique he uses is stipple engraving, where the image is built-up onto the glass by hand through hundreds of tiny dots. A client's patience is required as the work is time-consuming. On average each piece takes him a month to complete. His work covers every conceivable image from African wildlife to families outside their country piles. Once commissioned, James visits the location to see his project in the 'flesh', before returning to Scotland to complete the work. No job is too large or too small. James is a find.

What the clients say
'James has engraved the most beautiful goblet, which I commissioned to give to my husband for our 30th wedding anniversary... James provided an invaluable service in arranging the display and lighting of the glass, which makes the most special of presents.' Lois May Donaldson, client
'Since I first came across the stipple-glass engraving produced by James Denison-Pender, some six years ago, he has been commissioned by Diageo to design and create the Trophy for the International Wine and Spirit Competition Outstanding Achievement in Scotch Whisky Award, sponsored by Diageo. His work has shown creativity within the type of glass medium, ranging from goblets large and small, plates of different sizes, illuminated display cabinets... We would have no hesitation in recommending James to others.'
Patrick Millet, Scotch Heritage director, Diageo

D—G

Paolo Ducasse
5 Cherry Tree Walk
Oakridge Village
Basingstoke
Hampshire RG21 5RJ
T/F: 01256 41 0903
artyfaktory@yahoo.co.uk

Costs **Commission based only.**
Travel **Worldwide.**
Size of job **Box-sized.**
Attitude **Thinks out of the box, even though he makes boxes.**

Paolo Ducasse will put the historical context to the meaning of the name of your house in a rectangular, oak-framed box which he calls the Game of the Name. An artist with a multifarious past – he was formerly a documentary maker and an anthropologist with an interest in etymology – Paolo uses his bricolage of knowledge to create symbolic pieces of relief art. He does this by rummaging through old photos, books, whatever is disused and ignored, but has a personal context from a client's house and recycles them into his art pieces. The artwork is then suspended by wax inside the box; the image reflecting the meaning of the client's house or name. Each piece comes with an old-fashioned envelope explaining the symbols to the name. The point behind the work is that he tries to give the client a sense of identity, of belonging somewhere. When commissioned, he believes in finding out as much about the client as possible: he likes the client to be as involved in the work as he is himself. Don't limit yourself purely to the Game of the Name boxes. Paolo is extraordinarily inventive and will create other personal artworks. For a client, he moulded together large honeycombs, symbolizing the couple's life together, and injected each cell with the couple's DNA.

What the clients say
'Paolo Ducasse's Game of the Name make great presents, especially for Christenings and weddings. Having said that, the process will stretch you.'
Helen Kirwan-Taylor, author of *Home UK*

Belinda Eade
Studio 70
Great Western Studios
Great Western Road
London W9 3NY
T: 020 7266 0328 M: 07956 455 224
studio@belindaeade.com
www.belindaeade.com

Costs **Commissions from £25K to £30K upwards.**
Travel **UK.**
Size of job: **Small or large, as long as they are grottoes.**
Attitude **Who says grottoes aren't 2005?**

Grottoes were originally built by the Greeks as shrines to celebrate a water source. By the 17th century, they became the must-have garden accessory in Italian high society. Belinda Eade, grotto designer, still works the old-fashioned way for equally illustrious clients such as the Duke and Duchess of Northumberland at Alnwick Castle. She describes her work as art imitating nature: what may look like rough bits of rock on the outside is, in fact, a carefully thought-out structure. She lines her grottoes with beautiful shells or cut stone. The effect is like stepping into an early Byzantine church. Water plays an important part, with rocky cascades or bubbling pools. Belinda believes that 'if anyone has a natural spring, then they should definitely have a grotto,' but neither water nor a resident hermit in the English Romantic tradition are an essential feature if all you desire is a beautiful outdoor room to escape to.

What the clients say
'It was certainly worth it, and we are delighted… We are absolutely thrilled with the final result of Belinda's considerable work and good taste.' Sir Philip Naylor-Leyland, client
'I think Belinda created an absolute jewel. She was a joy to have around. She has created something that is extraordinary and special.' Robert Chapman, client

FA Firman

19 Bates Road
Harold Wood
Romford
Essex RM3 0JH
T: 01708 374 534
F: 01708 340 511
www.firmanglass.com

Costs **£100 upwards.**
Travel **Worldwide.**
Size of job **From glass ballustrading to a swimming pool.**
Attitude **Try our best at all times.**

FA Firman is a glass-processing firm that will laminate, etch, cut – in fact, you name it and they can do it. John Hodgson, managing director, says: 'Any niche project that someone else cannot produce, Firman will do it.' They have more in-house facilities than any other glass processors in London, including fabrication and installation of any metal work that goes with a project (they have an internal team of 60). This has made them the favourite with the architectural world, such as Raphael Viñoly who ordered a glass canopy supported by cantilevered glass beams (situated in Toyko). Each piece of 12-metre glass had to be tested to take 10 tons before it was installed. Elbowing the architects aside, they are happy to take on private commissions such as glass swimming pools and glass staircases. Their work can also be found at the Royal Opera House, London, and they also supplied the 3,500 glass pieces that make up the ceiling of the Bank restaurant, Aldwych.

What the clients say
'The company does a complete job from the glass and metal work to the foundry. Dependable and would most definitely recommend them.' Ann King, client

Kevin Glashier

93 Sussex Way
London N7 6RU
T/F: 020 7281 7821
M: 07956 36 39 34
kevin@kevinglashier.co.uk
www.kevinglashier.co.uk

Costs **£30 an hour.**
Travel **Europe.**
Size of job **From a house number to wall decorations.**
Attitude **Very conscientious when it comes to work, combined with beautiful craftsmanship.**

Anyone with a bit of imagination should consider commissioning Kevin Glashier.

A signwriter (who originally studied fine art at Goldsmiths), he has a unique craft of hand-painted lettering and numbering. He can apply the name and number of your house onto anything: the door, the wall, onto a glass outdoor lamp. He works with a variety of typefaces, including calligraphy, which he uses on picture mounts as well. He will also create signs (both projecting and flat) out of stainless steel, as well as brass. Don't limit him, though, purely to letters and numbers. He is also a skilled gilder, his work including ceilings, furniture and railings. His other talents lie in decorative finishes – in case you've ever fancied the family crest painted onto a wall – including reproducing wall decorations, which may have been worn away, to match the original in a room. Once commissioned, he will visit the client on site, produce scale drawings and alternative typefaces, before coming up with a quotation. His clients include Westminster Abbey, The Reform Club, M & C Saatchi, and John Jones, the specialist framers. No one has yet thought to put his skills to decorative use (as a birthday present, for example).

What the clients say
'Kevin Glashier has worked with us for about 15 years. He specializes in hand-painted lettering and, in the early days of his association with Carew-Jones, his projects included white and gold-leaf lettering on glass, as well as decorative gilding on furniture. More recently his work has included vinyl logos on contemporary pieces of furniture. The standard of his sign-writing has always been of the highest calibre, and he is one of the most conscientious people to work with.'
Nigel Carew-Jones, Carew-Jones & Associates

Mark Gowman
Redlands Farm
Duncton
Petworth
West Sussex GU28 0JY
T: 01798 343 187 F: 01798 342 539
pamgowman@btopenworld.com

Annabel Grey
20 The Street
Bintree
Norfolk NR20 5NE
T: 01362 683 569
M: 07860 500 356

Costs **Chest of drawers from £2K; Dining chair, £500 to £600, depending on detail. Pricing is broken down into design time plus estimation of hours and material costs.**
Travel **Based in West Sussex so he mainly works in the South East and London but will travel, depending on the job or if it is repeat clients.**
Size of job **Chairs and any other pieces of furniture.**
Attitude **A 21st-century Chippendale cabinet maker.**

Mark Gowman is a cabinet maker and a fully qualified antique restorer in the old-school tradition. Trained at West Dean College for Design, he can turn his hand to making any quality piece of furniture in the style of the 17th century through to Art Deco. Clients often bring him pictures from sales catalogues, magazines or even their own designs and he will tailor-make the piece to the client's specifications. Do not, however, take your Heals catalogue along, Mark's skills are traditional and he is interested only in making traditional pieces. As a restorer, he can do all the variety of finishes, carving, inlays and veneers, as well as make up numbers: if you have bought four dining chairs in the sale room and want six, he can make up the other two. He's been featured in *House & Garden*, but predominantly his skills are passed on by word-of-mouth. Having bespoke pieces made by Mark can become addictive. He says: 'Once clients get the bit between the teeth they enjoy the process.'

What the clients say
'The desk Mark made is absolutely stunning! It certainly is a solid piece of furniture and suits the room beautifully.' Mr and Mrs Shears, clients

Costs **Middle range.**
Travel **Worldwide.**
Size of job **Anything considered.**
Attitude **Fun, original designer who is very professional.**

Annabel studied for an MA in printed textiles at the Royal College of Art. Her expertise, however, lies in hand-painted fabrics and murals. Think big – some can be 45 feet long, such as the painted canvas she produced for London Weekend Television. She has a great eye for colour and design, ranging from bold geometric shapes to stylized flora and fauna. Simon Finch, rare book dealer, had her decorate his Arts and Crafts house in Norfolk, and has now commissioned her to do his bar in Majorca. Her talents, though, are not to be pigeon-holed just in painted canvas. She is also an expert in mosaics, as well as producing other funky projects such as her large mobile Perspex Christmas decorations. She has also produced work for Raymond Blanc's Oxford restaurant Le Petit Blanc.

What the clients say
'I have worked with Annabel for the past 25 years and am currently working on a project in Majorca with her. She has an interesting and unusual eye. Extremely talented and, when she gets down to something, she is really focused.' Simon Finch, rare book dealer
'She is a great girl, very creative and totally reliable. She gets the job done on time, and keeps within the budget. She is highly original.' Lady Margot Bright, client

Ian Harper
119 Taplow
Swiss Cottage
London NW3 3NU
T: 020 7586 4163
M: 07779 22 88 75
ianharper@ianharper.com
www.ianharper.com

Costs Commissions start at £500 upwards.
Travel Worldwide.
Size of job From special paint finishes to a faux-wooden
panelled ceiling.
Attitude Anything you fancy.

Ian Harper uses the ancient techniques of fresco
painting to create modern-day masterpieces. This is
no mean feat: fresco painters have to paint onto wet
lime-based plaster before it dries – there is little room
for error. Ian paints with natural earth pigments as
these bond with the lime plaster better than other
paints. He says: 'Personally, I love the use of working
with earth materials. If it is done properly, the colours
become more vibrant and beautiful as time goes by.
There is something very mysterious about it.' If you
have gypsy-like tendencies, don't worry; Ian will paint
onto removable plaster panels. He is also a master at
trompe l'œil, marbling, graining – in fact, anything that
needs a special paint finish. Clients include Raymond
Blanc, owner of Le Manoir aux Quat' Saisons. His
works can be found in Lord Rothschild's property on
Corfu, and the dining room at the Governor General's
Palace in Riyhad.

What the clients say
'Ian is a complete master of his craft, besides being a very
likeable person. He has done marvellous things for us here
at Le Manoir.' Raymond Blanc, Le Manoir aux Quat' Saisons

Mark Harvey
26 Rotherwick Road
London NW11 7DA
T: 020 8458 2373

Agent: Rabih Hage
69–71 Sloane Avenue
London SW3 3DH
T: 020 7823 8288 F: 020 7823 8258
info@rabih-hage.com
www.rabih-hage.com

Costs High end.
Travel Global, if the commission is right.
Size of job £2K for one piece of furniture to £200K for
a serious sculpture/installation.
Attitude Rock star with PhD.

Brad Pitt is a big enough fan to mention his name
on TV (Tom Cruise just buys the stuff). Mark Harvey
studied history and philosophy at Cambridge and
worked briefly at Clifford Chance before making a leap
into the world of three-dimensional furniture. His work
was featured in *House & Garden* and, virtually overnight,
Harvey was getting plum commissions all over the
world. His first medium was wood (woven wood that
looks more like sculpture than furniture), then he
moved into stone and metal and glass but always
keeping wood as his base material. His furniture is
described as '*sui generis*' (without precedence).

At 35, he is still a bit of a wanderer and now
wants to move to Hawaii. His work can either be
bought as is from his agent Rabih Hage or
commissioned via him.

What the clients say
'His design is very innovative and has a lovelyarchitectural feel.
The table he designed for me is like a Mondrian in wood. It's
very beautiful and fits in perfectly with our contemporary house.
He also made a side-table for us, which looks like a sculpture
underneath with a glass top.' Janet Rapp, client

Tim Hine
Studio G14
Kingsgate Workshops
110–116 Kingsgate Road
London NW6 2JG
T/F: 020 7328 2824
M: 07803 506 940
tim@timhine.com www.timhine.com

Costs **Commission based. A table is roughly £3K.**
Travel **UK.**
Size of job **Furniture.**
Attitude **Artist's temperament.**

Tim is a furniture designer, but his work process is more deliberate than this. 'I'm like an artist,' Tim explains, when it comes to his designs; 'the process develops over time.' This approach has made his work popular with Yohji Yamamoto, private collectors, interior designers, museums such as the National Museum of Scotland, as well as architects Munkenbeck and Marshall. He uses only the best timber he can lay his hands on, knowing that good timber, which is exquisite, is a rarity. His style is elemental, focusing predominantly on form – he finds that there is something sensuous about the simple geometry of his work. Do not approach him, however, to do built-in furniture, such as kitchens or wardrobes, or for decorative work: this is not his style. He is your man, though, if you want beautiful tables, chairs, chaises longues and other individual, free-standing pieces. Clients will get rough drawings, and a model. He is predominantly word-of-mouth, retaining faithful clients. His designs and craftsmanship are impressive, bearing in mind that he is self-taught.

What the clients say
'I was introduced to Tim Hine through the architect Alfred Munkenbeck. He made me a highly architectural dining-room table, which has now been recommissioned by several of my friends. He cares deeply about his work.'
Helen Kirwan-Taylor, author, *Home UK*

Scott Hyde
74 Bradgate Road,
Catford
London SE6 4TR
T/F: 020 8690 7991
M: 07939 047 494
scott@builtmedia.co.uk
www.builtmedia.co.uk/joinery

Costs **Very reasonable.**
Travel **London area.**
Size of job **Desks, benches, shelving, storage.**
Attitude **Pleasure in working the wood to create stimulating textures and effects.**

Scott Hyde is a joiner who also does one-off bespoke designs. He can do anything from desks, benches and shelving to in-built storage. His aim is to make furniture that looks good, and is discreet as well as functional. He mostly works in hard woods and, being eco-friendly, tries to source his materials from sustainable forests. He studied multi-media at Winchester School of Art, but has found his niche in working wood. As a former art student, his clients are predominantly from the art world, such as Fiona Banner, who was nominated for the Turner Prize. You don't have to be famous or part of the art world, though; Scott says he is happy to make furniture for the 'humble masses' – as well as taking on large or small jobs. He enjoys involving the client in the process of designing and as he has no fixed style, he reckons this makes him very adaptable. This is a small-scale outfit that produces beautiful hand-made joinery. His name is passed around purely by word-of-mouth.

What the clients say
'The best carpenter in the world. He was trained at Winchester School of Art, and he's just incredible. He loves wood more than anyone I've ever met.'
Rachel Meddowes, design editor, *Harpers & Queen*

Charlotte Ingle
50 Florida Street
London E2 6AE
T: 020 7729 2801
F: 020 7729 1292
info@charlotteingle.co.uk
www.charlotteingle.co.uk

InsideSpace
34 Mortimer Street
London W1W 7JS
T: 020 7299 6680 F: 020 7299 6690
enquiries@insidespace.com
www.insidespace.com
also at Selfridges, Oxford Street
T: 020 7318 3382

Costs **£250 to £350 a day.**
Travel **UK.**
Size of job **One room to many rooms.**
Attitude **Colour is not easy, otherwise we would all get it right.**

Costs **Wallpaper, £149 per square metre.**
Travel **Intergalactic or via email.**
Size of job **Giant photos to rolls of wallpaper.**
Attitude **Confident in their services.**

A colour consultant is someone who has a natural sense of which colour works where (and has training to back it up). The Royal College of Art trained Charlotte Ingle, who will come to the house and discuss what a client has in mind. If a shade of paint cannot be found from the normal suppliers, she will mix up her own colours to get the right one. She has an understanding of specialist finishes, and although she no longer does this type of work herself, she has a good team of people who can come up with a variety of different finishes. This is best done at the end of a project. Ingle is often called in by architects to solve their colour problems. Her work can be found at The Barbican Centre, Whistles, as well as the odd stately home such as Mount Stewart.

InsideSpace started as a website just over four years ago, providing distinctive prints and other artworks. They are now so popular with the likes of pop-princesses Sophie Ellis-Bextor and Louise Redknapp, as well as chef Jamie Oliver, that they have expanded off the web and into their own store. They can take any image, such as a picture of your favourite pet, and duplicate it onto wallpaper, acrylic panels for the walls, limited edition prints or just a giant photograph. They also work with a large number of artists to provide original art work, including contacts at the Royal Academy of Arts. Their most recent service is a pop art-style portrait of your child, or, failing that, of yourself.

What the clients say
'We commissioned Charlotte Ingle to create a hand-painted wall feature for the Zetter Hotel, London. Charlotte provided expect advice on the specialist paint and application, and project managed through to completion.'
Meriel Scott, creative director, Precious McBane

What the clients say
'The painting was done of my son Marlow; he was one of a surviving pair of twins. My grandmother had left me £500 in her will, and we thought that getting a painting would be a nice way of creating an heirloom for the future generation. We are very happy with the result.' Michelle Turner, client

J—K

John Jones Framing
4 Morris Place
Stroud Green Road
Finsbury Park
London N4 3JG
T: 020 7281 5439
F: 020 7281 5956
www.johnjones.co.uk

Costs From £25 to several thousands, depending on what you
want. Often cheaper than the high street. Now charge a pick
up and delivery fee (except for account holders).
Travel Anywhere in the UK.
Size of job Cheap and cheerful framing to priceless restoration.
Attitude Framing that is an art form.

John Jones, chairman (his son is now MD), can do
absolutely anything that has to do with framing. He is
the largest bespoke framer in the world but somehow
you always sense that he's alone in the workshop.
This is where Damien Hirst, David Hockney, Howard
Hodgkins and Julien Opie come and, frankly, that's as
good an endorsement as you can get. Oh, and they
just did a whole house-worth of framing for Alexander
McQueen. John Jones does wood, acrylic, steel, gold
leaf, modern, old, cheap and cheerful framing or
priceless restorations and plinths. They will also pick
up your masterpieces (for £25 in central London) and
come up with their own suggestion. They employ 90
staff, so are used to deadlines (two hours is a record).
Clients are art galleries and mothers with school
photographs to frame.

What the clients say
'John Jones are one of the most professional and specialized
framers in London. They are in a position to offer focused
advice.' James Ulph, Flowers East Contemporary Art Gallery
'They framed a batik given to my father from the King of Fiji for
me in Perspex – and I mean six-foot-long Perspex. John Jones
can do anything!' Helen Kirwan-Taylor, author, *Home UK*

Tracy Kendall
401½ Studios
401 Wandsworth Road
London SW8 2JP
T: 020 7640 9071
F: 020 8769 0618
info@tracykendall.com
www.tracykendall.com

Costs Established collection, regular wallpaper width, £105 per
square metre; bespoke, such as sequined wallpaper, £500 per
square metre.
Travel Willing to travel.
Size of job Wallpaper.
Attitude: Anything goes.

Sequinned, zippered, floral, whatever flights of fancy
you have for your wallpaper, one-woman-band Tracy
Kendall is your lady. Her work has gone as far afield
as New York, and can also be found at Babington
House, Somerset, Soho House and The Grove Hotel.
Commission a bespoke piece or choose from her
collection; either way, her wallpaper can be customized
to any print size or colour way. Her background is in
fine-art printmaking, allowing her the expertise and
knowledge to block her prints by hand. She is the
ultimate in wallpaper design; interior designers have
kept her a secret for too long.

What the clients say
'Tracy's work fits so well within my space; it strikes the right
balance between the completely modern furniture and the
Victorian interior.' Rachel Deacon, client
'Tracy is very original. She provides a very good service and
comes to your house to look at the space. I've used her and can
recommend her. It is like having art posted on your walls.'
Nia Morris, client

Susy Kennard
135 Riversdale Road
London N5 2SU
T: 020 7354 4345
M: 07780 862 548
susykennard@onetel.com
www.susykennard.com

Costs **£300 per square metre and upwards.**
Travel **Worldwide.**
Size of job **Mirrors to showers.**
Attitude **Puts some pep in an old-fashioned technique.**

Susy Kennard takes the old-fashioned technique of
verre églomisé (glass gilding) and brings it into the
21st century, onto glass showers, consoles, mirrors,
splashbacks and tables for the likes of the Duke of
Westminster and Emma Bunton. She gilds in gold,
silver and copper leaf to create fantastical designs.
Her background is in 18th-century decorative painting
and restoration, but now she is firmly in the hands of
the big boys such as Herbert Zandburg and Collett-
Zarzycki. She can also make glass panels look like
wallpaper from a distance. She is now into her '70s
Austin Powers phase, which involves bold, geometric
designs done in stunning moon gold. Look at her
website to understand Susy's 'wow' factor.

What the clients say
'Susy has an understanding of a certain style that is not
necessarily understood. She has these traditional skills and
uses them to bring about what the designer is trying to achieve.
She can create some serious elevated finishes. It is wonderful
when you discover a contemporary craftsman who gets it right,
being able to capture either the spirit of the old world or update
it. Her artistic flair is very much locked up into being able to
understand what we are trying to achieve. It is a pleasure to
work with Susy.' Hubert Zandberg, CK
'Susy is a very talented glass artist. We worked together on
a commission for a three-sided large glass-panelled shower
in browns and gold, which she designed and painted quite
beautifully – the result was unique in every way.'
Willa Elphinstone, designer

Renée Kopal
8 Hillside Road
London SW2 3HN
T: 020 8674 3487
M: 07970 331 992

Costs **£250–£500 a day.**
Travel **UK.**
Size of job **Walls.**
Attitude **This is not just a lick of paint**

Renée Kopal's work gives new meaning to the phrase
a 'lick of paint'. She is a specialist paint finisher
perfecting the art of imitation. She claims that she can
'make a marble fireplace out of MDF so realistic that
it looks like marble'. Or if the grand, baronial style is
more to your liking, she can 'make your room look
like an old castle inside'. She does both traditional
techniques such as stripling and dragging, as well as
more modern looks such as colour washes made to
look like concrete or hessian paper. The Sultan of Qatar
used her to put the final touches on two ancient halls
at Hackwood House. She also does jobs for English
Heritage and The National Trust.

What the clients say
'Renée is absolutely amazing. She's really cool and does
anything paint-wise you want to do. You also feel comfortable
with her in your house. She's fantastic and really talented.'
Jacqui Winterflood, client

Michael Lythgoe
71 Chosen Drive
Churchdown
Gloucestershire GL3 2QE
T: 01452 712 080

Made
75 Oxford Gardens
London W10 5UL
T: 020 8960 6969
M: 07973 748 027/07974 305 288
info@made.co.uk
www.made.co.uk

Costs From approx £45 to £2,000.
Travel UK.
Size of job Anything from a small sandpiper up to
a life-size swan.
Attitude Fascinated by his carving.

Costs Bespoke commission based.
Travel They will ship anywhere.
Size of job Cushions to bean bags.
Attitude Fluffy fun.

Michael Lythgoe carves life-like birds and fish from wood. What was a hobby inspired by a holiday jaunt to Cape Cod is now his full-time profession. The birds are based on the North American tradition of decoy ducks. Used by hunters, these beautiful carved birds would attract migrating ducks, geese and other wild fowl. The carving skills, however, were admired by collectors and decoy ducks started to find their way into residential homes. Michael's birds are carved from western red cedar as this wood has a wonderful stability. He also uses the grain pattern of the wood to create natural-looking feathers. The fish are carved from redwood, and tend to be more 'homogenized'.

The dynamic duo behind the bespoke-sheepskin soft-furnishings company Made, Tanya Thompson and Emily Bradbury, are the darlings of stars such as Kylie Minogue, Paul Weller, Damien Hirst, Harry Enfield and Tara Palmer-Tomkinson. They can make a 12 foot by 12 foot sheepskin bean-bag to fill a whole room, or you can design either a cushion or rug in any shape, colour or size and put your own design on it. Tanya says: 'We'll give anything a go.' The sheepskins come in either short fur, which works better with geometric patterns, or long fur for that sensuous and tactile I don't-want-to-let-go kind of feeling. Otherwise you can choose straight from their range off the website.

What the clients say
'Please let me recommend Michael Lythgoe. He carves the most beautiful birds out of wood and he's an excellent chap.'
Tony Bond, client
'We have been one of Michael's clients for a long time and have a lot of his work, both inside and outside. It's very interesting and suits our environment very well.' Monica Paice, client

What the clients say
'I've been buying Made's products for years. They're high quality, and amazingly tactile. When my son was born, I bought the bean-bag, the playmat and rug – both children have been swaddled in their sheepskin. They are good products, and are really good fun.' Sam Robinson, co-founder, The Cross
'I commissioned a large stars and stripes sheepskin for my son's bedroom. He stopped sleeping in his bed as a result. Tanya and Emily make the commissioning process painless and fun.'
Helen Kirwan-Taylor, author, *Home UK*

Marshall Phillips Ltd
38 Chiswick Lane
London W4 2JQ
T/F: 020 8742 8089
john@marshallphillips.com
www.marshallphillips.com

London Antique Restoration Services Ltd
4 Wilson Walk
London W4 1TP
T/F: 020 8846 9709
info@larsltd.com

Costs Pair of reproduction Art Deco-style chandeliers, £17K
Travel Worldwide.
Size of job Chairs, chandeliers and so on.
Attitude We know our trade.

Marshall Phillips is an Aladdin's cave of French antique furniture and light fittings. Elton John, the Goldsmith family, including Jemima Khan, and other celebs have all piled in through their doors. If you cannot find what you want, their sister company London Antique Restoration Services specializes in reproductions. They have their own in-house team of seven, with the skills to do small castings. Metalwork is their speciality. This firm is a find, especially if you want to make up a set of six chairs when you have only four, or to match an existing chandelier to make a pair. They will even reproduce furniture from a picture in a magazine. Everything is made-to-order.

What the clients say
'I can happily say that Marshall Phillips has a great sense of style and an impressive depth of knowledge of historical detail. We found him invaluable.' Joanna Wood, designer
'I know they can produce things that I want, and the final product always looks good. They are also honest. The whole workshop is fantastically sympathetic. I design the thing and it is done.' Looby Crean, Crean Interiors

Jennifer Merredew
13 Ermine House
Moselle Street
London N17 8DE
T: 020 8808 2586
M: 07932 764387
art@jennifermerredew.com
www.jennifermerredew.com

Costs Approx £5K–£15K, depending on the size of the ceiling.
Travel Worldwide.
Size of job From a kitchen to a great hall.
Attitude 'As long as it doesn't move, I'll paint it.'

Jennifer Merredew is an expert in painting traditional Scottish ceilings. The practice originated in the Elizabethan age, introduced by journeying artists from the Netherlands and perhaps Italy. The images are bold, vibrant and rich in colour, and while the beams have strap-work of repeated decoration and written script, the in-fill between the beams is a wealth of mythological figures and beasts, knights, pelicans, aquatic creatures and family crests. Quite often the images continue two or three feet down the walls – the designs are medieval in feel, but make a dramatic change to a bland, white ceiling.

Jennifer finds it is important to get to know her clients well. This allows her to incorporate into the design personal family details, such as family crests, children, favourite pets, which all make important reference points that add to the personal value of the work. Any ceiling can be painted, from great halls and hunting lodges to kitchens and libraries, in the country or the city. Nor do you need beams. Jennifer has a team who can insert faux-beams onto your ceiling to create the effect. Also, she can paint ceilings off-site, which can be installed at a later date by attaching to the client's original ceiling.

Trained at Edinburgh Art College and specializing in mural painting, her skills allow her to draw straight onto the ceiling in charcoal before black-lining the image with paint, and filling in the colour in between. Her main inspiration comes from the famous ceilings at Crathes Castle in Aberdeenshire. She has painted the ceilings at Forter Castle in Angus, home of the Pooley family, as well at Peter Nicholson's house in Fife, and you can find her work at Sterling Castle.

What the clients say
'Jennifer is an excellent artist, a creative designer and a thoughtful person. Everything she's done for me is better than expected.' Lady Judge, client

M – P

Juliette Mole
T/F: 020 7627 8586
M: 07812 773 482

Costs Varies per each commission.
Travel Potentially could travel.
Size of job One wall to a mansion.
Attitude Perfectionist.

The clients were loathe to part with this name. Trained at the world-famous L'Ecole Supérieure de Peinture in Brussels, Juliette Mole specializes in trompe l'œil in particular, although she is equally adept at wood graining, marbling and other specialist paint effects. Do not call her, however, to do colour washes – she can't bear it. 'There's very little skill in it,' she says. She is a great believer in creating a mutual trust between clients and herself, and will only take on jobs where she feels there is a certain chemistry. She is a skilled artist (and an actress as it happens), who also creates her own glazes from her own secret recipes. Commissions have taken her to New York and Hong Kong. She has worked for Mimmi O'Connell, literary agent Ed Victor, as well as the Lansdowne Club in Berkeley Square. Her work is always recommended by word-of-mouth.

What the clients say
'A trompe l'oeil artist by training, she's worked on several of our houses, most recently completing miles and miles of mahogany wood graining at our Scottish home. Her work is stunning; she can turn her hand to anything from faux *marbre* to torn metal. But you're lucky if you can get her…' Helen Fraser, client

Ornamenta
**South Kensington
London**
(by appointment only)
T: 020 7591 0077
F: 020 7591 0055
enquiries@ornamenta.co.uk
www.ornamenta.co.uk

Costs Commission based.
Travel Sends her wallpapers worldwide.
Size of job Wall-sized.
Attitude Flowers anyone?

Jane Gordon Clark designs bespoke wallpaper and fabrics. Whatever your imagination desires, from overblown flowers to modern, spatial graphic designs, Jane will help your idea become a reality. She has an in-house team of specialist craftsmen who hand-print the wallpaper either through block-printing or silk-screen printing. Well known for innovative ideas, Jane has also developed a site-specific collection, which are all digitally printed. Give her the dimension of a wall and she can create wallpaper where the image fills the entire wall space, such as her well-known Hot-House Flower collection. Clients can choose from all-consuming Pink Lilies to a fragile-looking Magenta Orchid. If you have your own concept in mind, like a cityscape, landscape, clouds or an historic painting, she can create wallpaper to your design – you could even transform your bedroom ceiling into the Sistine Chapel. The effect is uncannily realistic. Her designs are some of the most sought-after in the interior world. She sees clients by appointment only.

What the clients say
'We have worked with Jane on a number of recent projects to create stunning focal points within our interiors. Her versatility and imagination has allowed us to use a wide selection of images, varying from stunning orchids to "Batman and Robin".' Jo Bunton, Lifestyle Designs

Page Lacquer Company Ltd
Furniture Manufacturers and Specialist Finishers
Unit 3, Ferrier Street
London SW18 1SL
T: 020 8871 1235
F: 020 8874 8167
info@pagelacquer.co.uk
www.pagelacquer.co.uk

Paola Petrobelli
Unit 31
72 Farm Lane
London SW6 1QA
T/F: 020 7610 2846
www.paola@petrobelli.co.uk

Costs £200–£200K.
Travel Work all over the world.
Size of job Small pieces of furniture to super-yachts interiors.
Attitude Jacks of all lacquer.

This company specializes in lacquer which is a real art and the difference between a beautiful or a nasty piece of furniture. However, they are trade only, so if you want to use them, you will have to ask your designer or architect to commission them.

Although they build furniture as well as lacquering supplied joinery, they consider themselves essentially finishing specialists. Polyester lacquer, both solid colour and special effects; crackle glaze, canvas crackle and veneered finishes are their thing. A colour can be chosen from the standard range or a sample tailored especially for each project. They have worked on Kensington Palace Barracks refurbishment, Royal Bank of Scotland, Barclays, Lombard Street, Chanel and Harrods.

What the clients say
'Page Lacquer are the best in the field of polyester lacquer: very high quality – not cheap, but you get what you pay for.'
Richard Becher, joiner

Costs Commission based.
Travel Worldwide.
Size of job Tumblers to chandeliers.
Attitude Modern Venetian.

Paola is a self-taught glass designer (she was originally a molecular biologist) who creates vases, tumblers, lighting fixtures and objets d'art. Venetian-born, she has the glass tradition in her blood. When training herself in the skills of glass making she spent weeks in different glass makers' studios. This has given her a wealth of specialist contacts, and all her glass pieces are hand-blown by Venetian glass blowers. She is currently into chandelier making – but don't ask her to do classical chandeliers with arms – this is not her style. Hers tend to be squares of glass that look like sheets of paper hung at different heights. Clients are invited to her studio to discuss the commissioned piece before she does sketches and then a proper detailed drawing. Clients include Janet de Botton and John Stefanidis.

What the clients say
'Paola is the most creative glass designer I have ever worked with. Her chandeliers are elegant but never over the top. Her drinking glasses are quite amazing – everyone asks for her number once they have seen her work. She also makes larger pieces that can be filled with flowers or simply left as sculptures. All the work is blown by the very best Venetian craftsmen in Murano, and she can create personalized pieces that range from napkin holders to complete dinner services. There is no one else I have ever come across that can make such perfect bespoke glassware of every kind.' Mike Rundell, architect
'Paola is working in the great tradition of the Italian glass craftsmen. She has a wonderful sense of colour and comes up with imaginative forms.' David Rocksavage, client

Polidori Barbera Design
Studio 3
2 St Quintin Avenue
London W10 6NU
T/F: 020 8960 0272
M: 07747 032 568
polidoribarbera@aol.com
www.polidori-barbera.com

Costs **Walls, £110 sq m for plaster; furniture, £120–£140 sq m,**
depending on complexity.
Travel **Worldwide.**
Size of job **Cushions to walls.**
Attitude **To create contemporary, urban interiors through**
textured plasters.

When it comes to Italian stucco, Luisa Polidori and
Cristina Barbera are recognized as being the best in
the business. They mix plaster with coffee, spices,
sand, gold, silver and mango powder to give each
plastered wall its own unique identity and colour.
They also create a variety of finishes: matt, highly polished, textured and smooth. The smooth looks like velvet and comes in a selection of warm earth tones, from
reds and browns to naturals and aubergine. Creating
texture in a room is their strength – plaster can be
made to look like carved stone. Don't limit the plaster
to your walls, however; they cover furniture and make
pieces of relief art from it as well. Kelly Hoppen,
Todhunter Earle, Carter Tyberghein and Ahmed Sidki
of BowWow all work with Luisa and Cristina. The pair
have recently taken to designing their own cushions,
lighting and furniture.

What the clients say
'They are fantastic. We use them on most of our jobs. They are
very, very clever and have great success with their products.
Their work is unique; very good eye for colour. We always have
very happy clients.' Emily Todhunter, Todhunter Earle

Rooks Books
9 Coopers Yard, Crystal Palace
London SE19 1TN
(by appointment only)
T: 020 8766 6398
F: 020 8761 0933
gavin@rooksbooks.com
www.rooksbooks.com

Costs **POA.**
Travel **Worldwide.**
Size of job **Books, lights, sculpture.**
Attitude **Eccentric**

Before Gavin Rookledge turned his attention to
learning the art of book binding, he had come from
a fine arts background. He now combines the two skills
to create one-off pieces, be that an off-beat sculpture,
a traditionally bound book in leather or an unusual
light that looks like a giant woodlouse. His style has
been described as 'Gormenghast'. Always in demand,
Gavin has three full-time employees. State what you
want, such as lights or a sculpture, but a free rein
is best when commissioning. He always has
a consultation with clients before work commences.
He has been commissioned by the Queen and Bill
Gates – need we say more. Also a great source for
original gifts. All visits to the workshop are strictly
by appointment.

What the clients say
'Gavin's wonderful. He is so brilliant, and off-the-wall. He has
a great sense of colour, as well as beautiful craftsmanship.
He plays to the material's strength. If you want anything in
leather, he's the guy to make it. He's intellectually very creative.'
Lady Elizabeth Arnold, client
'We have commissioned Rooks Books to design very special
books: weddings, special events, birthdays, journals and baby
albums. He has the unique ability to create books that are
works of art, be they over-the-top or simple and elegant.
Rooks Books is our first choice of exquisite gift items for that
special occasion.' Vicki Saunders, client

Senior and Carmichael
Whitehouse Workshop
Church Street, Betchworth
Surrey RH3 7DN
T: 01737 844 316
F: 01737 844 464
rupert@seniorandcarmichael.co.uk
www.seniorandcarmichael.co.uk

Costs Commission based.
Travel Mostly UK. However, they have made furniture for clients in Europe, the USA, and as far away as Australia.
Size of job Chairs upwards.
Attitude Inventive, unusual pieces of furniture that are immensely functional as well as beautiful.

Rupert Senior and Charles Wheeler-Carmichael are cabinet makers with a difference. Trained in the traditional skills of cabinet making at Parnham College of Furniture, Dorset, they specialize in mechanical pieces. A mechanical desk they made for the Marquis of Bath, for example, looks from the exterior like a normal desk, but inside, hidden beneath the wood, lie springs and coils that allow for secret compartments. The mechanical workings also provide a form of security. Precious books can be displayed without any overt signs of the material being tied down.

Metal, glass and leather can be incorporated into bespoke pieces. They also produce a limited edition of pieces from wood salvaged from the great storm of 1987, which they call the Hurricane collection. These range from chairs, for adults as well as children, to a low table. When commissioning a piece, Charles advises that you visit his workshop so you can experience the sort of furniture they produce. They will then produce a few rough sketches before going ahead to make the piece. Awarded 12 Guild Marks from the Worshipful Company of Furniture Makers, Britain's hallmark for excellence in design and craftsmanship, Senior and Carmichael is out there on collectors' lips.

What the clients say
'I am delighted with the new desk. It's a mixture of traditional and modern craftsmanship, making it extremely practical as a work-station and very pleasing to the eye. I was also particularly keen that it should be entirely constructed from home-grown British wood.' Marquess of Bath, client
'The Folio Table has become one of my favourite pieces in the house and I often gaze at it in admiration. I decided to commission it because I wanted a completely contemporary piece of furniture that, at the same time, would suit the atmosphere of Petworth.' Lord Egremont, Petworth House

William Sitch & Co (Antiques) Ltd
48 Berwick Street
London W1V 4JD
T: 020 7437 3776
F: 020 7437 5707
wsitch_co@hotmail.com
www.wsitch.co.uk

Costs Individual quotes.
Travel London only. Pieces sent worldwide.
Size of job From cleaning and restoration to casting a replica chandelier.
Attitude Pipe-smoking light specialist who treats every piece on an individual basis.

HRH Prince Charles, No. 10 Downing Street, Ritz Hotel, Caroline Quentin, Colefax and Fowler, Boodles, The Reform Club, English Heritage and The National Trust are a small number of well-known clients who use William Sitch's lighting services. The business was established in 1776, and is still situated on the same premises. As well as a shop, they offer every service conceivable in regards to lighting, from a full cleaning and restoration service, which can also include plating and lacquering, to rewiring and reproductions. If you want a chandelier reproduced, bring it in: they will make a casting of the original and create a replica. They can also adapt vases into lamps. Although predominantly specialists in period lighting, they will create, where appropriate, modern pieces. They have recently made two huge lanterns, which Ronald Sitch calls 'shower units' because they are big enough to stand in. To make sure that the light you choose neither looks like 'a pimple nor a boil' in your room, Ronald suggests that you tell him the size, length, breadth and height of the room so that he can advise you accordingly. This is one word-of-mouth service prised from the trade's contact sheets, which make up 60 per cent of Sitch's business.

What the clients say
'A real charmer. Everyone knows him in the business.' Carolyn Trevor, architect

Joe Smith
Beech Cottage
Milton, Crocketford
Dumfries
DG2 8RJ
T: 01556 690 632 M: 07974 984 620
joe@joe-smith.co.uk
www.joe-smith.co.uk

Costs £600–£7K.
Travel Across the country.
Size of job This is art, so no limits.
Attitude Think big.

Smith trained under Andy Goldsworthy and is, as one client put it, 'the affordable version'. Joe Smith is an extraordinary sculptor. He takes traditional skills of dry-stone walling to build up to 11-foot-high vases, acorns, conifer trees or balls. His work is constructed from either slate or stone, though he can 'push [his sculptures] as far as they will go in terms of feasibility'. When asked if he has won any prizes, he wryly admitted to winning third prize at wellie-throwing at an agricultural show in 1989. His work has been commissioned by HRH Prince Charles, the National Trust for Scotland, Glasgow City Council and Scottish National Heritage. He's moving up fast: this is the right time to get in early.

What the clients say
'I saw a picture of his work in the book about Highgrove, and I longed for one of his pieces. He made me two vases, and then an obelisk. I think they are absolutely lovely. He is an excellent craftsman and an extremely nice man. I admire his work tremendously.' Lady Gunthrie, client
'I am knocked out by his work. I cannot help but sing his praises to the roof.' Robert Chapman, client

Mark Stephens Furniture
The Old Station Works
119–123 Sandycombe Road, Kew
Surrey TW9 2ER
T: 020 8948 3131 F: 020 8332 6040
M: 07771 782 621
mstepfurn@aol.com
www.markstephensfurniture.co.uk

Costs A dining table in solid oak, approx £3K plus VAT;
a solid oak/maple chair with upholstered leather seats, approx
£550 plus VAT.
Travel He will travel to wherever you might be.
Size of job Cabinets and furniture.
Attitude Organised enough to be able to organise you.

Mark Stephens is a bespoke cabinet maker. His style focuses on clean lines and strong features. The result is modern contemporary-looking furniture that is functional. He is particularly good with electrical detailing, such as TV cabinets where the TV can rise up on an electronic mechanism, or hi-fi cabinets that specialize in making sure all the ventilation for the equipment is correct, as well as hiding the acres of cabling. He is also good at creating mood lighting, such as bookshelves that are lit from behind. He uses a lot of North American and European hard woods that lend to the modern feel in his work. Dining tables, chairs, free-standing wardrobes, in fact anything domestic, can be mixed with other materials, such as stainless steel and glass. He makes beautiful dining tables with an inlay in silver or ebonized timbers. His other speciality is bespoke kitchens. As a man who enjoys cooking, he understands the need for function and form.

What the clients say
'Mark is a complete perfectionist. If there is one detail wrong, he will stay up all night worrying about it. I have commissioned several cabinets (cantilevered) and a small dining table, and they were perfect. He comes in and checks on them when he's in the neighbourhood. A thoroughly nice man who will spend hours going through every detail.'
Helen Kirwan-Taylor, author, *Home UK*

Timorous Beasties
7 Craigend Place
Glasgow
Scotland G13 2UN
T: 0141 959 3331
F: 0141 959 8880
info@timorousbeasties.com
www.timorousbeasties.com

Costs **Blinds, from £85 a metre; wallpapers, £70 a roll.**
Travel **Europe.**
Size of job **Fabrics and wallpapers.**
Attitude **Arty, in-the-know.**

Alistair McAuley and Paul Simmons met at Glasgow School of Art. The company was set up in 1990 as a two-man revolt against minimalism. They design and produce hand-drawn, hand-printed wallpapers, fabrics, roller shades and accessories in both traditional and contemporary prints. There is everything from vintage-looking pineapples and pheasants to graphic, optical patterns and even bee and insect prints (perfect for a cool kid's room). They pride themeselves on being flexible and will come up with three or four ideas, and narrow it down until the client chooses one. They have designed fabrics for everyone from Liberty to Boussac; the Strata bar has been graced with their prints; they have revamped the Arches Theatre in Glasgow, as well as creating papers for MTV's documentary series *Real Life* and fabrics for Philip Treacy's Haute Couture show in Paris in 2001. Their products are stocked at Holland and Sherry in New York, as they are trying to establish a presence there.

What the clients say
'From our perspective Paul and Alistair are very easy going, nothing is a problem. Their service has never let us down. To sum up they are honest, hard-working, fun and professional.'
Jim Hamilton, Graven Images

Chris Topp & Co
Carlton Husthwaite
Thirsk
North Yorkshire
T: 01845 501 415
F: 01845 501 072
enquiry@christopp.co.uk
www.christopp.co.uk

Costs **High end.**
Travel **Supply worldwide. Travel predominantly in the UK.**
Size of job **From a nail for £4 to a £300K job.**
Attitude **Friendly, helpful and passionate about wrought iron.**

'We're diehards,' says the very wry Chris Topp, managing director of the only wrought-iron manufacturer in the world – one very good reason to recommend them. The second reason is that they provide a complete service in the design and manufacture of new ironwork, as well as being knowledgeable restorers of ancient ironwork (predominantly 1600s onwards). Topp's workshop is where the Victorian age meets the demands of the 21st century. Due to the nature of wrought iron, everything is done by hand, including the manufacture and use of rivets and tenons (wrought iron cannot be welded); they even make wrought-iron nails. As metal workers, they are adept at working in bronze, brass, copper, iron, cast iron and mild steel. Suggest to them the type of thing you like, such as a highly detailed gate, give them a rough indication of budget, and they will create the design and make it for you. The Queen, Westminster Abbey, Globe Theatre, Tower of London, Princeton University, St Paul's, Chatsworth and the Houses of Parliament have all used their service. They have even made replica cannons for Henry VIII's ship Mary Rose.

What the clients say
'In terms of Chris's work, it is very good. He has a can-do attitude. He achieves what we want and puts his back into the work. As a problem solver, he comes up with methods to get the job done. He is one of the few people who can deal with cast iron in the country.'
Michael Simpson of John Simpson, architects

M – C

Urban Glass Works
15 Orsman Road
London N1 5RA
T/F: 020 7729 8718
john@johnreyntiens.com
www.johnreyntiens.com

Costs Commission based. State what you can afford.
Travel Worldwide.
Size of job Windows to lighting to sculpture.
Attitude Like father, like son.

This is stained glass for the connoisseur. John Reyntiens is following in his (very famous) father's footsteps as number one in the business. He has made glass since he was nine years old ('it was a convenient way of making pocket money'). With such an apprenticeship, he has rare, traditional skills, but applies modern techniques. Clients include – listen to this – the Queen (Windsor Castle restoration project) and Versace, but this doesn't mean you cannot afford him as well. He can take a small glass window and create an intricate mosaic of glass such as the one he did for June Summerill of the kitchen store Summerill and Bishop. Don't think of John purely in the terms of windows. If the commission involves glass, he'll make anything from sculptural pieces to lighting and mobiles – he'll tackle any job. Always experimenting, John is currently into slumping (kiln-formed glass where the glass is left to melt over another object). Look out for his Millennium window at the City of Birmingham Museum and Art Gallery. It was the first bit of public art commissioned since 1911.

What the clients say
'We were very pleased with John Reyntiens. He had to win the selection for the Millenium window project along with other UK glass designers. John was given a very loose brief and shown the location. He came up with some very abstract sketches, and we chose one of them. John is very skilled and very creative. I've got nothing but praise for him.' Stuart Dalby, project manager, City of Birmingham Museum and Art Gallery

Wilkinson Plc
5 Catford Hill
London SE6 4NU
T: 020 8314 1080
F: 020 8690 1524
Mayfair showroom: 020 7495 2477
enquiries@wilkinson-plc.com
www.wilkinson-plc.com

Costs Cleaning service, £45 an hour plus travel expenses.
Restoration, £100 upwards.
Travel Worldwide.
Size of job Chandeliers.
Attitude 'We'll get your glass looking as good as new.'

Wilkinson's are renowned as glass restorers, specializing in chandeliers. With the Royal Warrant and half the royal households in Europe using their services, they couldn't come more highly recommended. They supply a complete restoration service that covers everything from cleaning to making reproductions. If you want your chandelier cleaned, they can either go to your house, dismantle, wash, dry and reassemble the chandelier, or they can take it away to their depot. If the silver-plate on the metal framework is losing its lustre, they can renew this, too. They try and find the best solution for each job. It is their glass restoring, however, that truly shows dedication to detail. If the chandelier has a Venetian pedigree and needs new glass droplets, they have dedicated Venetian glass blowers in Venice to make them. The same applies if the chandelier originally came from Austria. They are sticklers in ensuring that the glass matches the original. They can also reproduce an original chandelier or make a copy from a photograph. Turn to them as well to restore other glass products, such as wine glasses where the foot or bowl has snapped off – a new foot or bowl is made and attached to the old piece of glass. They can even take chips out of favourite crystal glassware. Another amazing find we think.

What the clients say
'I do extremely high-quality restoration work. I've been using Wilkinson's for 32 years. I've always found them to be extremely helpful and extremely good at their job. They are great, absolutely super.' Frances Jevons, restorer

PILGRIM PAYNE & CO BAILEY
ABSOLUTELY SPOTLESS UPH
AVALON RESTORATION LTD
STAUNCH AND CROSS HAD
TRACKING & HANGING WALK
CHRISTOPHER HOWE DEACO
THE KEYHOLDING COMPANY
BAILEYS HOME AND GARD
THE KITCHEN DOCTOR STAU
WALK ON WOOD LTD MARBL
BAILEYS HOME AND GARDE
SIMON DODSON RESTORATI
STONETECH UK LTD PILGRIM

HOME AND GARDEN OVENU
STERY CLEANING ALL CARE
STORE PIMLICO PLUMBERS
ST **DOMESTIC DIVA** JAMES
N WOOD LTD WOMERSLEYS
FINISHES MARBLE SHINE LTD
MON DODSON RESTORATION
SUDS STONETECH UK LTD
CH AND FLOW OVEN CLEAN
HINE LTD DEACON FINISHES
HADLEY ST JAMES AVALON
PIMLICO PLUMBERS SU
YNE & CO DEACON FINISH

DOMESTIC DIVA

You can't help but have noticed how many housekeeping magazines and columns there are out there. To flatter myself, I was writing a column called 'Mrs Mop' for the *Financial Times* long before anyone else had thought of it. I was inspired to do this by my girlfriends, many of them Oxford graduates who once held senior jobs in banks and law offices, who were now absolutely obsessed with their homes and children. Nigella, for all her cooking skills, is a lousy housekeeper (she admits it). My friends have taught me how to organize a linen cupboard, train a nanny and keep the husband happy (food is everything). They have taught me the nuances of thread counts. My friend Jacky made me sit up and take notice of what rubbish goes into detergents (and hence into my children's lungs). Faith Popcorn calls those of us who read the cleaning tips in magazines then instruct others to do the work 'homemaking voyeurs'.

I can be found longingly stroking feather dusters at Labour and Wait (see page 201). I label the outsides of drawers (I learned this trick from Fergie) and confess a deep attachment to my mop. There is plenty of research to support the idea that cleaning is good for you. 1) It uses almost every muscle in the body, and 2) it's cathartic. Women in Britain spend 17 hours a week cleaning – it might as well be fun.

Why are women today so obsessed with cleaning, cooking and floral Cath Kidston's aprons? Susan Strasser, a professor of history at Delaware and author of *Never Done: A History of American Housework*, has examined the phenomenon closely. The further we get from the task itself (cooking, cleaning, ironing), she says, the more we romanticise it. Companies like Cath Kidston and Cabbages and Roses remind us of our grandmothers. We associate lavender-infused ironing water we buy for £5 with the linen sheets we slept in as children. Professional women today are busier than ever, but that doesn't mean they don't long for a clean house and home-baked biscuits on the table. I honestly feel sorry for the husbands whose wives don't care about this. Loving your home is loving your family.

OK, we now have green tea and patchouli washing-up liquids on the market, but we also have masses of things in our homes that used to exist only in office buildings, such as stainless steel, glass, granite, resin and Perspex. The organic movement has made people shun anything that is not 'natural'. These materials, which set you back thousands of pounds, cannot be cleaned with Ajax. They require specialist products and specialist cleaners. I don't think the architect David Chipperfield had any intention of causing despair in the hearts of London cleaners, but the super-modern, no-objects-on-any-surfaces school of architecture is generally loathed by those employed to keep them looking that way. One coffee mark on the honed granite and it's over.

As for carpets, according to our pin-up Graham Doyle (who runs the most excellent carpet and soft furnishing cleaning company Pilgrim Payne), a natural fibre carpet should be cleaned only every few years unless you suffer from asthma. If a carpet cleaner says it should be done 'every month, like your cycle', he's lying. Cleaning rots the underlay.

We have included information about stores that sell wonderful products and sources for eco-friendly products. According to Mike Sweeney, CEO of the British Institute of Cleaning Science, those new microfibre cloths now sold in the supermarkets are as effective as a one per cent solution of hydrochloric bleach. We have tried and tested quite a few of the services included or we know someone else who has (which is how we came to get the number).

COs and how to mop properly

Speaking of cleaning, cleaners are now officially called 'cleaning operatives' (COs). According to Mike Sweeney, the domestic cleaning industry is worth £2.5 billion annually (much more if you add the black economy). A good cleaner (i.e., one who has been trained) knows to start with 'wet tasks' (bathrooms, kitchen), before moving onto 'damp' tasks (dusting, skirting boards and radiators etc.), followed by 'suction' (this way, all the dust goes into the vacuum cleaner). A good CO never lets the mop leave the ground. She uses figures of eight or back and forth movements to bring the dirt to a central collection point. Aren't you glad you know this?

If only we all had a handy handy man

Sadly, there are few around. Some builders offer maintenance contracts (mostly only to existing clients). In the meantime, we all have loos that get blocked up. Maintenance is a growth industry. Several companies, like Pimlico Plumbers, Household Division and the Keyholding Company in London offer help – fast (at a price). There will be more in the future, that's for sure. In the interim, be like Mrs Mop and learn to use a drill.

Dos and Don'ts

- Do expect services to go up and down in quality the whole time (it's down to the staff), though, because you have a middle man, you have someone to complain to.
- Don't spend five grand on a new floor, then not use products given to you by the merchant. Do show your CO (if you have one) how to use products and make sure relevant clothing is worn.
- Do think of the planet. Most household products are the equivalent of Agent Orange. They end up in our rivers and fish are already getting weird. Eastern European COs think nothing is clean unless bleach has been applied.
- Do not try to get stains out of anything expensive without first consulting an expert. Most supermarket brands of stain remover will leave a ring.
- Do accept the way a man cleans – or do it yourself.
- Do train children to make their beds and put dishes in dishwashers. Where do you think dad learned his bad habits?
- Do try and maintain a balance between cleanliness and obsessive compulsive disorder. You're supposed to be making a nest, not running a reform colony. A few specks of dirt are good for you and boost your natural immune system.
- Do make sure your home is ecologically sound in the first place by using specialist building materials (e.g., Womersley's, Construction Resources) or at least buy environmentally friendly cleaning products from specialist suppliers (e.g., Healthy House). Failing that, vinegar will clean just about anything – from mirrors to lime-scaled toilet bowls – and soda crystals does a wizard job on drains when mixed with boiling water.

PILGRIM PAYNE & CO

Pilgrim Payne & Co Ltd
290–294 Latimer Road
London W10 6QU
T: 020 8960 5656
F: 020 8964 0598

Costs Free estimate, then £60 call-out plus VAT.
Travel Throughout London and within the M25. Will consider
further afield.
Size of job From spot removal to whole house.
Attitude Service is at your convenience, not theirs.

Pilgrim Payne, established in 1850, cleans and
reinstalls curtains, carpets and upholstery on site,
and will collect, renovate and return fine rugs and
tapestries. (Miracles worked include removing tar
footprints from a staircase carpet, and dark ink from
a cream sofa.) They will also reline and alter curtains,
refit loose covers and do reupholstery. It's little wonder
that due to customer demand, they now offer an
interior design service.

It's not unusual for Pilgrim Payne to offer discounts.
'It's our policy,' says managing director Graham Doyle.
'We're interested in our customers, and 92 per cent say
they will never use anyone else.'

Doyle's men may ask customers to sign
a disclaimer, but should a problem arise they don't
hold it against you. 'We don't say: "But you signed."
We say: "How I can help?"' says Doyle. One German
lady insisted her curtains hung differently after the
cleaning. Doyle showed up with a stepladder and spent
three hours with her. 'She told absolutely everyone she
knows about us. She's now our best customer. My view
is, if you say to someone who's got a problem, "I'm
here to solve it," they're amazed,' he says. So are we.

What the clients say
'They get the Academy Award for domestic service.'
Helen Kirwan-Taylor, author, *Home UK*
'A real person on the other end answers the phone quickly, calls
back when they say they will, and gets someone to you ASAP
who is nice, sensible, quotes intelligently, does the work very
quickly, comes at a time to suit you and does not keep you
waiting. They do not suddenly start quoting for things that don't
need doing. If the work you want them to do is impossible, they
tell you. If a stain will still be there, however faint, they will
explain exactly how visible it will be and they are right. I cannot fault their old-fashioned personal service.'
Jamie Jago, Jago Dean PR

Baileys Home and Garden
The Engine Shed
Station Approach
Ross on Wye
Herefordshire HR9 7BW
T: 01989 561 931
www.baileyshomeandgarden.com

Baileys Home and Garden sell everything and the kitchen sink (lovely old-fashioned butler's ones). The products for the home, office, garden, kitchen, bathroom, children and family dog have all been chosen by owner Sally Bailey, and if it all looks like it's from a glossy magazine shoot, that's because it is. Nearly every interiors editor includes Baileys Home and Garden on their pages; the items are functional and photogenic, with a nostalgic 1930s to 1950s look (some are actual vintage items).

And then there are the cleaning products. Even if you are a stranger to a bit of spit and polish, you'll love the aesthetic appeal of the Madagascar bristle brush and goat hair dusting brush (£5.50 each), the artisan's studio smell of Baileys Leather Polish (£6.50/250ml), and Good for Wood (£13.50/l) to treat wooden salad bowls, chopping boards and work surfaces. And they're attractive enough to leave out on full view on the counter.

Caldrea
at Harvey Nichols, London
T: 020 7235 5000
www.caldrea.com

If you thought cleaning couldn't possibly be glamorous, you're wrong. The slogan of New American homecare line Caldrea is 'The spirit of keeping home' and it has managed to make its cleaning fluids and accessories must-have home items. Billed as 'aromatherapeutic household cleansers', Caldrea's products are not only beautifully designed and packaged, but 'earth friendly'. From the white-spruce-scented Kitchen Surface Cleaner to the pearwood and horsehair French Door-Dusting Brush (perfect for hard-to-reach corners and Venetian blinds), each item works as brilliantly as it looks. Domestic bliss.

Good Home Company
at Selfridges, London
T: 0870 837 7377

Nostalgia for simpler times is the inspiration behind The Good Home Company's homecare line from the USA. The gentlest ingredients available are used and the products are only 'tested on good people, not good animals'. Despite the thoroughly contemporary and pricey prices, the products are irresistible, and sold in elegant glass bottles with metal and rubber clasps, as if they were the finest liqueur or rare olive oil.

The laundry detergent is all natural, biodegradable and comes in such summer-in-the-Hamptons scents as Beach House, Lavender and Pure Grass. Particularly ingenious are the vacuum beads – pop a sachet of 25 scented beads into your vacuum cleaner and fresh fragrance will waft through the exhaust every time you use it, scenting the whole room. How nifty is that?

Healthy House
T: 01453 752216
info@healthy-house.co.uk
www.healthy-house.co.uk

This family-run business was established 15 years ago, initially to help people with allergies, but its products will be of fascination to anyone interested in a solvent-free home. There are products sympathetic to sufferers of asthma, eczema, Multiple Chemical Sensitivity, electromagnetic and geopathic stress, and seasonal affective disorder (SAD). A cult item is the Polti Vaporetto Lecoaspira Steam-Vacuum Cleaner (a hefty £349), which combines steam cleaning with high-suction vacuuming so you can blast dust mites from upholstery and mattresses to a depth of three inches without having to use chemicals, and bring an extra degree of freshness to vacuuming hard and soft flooring. (It traps the dust in water and then you just pour the liquid away.) Another household must-have are the microfibre cleaning cloths (£4.99 each), which neither contain nor use chemicals and are so well designed that only water and elbow grease are needed to clean most hard surfaces. A fascinating mine of information.

Labour & Wait
18 Cheshire Street
London E2 6EH
T/F: 020 7729 6253
info@labourandwait.co.uk
www.labourandwait.co.uk

Mrs Beeton would have approved of this tiny shop in Shoreditch; indeed, many of its products would not have looked out of place in her kitchen. Quite simply, Labour & Wait sell the most beautiful, timeless, nostalgic-looking but practical and long-lasting home products out there. There are specialist brushes from Sweden (from £5), cool suede toolbelts for lumberjacks and carpenters (from £15), chic beige leather work gloves with cotton lining (£10), and you will want to carry their ostrich feather duster (£18) as a fashion accessory – it's that beautiful. These products are so functional and yet so stylish, you feel like a whole, new clean just looking at them. A must-see shop, or order from the website if you can't make it to the East End.

Lakeland
Lakeland Limited
Alexandra Buildings
Windermere
Cumbria LA23 1BQ
T: 015394 88100
www.lakelandlimited.com

Lakeland is the secret weapon in every Domestic Diva's arsenal. It is a fascinating catalogue company that offers products for levels of cleanliness and tidiness you never knew existed. It sells things like Band-It Dishwasher Loops (£2 for three), elasticated strips to strap in your stemware so it doesn't topple over when you open the dishwasher door, and Clip-On Tea Towel Loops (£2.95 for five), so you can elegantly hang your tea towel to dry from a hook without having to sew on a loop yourself. It's only when you read about these tempting, affordable items that you realize how irritating it's been not to have them.

The catalogue's friendly tone makes for an entertaining read, and the service is faultlessly efficient. The company is still family-run and was founded 40 years ago in the Lake District, initially to supply local farmers with polythene bags for packing poultry. It's gone rather more upmarket since then and now offers more than 4,000 products through 11 catalogues that are sent to one million homes each year (there is also a flagship store in Windermere and smaller branches from Scotland to Cornwall – visit the website for details). Apparently, more than 6,000 orders are despatched every day. Looks like Britain's cleaning up its act.

Miscellaneous
www.howtocleananything.com

If you actually like getting your own hands dirty, then visit this website ASAP. An international group of cleaners has joined forces to produce a site with more than 1,000 cleaning tips for inside and outside the house, ranging from how to remove burnt food from the bottom of stainless steel pans to how to wash kangaroo urine from sleeping bags and even tips on the 'annual fishpond clear-out'. A fascinating, cult read.

1st Call Appliance Service
PO Box 2872
Gerrard's Cross
Buckinghamshire SL9 7ZJ
T: 01753 884 866/020 7221 3312/020 8801 3141
call1st@aol.com

Costs A flat fee of £42.50 plus VAT to £59.50 plus VAT. There is
no separate fee for call-out and for work, but if 1st Call comes
to your house and you decide not to proceed with the job, the
flat fee must be paid.
Travel Work within the congestion charge zone, mainly north,
north-west, south-west and west London and Middlesex.
Size of job Vacuum cleaners to tumble driers.
Atttitude To the rescue.

For the past 30 years, Martin Baggett and his team of
engineers have been rescuing households in domestic
distress. If your washing machine, tumble drier or
dishwasher has broken and the manufacturer is slow
in coming to fix it, ring 1st Call. Baggett and his team
have the stock and expertise to repair more than 20
household brands the same day or the next (Monday
to Friday, 9am–5:30pm). Engineers arrive with a van
of spare parts, so you're saved the irritation of order-
ing and waiting weeks for those, too.

What the clients say
'1st Call engineers don't just get Christmas cards; they get
kisses.' Helen Kirwan-Taylor, author, *Home UK*
'They're so good and so reliable. When you're dealing with
some of the German appliance service departments, it gets very
frustrating. 1st Call are quick and get the job done.'
Sally Sahin, Bloomsbury Property Services

Absolutely Spotless
106 Wellesley Road
London W4 3AP
T: 020 8932 7360/020 7839 8222
F: 020 8747 0598
spotless@ukonline.co.uk
www.absolutelyspotless.co.uk

Costs General clean of one-bedroom property (including
descaling sanitary ware and cleaning the fridge), £110–£130;
five-bedroom property, £200–£250. Carpet cleaning, approx
£1 per square metre; upholstery cleaning, approx £10 per seat
(so a two-seater sofa, £20); window cleaning, inside and out,
approx £10–£20 for a one-bedroom property and £50–70 for
a five-bedroom property.
Travel London and the Home Counties.
Size of job Minimum charge £90.
Attitude 'Our name is our aim.'

Absolutely Spotless cleaned the *Big Brother* house
during filming of the TV series. If you tuned into the
loutish antics of the contestants, you'll know that if they
can clean that, they must be good – and very patient.
    This dynamic team of fit young Kiwis and Ossies
has offered professional cleaning to private and
commercial clients for the past ten years. Whether you
need a spring clean, end-of-tenancy clear-out, mop-up
after the builders, gleaming windows or a spot
removed from a sofa, the site is surveyed by an
Absolutely Spotless supervisor who gives a free quote
before a van filled with a trained, insured blitz squad
and all the right equipment and materials arrives to
bring order back into your life – one contented
customer fainted with delight on seeing them scrub
her grouting with a toothbrush. Offering a 24/7 service
at short notice, theirs is certainly a number for the
domestic emergency file, too.
    Clients include interior designer Kelly Hoppen,
and if they're good enough for the Queen of Beige
Suede, they're good enough for you. They also have
leading London estate agencies such as Kinleigh,
Folkard & Hayward, Behr & Butchoff, Oakleys and
Ellis & Co on their books.

What the clients say
'I used them to clean a filthy flat recently that belonged to a
friend. The team were so hunky and good-looking, I kept coming
in to supervise them.' Helen Kirwan-Taylor, author, *Home UK*

Aga Clean
T: **07815 475 856**
stuart@agaclean.co.uk
www.agaclean.co.uk

All Care
16C Brondesbury Villas
London NW6 6AA
T: **020 7625 8888**

Costs £65 an hour.
Travel **Based in Yorkshire but will travel all over the UK.**
Size of job **Aga.**
Attitude **Wherever we can reach, we clean. We bring Agas back to their former glory.**

Literally half a dozen handwritten letters came in praising this service. When Stuart and Karen Nelson desperately needed someone to clean their Aga and discovered no one near their home in Yorkshire was offering a cleaning service, they were obliged to set up their own. Just a few weeks after opening their Aga-only cleaning company, the phone started to ring off the hook.

Working as a two-man team, a two-oven Aga takes around two hours to clean, and a four-oven Aga about three hours. All the materials needed for the job, including a steam cleaner, are provided by Aga Clean, which has cleaned more than 500 Agas and come across every form of encrustation and oily deposit since it opened three years ago. If cleanliness is next to godliness, then it is entirely appropriate that their current job is blitzing the Aga at the Bishop's Palace at Hereford Cathedral.

What the clients say
'We enjoyed Stuart and Karen's company. They have captured a unique hole in the market for busy people who actually use their Agas to their full potential. When my engineer came to service it, he was most impressed.' Mary Vyvyan, client
'They did a super job! I have no hesitation in recommending them.' Irene Dunn, client
'After Stuart and Karen had been, my Aga looked ten years younger and it was cleaner than I had ever thought possible. The result was amazing. The condition of my Aga had been transformed before my very eyes.' Caroline Rennie, client
'Stuart and Karen have come to us twice. On both occasions they were punctual, extremely efficient and professional, very cheerful and friendly, and we were very pleased with the finished result.' Mrs Nolan Parker, client

Costs **Charge by the job, not per hour. A typical one-bedroom property costs £100–£120; a two-bedroom property, £120–£140; the price rises incrementally.**
Travel **All over London and within the M25.**
Size of job **Minimum charge £45–£50.**
Attitude **No worries.**

This dynamic team of New Zealanders and Australians was set up in 1987 and since then has been blitz-cleaning for Sainsbury's, Prêt à Manger, property developers (cleaning up after builders and doing end-of-tenancy cleans) and you and me. All Clean will completely make over your property: a team of three to four will arrive with all necessary materials and clean every room in the house – vacuum, polish, mop, wipe, tidy and even make beds. Carpet cleaning and windows are available by separate negotiation. And when they say clean all over, they mean all over: it is not unknown for a nice man from All Clean to be found up a ladder trimming the tree in your front garden.

Avalon Restoration Ltd
Avalon House
85 Picardy Road
Erith
Kent DA17 5QL and branches
T: 0800 052 3300/020 8319 0997
enquiries@avalon-ltd.co.uk
www.avalon-ltd.co.uk

Costs Ring for an estimate – each job is individually priced, depending on the degree of damage. Carpets and curtains are charged per square metre.
Travel London, Kent, Sussex, Essex and Surrey. Can refer you to local team partners nationwide.
Size of job Will consider anything.
Attitude The appliance of science. Staff are proud of their knowledge of psychrometry (that's the atmospheric mixture of air and water, to you and me), humidity, combustion levels and all the other stuff you dozed through in chemistry and physics lessons.

Want an education in microbiology and a clean carpet and curtains?

Avalon has been dealing with drama since 1971: although many of its clients are residential and just want carpets cleaned (including a recent one for a Lloyds of London client, valued at £100K), Avalon is also a disaster specialist for fire, flood, trauma and crime scenes, so your ketchup stains aren't going to raise any eyebrows. You can have your upholstery cleaned and stain-protected on-site, curtains cleaned (off-site), everything zapped with antistatic, and get your household goods deodorized and flame-retarded. You can then keep up the good work with Avalon's range of specialist cleaning products, such as the exotically named Powdered Haitian Cotton Upholstery Cleaner, available online.

Avalon goes about its business with forensic zeal. You'll learn that in fires, dry wood, paper and natural fibres produce a non-smeary residue; and plastic, foam rubber and polymers produce large black smears. You'll nod in fascination that there are 100,000 species of mould, and that it can grow anywhere, as long as there is moisture. Runny nose? Chronic fatigue? Weak lungs? Aching liver? That could be the super toxic *stachybotrys chartarum* mould, which Avalon will happily remove from the darker reaches of your cellar.

Bell House Restoration Ltd
Antique Furniture Restorers
20 – 22 Beardell St
London SE19 1TP
T: 020 8761 9002
F: 020 8761 9012
bellhouserestore@aol.com

Costs Will take on anything that can be repaired, from £50 to £50K. Cost depends on the degree of damage and how long the job will take.
Travel Travel all over the UK and abroad.
Size of job Lamps to family heirlooms.
Attitude Serious, ponderous and meticulous. Quietly and slowly get on with the job.

Managing director Rupert Humphrey is a cross between Prince Charles and a maths professor. We were bombarded with glowing references for his firm, and on meeting him, you'll want to break more furniture just so he can come over again. He is also one of the few men in England who can get red wine stains off white satin, which will endear him to anyone covering blotchy upholstery with throws.

Bell House Restoration has been making and restoring furniture for more than 20 years. As well as a full furniture service that embraces everything from repairs to gilding, upholstery, carving and treatment for woodworm, Bell House can create a chair to match a set or a table leaf to match an existing table. Although the emphasis is on fine antiques, Bell House does the occasional contemporary piece, as well as Art Nouveau, Art Deco and 1930s Modernist work, and porcelain and metal restoration.

Working as a small team of 6 to 12 craftsmen, Bell House will come on site for a free quotation, and are renowned for their personal service. Consequently, it has a long list of prestigious regular clients that includes the Palace of Westminster, English Heritage, Christie's, the royal palaces and antique-collecting celebs such as John Cleese.

What the clients say
'Rupert came via my mother-in-law. He's fixed the same lamp twice (because the kids keep breaking it) and you still can't tell.' Helen Kirwan-Taylor, author, *Home UK*
'They are extremely pleasant, professional, old-fashioned. They go down particularly well with our American clients. They are our preferred company for all insurance matters.'
Gillian Atkinson, insurance claims manager

Deacon Finishes
Lawrence House
St Augustine's Business Park
Whitstable
Kent CT5 2QJ
T: 01227 791999
F: 01227 791777
www.deaconfinishes.co.uk

Costs Free quote or send drawings by e-mail. Prices vary,
depending on size of the job.
Travel Nationwide and abroad.
Size of job No job too small.
Attitude Great pride in their reputation and true professionals.

Jason Barnes and David Hadlow, the directors of
Deacon Finishes, set up shop five years ago after more
than 30 years in the business between them. Now their
company is one of the most successful in its field,
restoring, cleaning and building wooden flooring and
panelling. They also spray and French polish and
undertake graining and broken-colour finishes. Their
long list of prestige projects includes the Houses of
Parliament, for which they refurbished the wooden
panelling; the King's Drawing Room at Kensington
Palace, for which they revived the flooring and oak
panelling; City titans Lloyds and KPMG, for which they
supplied all the doors and unitry for their power-
broking boardrooms; and shopfitting for gleaming
branches of Monsoon and LK Bennett. Somehow they
still find time to take on private clients, and offer on-
site polishing, collection and delivery, and also work
out-of-office hours. Generally, Deacon can offer one-
week turnarounds, depending on the size of the job,
and with a 6,000 square foot spray shop, they can
handle huge quantities of panelling, skirting and
furniture. A real find.

What the clients say
'We know that when we call on them to undertake a project for
us it will be carried out with the utmost care and attention;
whether attending one of our sites for our "blue chip" clients or
polishing a piece of our bespoke joinery in their fully equipped
spray factory. Their workmanship and professionalism are
a major asset to us.'
Cathedral Contracts, interior contracting company
'Their work easily meets the high standards we require. They
offer a friendly, efficient service.'
Cynthia Jameson, general manager, Czech & Speake

Simon Dodson
Antique Furniture Restoration and French Polisher
The Workshop
Lower Seagry Farm
Chippenham
Wiltshire SN15 5EW
T: 01249 720 770
M: 07968 223352

Costs Prices vary depending on each piece, but a ballpark fig-
ure is £17.50 an hour.
Travel He generally sticks to the counties around him –
Wiltshire, Gloucestershire and Oxfordshire. Be warned, he is
not a fan of London.
Size of job Anything that can fit into a workshop.
Attitude: Charming one-man band.

'I'll have a go at anything broken,' Simon Dodson
volunteers. And true to his word, he'll take on anything
made of wood, be it Tudor or Ikea. The classic country
boy made good, Simon is an unbeatable restorer.
He started his training in Cirencester in 1988 and
received his City and Guild certification in Furniture
Craft in Bristol. By mid-1991 he was working solo in
Cheltenham and, despite having no telephone or his
own workshop, word-of-mouth recommendations led
to a long line of customers.

Most of his work is with antiques, and if for some
extraordinary reason he can't complete the task at
hand, he usually knows someone who can and, in true
charming style, is happy to recommend them.

All of his current jobs are from repeat customers,
impressed by the fact that Simon will not finish a job
until, in the client's eyes, it's perfect.

What the clients say
'His manner was absolutely charming, most obliging. He treated
the piece with such respect. He transformed it, so it now looks
like a treasured antique. It's beyond what I expected it to
look like. He's very professional and accommodating, and I will
continue to use him. He is absolutely marvellous.'
Mrs Dalgliesh, client

**David Gunton's Hardwood Floors
at The Parquet and General Flooring Company Ltd
Grange Lane, Winsford
Cheshire CW7 2PS
T: 01606 861 442
F: 01606 861 445
floors@wideboards.com
www.wideboards.com**

Costs **from £250 per sq m. An average room of 20 sq m
costs £8,500.**
Travel **Nationwide and abroad.**
Size of job **Whole floors.**
Attitude **Boy, does he know his woods.**

David Gunton used to work 9–5 in L'Oréal's workshops
and would sand wood floors for a laugh in his spare
time. Then friends increasingly asked him to tend to
their floors – so much so that he was almost obliged
to become the full-time, bespoke hardwood flooring
specialist that he is today.

He employs a team of Hindu craftsmen, who
are nothing short of superb and he can't praise them
highly enough. 'Philosophically and culturally, they
make wonderful workmen – honest, loyal and
trustworthy… they see everything through to the
very highest standard.'

He worked in Windsor Castle after the fire in 1992.
Currently, he is making 12-metre-long, 1-metre-wide
English oak floorboards and installing them over
underfloor heating. And he's offering them with
a 100-year warranty, though he expects them to last
well over 1,000 years.

What the clients say
**'The best. The work he does is exquisite. I can't praise him
enough.' Mark Gillette, interior designer**

**Hadley St James Residential
748 Fulham Road
London SW6 5SH
T: 020 7731 8900
F: 020 7736 7660
M: 07799 893 083
danny.saffer@hadleystjames.com
www.hadleystjames.com**

Costs **Fairly expensive (£12 an hour for a cleaner), but the
plumbers are less expensive than Pimlico Plumbers.**
Travel **Greater London, southern England, along the M25.**
Size of job **From tiny to humongous.**
Attitude **These are true professionals, not fly-by-night wheeler-
dealers trying to make a quick buck.**

Company director Kit Hall sounds like a colonel in
the Royal Scots Dragoons; in fact, he was originally
a money manager in the City before deciding to devote
himself to servicing houses and offices across the west
of England. With a turnover of more than £4 million,
you can confidently assume that Hadley St James
knows its stuff. They were recommended by designer
Catherine Pawson.

Hadley St James specialize in maintenance and
cleaning: windows, carpets, interiors, ovens,
bathrooms, marble and fabrics. If they can't clean or
repair something for you, they will find someone who
can from their extensive database of electricians,
plumbers, decorators and artisans. 'Give us 48 hours
and we guarantee to find you what you need,' says
Hall with confidence. And with a client base that
includes Deustche Bank, Colefax and Fowler, two-thirds
of London's private schools, leading estate agencies
and all the well-heeled postcodes, they must be doing
something right.

What the clients say
**'They've been here twice to clean my carpets. Both times they
were punctual and, more importantly, they got out the coffee
stain that no one else could. I would have saved myself a lot
of grief had I known about them earlier.'**
Helen Kirwan-Taylor, author, *Home UK*

Highgrade
2 Bushey Hall Road
Watford
Hertfordshire WD23 2EA
T: 01923 227 207
F: 01923 236 400
www.highgradecleaning.co.uk

Costs Free quotation. No standard rate; each project is priced individually, depending on size and condition.
Travel London and the South East.
Size of job Minimum £60.
Attitude Have a reputation to look after, so will be honest about expectations and do the job with dedication.

When Harrods, Selfridges, Liberty and John Lewis continually recommend a company to their clients, you can rest assured that it must be good. In business since 1968, Highgrade has cleaned the carpets and upholstery of more than 30,000 clients.

Now for the science bit. Highgrade use a foam shampoo system that converts hot water and special powder detergents into foam, which is brushed into and simultaneously extracted from the fibres, so no rinsing is required. Many of Highgrade's rivals use water-extraction (steam) machines that spray water and liquid detergent into the fibres and then extract them through suction rather than brushing. A method that, while fine in the short term, apparently can attract dirt and make future cleaning more difficult. Highgrade also offers a stain-proofing service so that you won't need to call them in again – can 30,000 people be wrong?

What the clients say
'We've used them for years – they're the best in the business. When you're a shop like Harrods, you can only recommend people of the highest level to your customers. They satisfy all our criteria.' Steven Bates, director – fitted carpets, Harrods

HomeClean
273 Eversholt Street
London NW1 1BA
T: 020 7383 4958
teresa@homeclean.co.uk
www.homeclean.co.uk

Costs Annual maintenance fee of £189 plus VAT per property for the first year and £95 plus VAT for subsequent years. Short-term fees: 1day, £20 plus VAT; 1 month, £59 plus VAT; and so on. The client pays the cleaner £6 an hour, for a minimum of two hours a week.
Travel Throughout London.
Size of job Temporary to full-time.
Attitude Proud of thoroughly vetting staff's credentials, which is good news for you.

HomeClean is the cleaning world's equivalent to a dating agency: it is one of the largest domestic cleaning agencies in London and acts as a matchmaker, finding cleaners that are right for your expectations and organizing cover for holidays, illness, etc. It's left up to the client to pay the cleaner and provide cleaning materials, equipment and access to the property. Essentially, this is a service for people who want to know that their cleaner has been interviewed and reference-checked (references are available on request), and who like a systematic clean – HomeClean offers a pad of checklist forms, where you tick the boxes of things you want done and leave it for the cleaner.

H–K

The Household Division
5 Upper Richmond Rd
London SW15 2RF
T: 08708 304 460
enquiries@thehouseholddivision.com
www.thehouseholddivision.com

Christopher Howe
93 Pimlico Road
London SW1W 8PH
T: 020 7730 7987
F: 020 7730 0157
www.howelondon.com

Costs All services are priced per day. The daily rate is £200 for non-members and £180 for members. Any job over two days merits a quote. Handymen cost £33 an hour for non-members and £30 an hour for members.
Travel London based, but will endeavour to go as far as the M25 borders.
Size of job Handyman to loft conversion.
Attitude Takes on headaches so you won't have one.

Costs Italian cowhides, from £9.99 per sq ft (average hide 8 sq ft); goatskins, from £13.22 per sq ft (average hide 17 sq ft).
Travel Clients generally e-mail pictures for a free quote; if items are too large to bring in or if clients have several pieces, the team will travel nationwide and abroad by separate negotiation.
Size of job Minimum 12 skins (from a large selection).
Attitude Thoughtful and artistic.

When he saw that the shower unit was held on with tape, chartered accountant Adrian Gribben realized his destiny. Fed up with being ripped off by tradesmen, he abandoned his first profession and set up Household Division in 2001. It started as a building service for professional residential Londoners who needed good tradesmen but didn't have the time to find or wait for them. Gribben now provides everything, from a lone handyman with a screwdriver to entire building crews for refurbishing a property. He maintains customer privacy and won't name-drop, but Household Division is now the preferred maintenance company of lifestyle management and concierge service TenUK.

Household Division vets all the tradesmen on its staff and they are therefore reliable as well as skilled. The company also runs a keyholding programme so that you needn't be on site to let workers in and out. By paying £5 per month for a set of keys to be held by the company, you receive discounts of 10–40 per cent.

In response to customer demand, Household Division now also offer a handyman service, where two men will come and complete any task around the house, from leaking taps to flat-pack assembly. Husbands everywhere are breathing sighs of relief that Sundays are now DIY-free.

What the clients say
'They sent me this amazing American actor who also does handywork. He taught my son Shakespeare while he meticulously went about his job. When they screwed up (once) they sorted it out at no cost.' Helen Kirwan-Taylor, author, *Home UK*
'They've been excellent. They've done work on both of my children's properties from installing a bathroom to painting and repairing sash windows and plumbing. It's worked out very well. I have recommended them to others.' Frank Hickson, client

This is an antique business that does something no one else is prepared to do anymore: dyeing. Renowned for his hand-stitched horsehair seats and down-filled cushions, Christopher Howe (who trained as a sculptor) offers a fabric and leather-dyeing service and has gained a reputation for making sophisticated, classic items in Juicy-Fruit colours. If he can't match the colour you want from his collection, he'll dye one for you. The company also restores pieces and will even clean any emergency splotches (for existing clients only). Clients include David Mlinairc and Chester Jones.

The Keyholding Company
2 Cotswold Mews
30 Battersea Square
London SW11 3RA
T: 0870 770 6880
services@keyholding.co.uk
www.keyholding.com

Costs Basic membership fee, £6 a month. Then £12 for first 15 minutes and £12 for each additional half hour; tradesmen supplied at a flat rate of £55 an hour plus materials.
Travel London based, but plans to expand in the future.
Size of job From decorating to boilers.
Attitude Can do!

Charlie Gordon Lennox (previously a landscape gardener) was the first to come up with the idea of a key-holding service. 'People are sick and tired of being held hostage to delinquent tradesman,' he says, which is why he founded the company in 1998.

The company keeps a set of your keys and dispatches a member of staff on a moped or motorcycle to your house to supervise any work. Gordon Lennox does the shouting for you: 'We have 150 contractors (from electricians to dogwalkers to launderers) on our books, and we have volume – that gives us buying power.' His clients, he says, are anyone who is fed up with the fact that 'British service takes twice as long, costs twice as much and is twice as aggravating.' Clients include Phil Spencer, presenter of Channel 4's *Location, Location, Location,* city people and anyone who can't be bothered to sit and wait for the plumber.

The 24/7 service is 90 per cent domestic and 10 per cent commercial, and ranges from supplying tradesmen to being there if your alarm goes off, checking on a property if you're away (including watering the plants and collecting or forwarding the post) and being at your front door within 20 minutes if you lose your keys.

What the clients say
'They are a superb outfit. They have helped me out of a couple of difficult situations. They're efficient, useful and easy to deal with. I think they have an original idea.' Phil Spencer, Garrington Home Finder and *Location, Location, Location*

The Kitchen Doctor
Oak House, 1 Sevenoaks Road
Pratts Bottom
Kent BR6 7SF
T: 0500 855 555; 01689 850 000
F: 01689 852 222
james@thekitchendoctor.com
www.thekitchendoctor.com

Costs Approximate estimate given over the phone. Site visits charged by the hour and include first hour of work (£85 including VAT, plus materials); if more than 1 hour is needed, the first hour is deducted from the final bill, and subsequent hours cost £41.36 each. In general, replacing a hinge costs from £5; refurbishing an entire kitchen can cost between £2K and £3K.
Travel Anywhere in the South East.
Size of job Replacement doors, worktops, whole kitchens.
Attitude 'We do all sorts.'

James Horgan founded The Kitchen Doctor 20 years ago, filling a crucial gap in the market: to replace or repair practically any element of a modern kitchen. Kitchen Doctor's team of nine cheerful workmen do drawers, doors, worktops, hinges, appliances and fitted kitchen components, normally within a week of your first phone call – and they work in the evenings, not just 9 to 5. The Kitchen Doctors are experts in the NEF range, but also supply bespoke worktops, doors, fixtures and fittings. So, if a new kitchen isn't within your budget, revamping your existing one could be the solution, as clients from Chester Square to Walton-on-Thames have discovered.

What the clients say
'They did an excellent job in my kitchen, replacing worktops and fitting a new sink. The workmen arrived on time and left everything immaculate, and returned promptly to complete the work after the floor was laid. I have received several compliments as to how nice it all looks.' Mrs M J Swanley, client
'Our kitchen is an odd shape, with very uneven walls and floor. In a few hours Kitchen Doctor completely transformed its appearance. It now looks streamlined, elegant and immaculate. The degree of workmanship and attention to detail was superb. We have no hesitation in recommending them for future work as they are polite, courteous and scrupulously tidy.'
E W and R T, clients

M–N

MJ's Carpet & Upholstery Cleaning
4 Dorset Way
Hillingdon
Middlesex UB10 OJR
T: 01895 231 815
M: 07747 841 511

Marble Maintenance Company
3 St Mark's Mansions
Balderton Street
London W1K 6TQ
T: 020 7491 7497
M: 07730 896 690

Costs Free site visit and quote. Each job is individually priced.
Travel London and Greater London.
Size of job From one spot to the whole house.
Attitude Friendly, family-run firm.

Mark Slaney set up MJ's five years ago after a decade in the carpet and upholstery cleaning business. Fortunately for his clients (who include the Gettys and several property consultants), he has since branched into cleaning, polishing and re-sealing of hard surfaces, too, such as stone, marble and vinyl. Curtains can be cleaned on- or off-site and MJ's are happy to treat furniture upholstered in leather, suede and fine fabrics.

What the clients say
'Mark has done work in my properties for four years. He's absolutely efficient. He used the best products and machinery and works very hard.'
Merlyn Law, Law & Co, property managers

Costs Free quote and site visit. Will charge for testing of a trial area (£80). Each job individually priced. Can be expensive, but won't leave until the job is done properly.
Travel Mainly central London.
Size of job From one bathroom to entire palace.
Attitude Complains bitterly about British service, and therefore ensures his own service is tip-top and everyone's happy.

Irish Gerry Lawless is almost too cool to be in the business of cleaning marble. He loathes the English attitude towards work, which means you can expect to see him in your house long after the kids have gone to bed.
Clients include Ringo Starr, the Bransons and the St James's Club in Piccadilly, but his passionate interest is in the stone, not its owner. His philosophy is to be 'sympathetic to stone'. He hates chemicals, prefers not to use power washers (they eventually cause chipping and wear away layers) and instead uses a range of up to 20 different light liquid solutions and a lot of tender loving care to treat your stone.

What the clients say
'He somehow mesmerized me with his lyrical description of the art of marble cutting. He's an artist who will work all night if he has to.' Helen Kirwan-Taylor, author, *Home UK*
'Gerry is the only person we recommend to our clients: they all call back and say how great he is. He is reliable and deals with everyone and everything – small or large – with the same attention.'
Andrea Magale, resident architect, Limestone Gallery, London

Marble Shine Ltd
Unit 7
Betchworth Works
Ifield Road
Charlwood
Surrey RH6 ODX
T: 0870 011 6393/01293 863 362/863 363
F: 0870 011 6394/01293 863 778

Costs **Free estimate and advice on after care. They don't charge by the square metre, but by the day (approximately £265 plus VAT).**
Travel **Work a lot in central London but will travel nationwide.**
Size of job **Mrs Jones fireplace to an entire palace.**
Attitude **Know their stone. Honest about what can be achieved and won't be fazed by your floor's quirks.**

I discovered Marble Shine coming out of one of the most soigneé houses on the street. They clean marble, terrazzo, granite, limestone or any other natural stone the earth's core has thrown up at you. Simon Cowell uses them – which may or may not be a good thing.

A favourite with conservation and modern architects, the firm run by brothers Neil and Stephen Golder has been restoring, cleaning and repairing (where possible) historic and contemporary floors of 'blue-chip people', as they put it, for the past 18 years.

What the clients say
'Absolutely I would recommend them. We have used them on a regular basis since we started and recommend them to our clients.' Toby Jerman, Alex Stables Stone Productions Ltd
'He turns up on time – does the job without any fuss or mess and knows what he is doing. He's not afraid to say no if he can't do it. Honest and reliable.' Joanna Lindsey, designer

NKF Metal Services
Eastern Industrial Estate
Kencot Way, Erith
Kent DA18 4AB
T: 020 8310 2199
F: 020 8310 2204
nkf@btconnect.com
www.nkfmetals.co.uk

Costs **A standard kitchen is approximately £1K and tak[...] two weeks. Ring for a quote as there is such a wide range of features: a sink can change the price dramatically.**
Travel **Generally work within the M25. They will travel for larger jobs and supply further afield, but may not install.**
Size of job **From a worktop to an entire kitchen.**
Attitude **Honest and excellent.**

If you can't afford a new kitchen, NKF will take yours away and bring it back clad in gleaming stainless steel. Both managing directors, John O'Shay and Steve Jarratt, worked with aircraft components before stainless steel came into vogue as the interior designers' favourite work surface. They now work as a two-man team, but should a large-scale contract or unique commission arrive, they have associates and freelancers on hand to help.

John and Steve will clad your entire kitchen or individual units such as counter tops, kitchen islands, splash backs and table frames. They will even create and clad garden features.

What the clients say
'We have been using NKF since 1991. They are brilliant, hard-working and competitively priced.'
Mike Walker, director, Tempus Stet (Design)

Oven Clean
16 Market Place
Chalfont St Peter
Gerrard's Cross
Buckinghamshire SL9 9EA
T: 0800 731 7913
www.ovenclean.co.uk

Costs **Single ovens, £35; double ovens, £80. Separate menu of charges for hobs, extractors, ranges, microwaves and barbecues.**
Travel **Nationwide.**
Size of job **Ovens.**
Attitude **We scrub them til they're clean.**

If you ring Oven Clean's main number, they will give you the mobile number of the nearest serviceman in your area so you can negotiate with him directly. He will arrive in a van filled with cleaning fluids and a gas cleaner. The cleaning is old-fashioned and thorough (a double oven can take up to four hours), as Oven Clean does not believe that steam-cleaning rivals can match its good old elbow grease and top-of-the-range solutions. Best of all, the cleaners are sensitive to your kitchen floor, smother everything with newspaper and leave minimal mess.

Among their satisfied customers are such British stalwarts as Windsor Castle, John Lewis, which recommends them to clients, and Sunningdale Golf Club.

What the clients say
'It took most of the morning but boy was the oven clean! It's a hard job and they deserve a tip.'
Helen Kirwan-Taylor, author, Home UK

Ovenu
67 Barkham Ride
Wokingham
Berkshire RG40 4HA
T: 0870 880 1222
F: 0118 973 1876
www.ovenu.co.uk

Costs **Single oven, £64 plus VAT; double oven, £79 plus VAT.**
Travel **Nationwide.**
Size of job **Ovens.**
Attitude **'We've yet to encounter an oven that does not look like new after treatment.'**

Rik Hellewell, managing director of Ovenu, trained as a mechanical engineer before entering the carpet and upholstery cleaning business 12 years ago. Then, on the suggestion of a barbecue enthusiast friend, he designed a barbecue and oven-cleaning machine.

If hours of noxious aerosols, rubber gloves and hard scrubbing isn't for you, Ovenu has the solution: a totally caustic-free range of products, fully trained technicians and registered equipment to do the dirty work for you in three hours. Detail is key, as Ovenu will deep clean all shelves, racks, liners, doors, knobs, dials and seals, bringing your oven back to showroom condition.

What the clients say
'The oven was so clean that we hesitated using it again. We have since recommended Ovenu to all of our friends. We wrote them a thank you letter, that's how impressed we were.'
Martin and Anne Gray, clients

Pimlico Plumbers
136 Lambeth Road
London SE1 7DF
T: 020 7928 8888
F: 020 7928 3333
sales@pimlicoplumbers.com
www.pimlicoplumbers.com

Costs **Standard hourly rate between 6am and 6pm, Monday to Friday, £70 plus VAT an hour with a minimum one-hour charge. Rates for all other times are £95 plus VAT an hour with a minimum one-hour charge. There are no hidden extra charges.**
Travel **Central London.**
Size of job **Any kind of problem, any size.**
Attitude **'We need to leave the customer happy, and try to be the plumbing equivalent to Harrods or M&S in terms of service.'**

When Charlie Mullins, the founder and managing director of Pimlico Plumbers was an apprentice plumber, he says: 'There was a general bad feeling towards plumbers, that we were all cowboys, and I sensed that if I provided a quality service, people would be happy to use us again and again.' Smart boy. Since setting up Pimlico Plumbers in 1978, the company has won the National Plumber of the Year Award several times, was the subject of a recent BBC documentary, *Posh Plumbers*, and the corridors of its London head office are lined with signed photographs and glowing letters of praise from their many celebrity clients (Eric Clapton, Noel Gallagher, Britt Eckland and the notoriously fussy Michael Winner, to name a few).

This dedicated 24/7 company covers plumbing, heating, electrics, carpentry, drainage, roofing and general domestic building tasks. All work is guaranteed. 'If we make a mistake, we'll go back to solve it, no questions asked,' says Charlie Mullins. Apparently, 90 per cent of candidates for the rare vacancies at Pimlico Plumbers don't make it through the first interview. Of the 10 per cent that do, these are kept on for a trial period of one month, and then their work is reviewed. We have heard one or two complaints about plumbers exaggerating costs and a botched job or two. For the most part, they have a great reputation.

What the clients say
'I called your MC at 4.50pm and a plumber arrived within 40 minutes... I consider this so excellent that I'm sending you one of my books!' Michael Winner
'They have three good qualities: they are on time, they are neatly dressed and they clean up after themselves. It's a well-disciplined firm. They're not cheap but they are good value.'
Mr Pickford, client

Restore
Taggs Boat Yard
44 Summer Road
Thames Ditton
Surrey KT7 0QQ
T/F: 020 8398 4703
info@restoreltd.co.uk
www.restoreltd.co.uk

Costs **£25 per hour.**
Travel **Mainly London and the commuter belt, but happy to travel nationwide and abroad.**
Size of job **From small mirror to big table.**
Attitude **Charming, energetic and efficient young couple.**

This is a husband-and-wife team. Gavin Fisher was taught furniture restoration from childhood in Devon, and worked as an in-house restorer in a relocation company before meeting fellow practitioner Sophie and founding Restore six years ago.

Concentrating on antique furniture – especially armoires – and specializing in mahogany and rosewood, Gavin and Sophie will work as a team on- or off-site and bring in extra help for larger jobs if necessary. They keep their client base small, usually not taking on more than 40 or 50 pieces at any one time, to maintain their very personal service. Typical commissions are an inherited chest of drawers or a dining table that needs to be revived, and though they prefer not to work with contemporary furniture as some modern lacquered finishes don't respond well to treatment, they will take on what they can.

What the clients say
'After the beautiful work done on my mirror, I can't tell where the damage was. It looks fantastic. I will recommend them highly to anyone I know that requires work of this type.'
Mark Bailey, client
'They are both a mine of information.'
Nicki Manzoni, client
'They did a fantastic job on our table. It looked great!'
Mrs Riggs, client

R–S

Ryness
43 Westbourne Grove
London W2 4UA
and branches
T: 020 7792 5787
sales@ryness.co.uk www.ryness.co.uk
(Ryness electricians: 020 7239 8338
or e-mail electricians@ryness.co.uk)

Costs Free site visit and estimates from the electricians'
department. First hour £50 plus VAT, thereafter £30 plus VAT.
If a job takes a day, there's a flat fee of £240 plus VAT.
Travel Main operations within the M25; London and Surrey.
Size of job From changing lightbulbs to lighting up the
whole house.
Attitude Light up your life.

Ryness sells everything from twinkly fairy lights for
your Christmas tree to security floodlighting, slick
21st-century penthouse downlights to Edwardian repro
'banker's' desk lamps. What you probably don't know
is they will send fully qualified, certified, and experienced
electricians to your home for free and advise on
lighting systems, and can also recommend and install
intercoms and door entry systems.

The fact that they brought in Andrew Lindsay, an
ex-Goldman Sachs financial whizz kid as managing
director, proves that they're a serious player in the
illumination stakes. Well, they do 'do' Buckingham
Palace, as it happens. 'Service is what we care about
most,' says 27-year-old Lindsay. The former Olympic
gold medallist says: 'To be number one you have try
harder.' For starters, he wants to make Ryness stores
more cutting edge – as in the latest addition on the
North End Road. Clients are little ladies who need light
bulbs to hotels such as the Dorchester.

The company's proud of the fact that most of its
staff stay on for at least ten years, so the knowledge,
advice and experience customers receive is impressive.

Staunch and Flow
211 Piccadilly
London W1J 9HF
T: 020 7666 5566
info@staunchandflow.co.uk
www.staunchadnflow.com

Costs £65 an hour.
Travel Kensington area mostly, but will travel.
Size of job Will tackle anything.
Attitude 'We'll show you.'

Richard Nissen started life as an architect (he trained at
Bartlett). He then developed The Virtual Office, which
he still runs in Piccadilly. 'I realized that more and more
jobs will eventually go offshore,' he says, 'and only the
trades will remain.' He enrolled in plumbing school (he
says it takes longer to qualify as a plumber than to get
through Cambridge) and then started up Staunch and
Flow two years ago. As it happens, one of his
plumbers is an Oxbridge graduate, while another
worked as an accountant before. He now employs five
full-time plumbers (one female), some of whom are
trained apprentices. Because the plumbers are based
in Kensington, a call-out could be within an hour. 'It all
depends on where we're working at the time,' he says.

What the clients say
'They're extremely decent fellows, very different from old-
fashioned plumbers. They've done several jobs for me and
I can't fault them in any way. I even called them on a non-
plumbing problem recently and they were fantastically helpful.'
Jenny Cazalet, client

Stonetech UK Ltd
67 Chancery Lane
London WC2A 1RH
T: 020 7623 9898
stonetkuk@aol.com

Suds
8 Chelwood Close
Ewell
Surrey KT17 3AF
T: 020 8393 7656

Costs Varies, depending on the job, but from £100 into thousands.
Travel Nationwide; will also travel abroad with their own crew.
Size of job Will look at anything.
Attitude Take great pride in their work and find it personally satisfying, so will always achieve their best.

Stonetech is an 11-man band that will fix, replace, clean, restore and polish all your stone and provide you with specialist cleaning products for after they've gone. 'We're just as happy to do a small domestic job for Mrs Bloggs as a major commission, though,' says a member of the team. Be warned: they are very good at their job and very popular, so you may need to wait a few weeks for an engineer to come round for a free survey and quote, but the results will be worth it.

As for the clients of the company specializing in marble, granite, terrazzo and stone? 10 Downing Street and Buckingham Palace to name just a few.

What the clients say
'Stonetech are unfailingly efficient and courteous – we use them on all our luxury developments.'
Charles Tyler, managing director, Tyler London

Costs Outside London, £45 plus VAT for first half hour, then £10 plus VAT per half hour plus parts; inner London, £55 plus VAT for first half hour; thereafter £10 plus VAT per half hour plus parts.
Travel Surrey, south-west, south-east and central London.
Size of job Any appliance worth fixing.
Attitude Sensible and quietly get on with the job.

Music to anyone's ears: no more long waits for the Miele man (who claims a week is speedy service). As long as it's nothing to do with gas, refrigeration or microwaves and is bigger than a toaster, this popular, in-demand team of three will repair your domestic appliances. Ring them the next time your oven, hob, washing machine, tumble drier or dishwasher gives up the ghost, as hundreds of private residences, the Crown Estate and many letting agencies do.

Suds represent the majority of household name retailers, but be warned: like you, they can't bear companies that take weeks and weeks to show up or send parts, and simply refuse to represent them (bad news if you own anything by SMEG). Suds does not do emergency call-outs, though someone will generally arrive within a day of your call, depending on location. See: it can be done!

What the clients say
'Suds are a small and efficient company. They are knowledgeable, efficient, skilful, polite and, in my experience, punctual. No one likes waiting around for repairers who fail to turn up on time. I recommend them to my clients…'
Julian Mercer, property developer

T – W

Total Floor Care
3 School Lane
Combwich
Somerset TA5 2QS
T: 01278 652 150
F: 01278 653 846
info@totalfloorcare.com
www.totalfloorcare.com

Costs Free site visit and quote. Each job individually priced, depending on material and expanse (whether the floor is on one flat level or if there are lots of stairs).
Travel London, M4 corridor and down to Plymouth.
Size of job From 2 sq m area upwards.
Attitude Softly spoken, quiet and expert.

When they say total floor care, they mean it. They clean, refurbish, sand, repair, stain, wax, lacquer or oil your floor, be it made of wood, rubber, vinyl, lino, Amtico, seagrass, sisal or carpet. With a 50–50 split between private residential and commercial clients, Total Floor Care will also supply packs of specialist cleaning products for you to try on your own. They were recommended to us by Crucial Trading.

Founder Tim Derbyshire had 20 years' previous experience selling flooring, so he is familiar with the performance of most ranges. Andy Jones, the technical manager, trained in carpentry, joinery and cabinet making before realizing that caring for wooden floors was his calling 22 years ago. They've worked at Madame Tussaud's, the Royal Crescent Hotel, Bath, and for GMTV anchorwoman Fiona Phillips.

What the clients say
'We are very pleased with the quality of their work. We have a lot of people traffic, and the work needs to be of a high standard and long lasting. Total Care provides that.'
Helen Love, general manager, Royal Crescent Hotel, Bath

Tracking & Hanging
T: 020 8674 9142
M: 07860 330 191

Costs £40 call-out charge, which includes the fitting of the first item. After that, £10–£20 per item.
Travel London, nationwide and abroad.
Size of job From one blind to the whole house.
Attitude Let's get to work!

Lee Butler of Tracking & Hanging is the interior designer's secret weapon. 'We do all the things that people think they can do themselves – but can't,' he says. He and his team will hang and repair blinds, curtains and put up poles and tracking for a perfect drape and fit. With typical modesty and discretion, he refuses to name his famous clients, but the list of his destinations – Kuwait, Switzerland, Ibiza, Mustique – and jobs – stately homes, villas, boutique hotels – certainly gives a clue to the calibre of his work. 'But I'm just as happy to do anyone,' he says cheerfully.

What the clients say
'Lee and his team do all my curtain and blind fittings. They are efficient, helpful and good at what they do. I've been using them for 16 years.' Lindsay Behrens, Behrens Interiors

Walk on Wood Ltd
Tiptree Villa
20 Newland Street
Witham
Essex CM8 2AQ
T: 01376 518 243
F: 01376 503 949
M: 07867 535 437

Costs Free estimate; prices from £20 sq m, depending on size of job and condition of floor. They can also put in floors.
Travel Throughout south-east England.
Size of job Will look at any job.
Attitude Love wood – try to use non-toxic, natural products as much as possible.

This lovely family-run firm specializes in traditional flooring and carpentry, and offers refurbishment, sanding, sealing, waxing, painting and cleaning of all historic and contemporary wooden floors. Clients include the Hurlingham Club in London and the Royal Opera House, but Walk on Wood are also happy to do more modest expanses of wooden floor in private homes. Eco friendly, Walk on Wood is one of the few British suppliers of the latest water-based, non-toxic cleaning products by BonaKemi, a Finnish company, which clients can purchase to maintain their floors.

What the clients say
'They sanded my kitchen floor when others said it couldn't be done. They were meticulous – and nice to my children.'
Helen Kirwan-Taylor, author, *Home UK*

Wheelie Bin Company
Mwyndy Cross
Mwyndy
Pontyclun
Mid Glamorgan CF72 8PN
T: 01443 237 800 F: 01443 229 000
info@wheeliebin.co.uk
www.wheeliebin.co.uk

Costs £2.50 – £3.50 for one bin.
Travel Nationwide.
Size of job From one bin onwards.
Attitude Does the job you hate.

If those rubbish bins on your doorstep are getting a bit whiffy, the Wheelie Bin Company will despatch a team of men in bright yellow trucks to pressure wash, dry, line and perfume your bins on a weekly, bi-weekly or monthly basis. Hotel groups, restaurants and hundreds of private clients fed up with gruesome residues from split bags of rubbish sticking to the sides of their bins have taken them up on their offer. It all takes under five minutes, for the price of a handful of change. Getting the initial appointment may take a while, but at least you can log on to the website and watch video clips of Wheelie in action while you wait.

Womersleys
Walkley Lane
Heckmondwike
West Yorkshire WF16 0PG
T: 01924 400 651
F: 01924 403 489
info@womersleys.co.uk
www.womersleys.co.uk

World's End Waste
633 Pensbury Place
London SW8 4TP
T: 020 7351 0182
F: 020 7720 9159
worldsendwaste1@aol.com

If you really want to take clean living seriously and introduce it to every aspect of your life, Mark Womersley's your man. Cement, plasterboard, carpet adhesives and MDF are his enemy. Instead, his company provides a range of natural building materials for the construction of eco-friendly new-builds, and the refurbishment of historic buildings, including the medieval York Minster, York's ancient Roman city walls and the Cistercian Fountains Abbey in North Yorkshire.

All the materials Womersley sells for building, plastering, rendering, insulating and decorating the home allow the building to 'breathe', are free of dangerous chemicals and therefore do not pose a health hazard. The products are based on historic recipes and provide traditional finishes so, for example, Womersley has reinstated the linseed oil and waxes that were traditionally used to feed and protect internal and external timber, and to seal timber windows and doorframes.

Visit the website to order his Burnt Sand Mastic with Double-boiled Linseed Oil (£20.73/10 litres), based on an original Georgian recipe, which has a much more palatable list of ingredients than its modern petrochemical-filled competitors, as do the other natural resins, waxes and mineral-based pigments that were traditionally used to decorate historic homes. You may also fancy some lime wash (£17.50/3litres), natural emulsions in historical colours (£52.40/5litres), fungicide (£28.20/5kg) or concrete cleaner (£28.75/5kg) while you're at it.

And if you really want to get serious, Womersley also runs courses on traditional historic building practices and materials for conscientious homeowners and DIY enthusiasts.

Costs A tipper lorry is £160 plus VAT per hour, but less if you don't fill it. A skip is £130 plus VAT for two weeks.
Travel London based, and as far as the M25.
Attitude Professional and efficient.

Having a feud with the council over your builder's detritus? Ring World's End, an easier alternative to organizing the rubbish collection yourself. Indeed, it even provides celebrity skips, having supplied nice shiny ones for the *House Doctor* TV series. Just call 24 hours beforehand and World's End will do the clear-out for you and organize a private dustcart to avoid all fraught phone calls with your local authority. With a large roster of private and corporate clients, this answer to your prayers has, unsurprisingly, been incredibly successful and in business for the past 15 years.

What the clients say
'They were clearing out the office next door. Now I see them absolutely everywhere.' Helen Kirwan-Taylor, author, *Home UK*

THE DOOLEYS ARCHITECTUR
HENRIETTA COURTAULD LA
DUNCAN HEATHER AND AS
PRACTICALITY BROWN LTD B
RIO POOL CONSTRUCTION C
MICHAEL LITTLEWOOD LAA
LUCIANO GIUBBILEI GARDEN
DEL BUONO GAZERWITZ CE
JOE SWIFT HENRY VEREKER
HELEN TINDALE ALICE COPT
JO BOGGON KARENA BATST
LANDSCAPE LONDON HENR
LAARA COPLEY-SMITH THE

L PLANTS AVANT GARDENER
OSCAPE LONDON JOE SWIFT
OCIATES KARENA BATSTONE
TTER WAKEFIELD JOAN EDLIS
MPANY LTD JONATHAN BELL
A COPLEY-SMITH JOE SMITH
DESIGN **GARDENERS** LIMITED
R LANDSCAPE MARTIN KELLY
ARK LUTYENS ASSOCIATES
AT ARCHITECTURAL PLANTS
IE PRACTICALITY BROWN LTD
TA COURTAULD LANDSCAPE
OLEYS CEDAR LANDSCAPE

I think I did absolutely nothing right when it came to turning my attention to the outside space of our London family home. With the usual budget issues – the result of getting carried away and massively overspending (ring any bells?) – as well as lack of planning, our garden was left as an afterthought. BIG MISTAKE.

To make even the most basic improvements would have meant tons of earth being dragged over my new power-floated concrete kitchen floor – a scenario that, after a year of building works, none of us could face. Thereafter followed a series of 'I know!' ideas that were, to put it mildly, disastrous and expensive. Take the 'I've just read Pawson's book moment', which resulted in extending the kitchen floor outside in a very indoor/outdoor kind of way. The resulting high-maintenance, slime-loving, hazardous surface threatened to endanger the life of anyone daring to walk outside. My garden was a bleak black hole that no one, not even my children, wanted to enter.

The message here is, if you are redesigning/building, etc. plan your garden early. Interview for your garden designer when you are interviewing for architects. From what we gathered, it's rare that an architect will flag up the idea of bringing the garden designer in at the beginning (except for Good Architects who recommend ones they know compliment their style) and risk the possibility of the precious budget being eaten into.

Many of the designers we spoke to describe the gardens in terms of creating another room/dimension to a house, and anyway you are more likely to drag your guests off to see the new garden than the new drawing room (we hope). With that in mind, the percentage cost of having a dreamy outside space in relation to the total budget is low.

Fees
Negotiate. Unless you are a super-high-maintenance client, in which case add a minimum 20 per cent of overall budgets.

Most designers will work on an hourly rate. How they land on a price will depend on whether you simply want a verbal consultation – this will probably be charged out by the day/half day; the finished plans to go and do what you like with – this will be a higher than normal hourly rate/day rate; or the full blown design and build, which will work out to be a lower hourly/day rate.

You may want the plans and have your own man to build, in which case many designers will charge a lower hourly rate to monitor the builder.

Asking your designer to source products will also be charged at an hourly rate.

The initial spend need not be high. Many of the designers in this book will do a master plan that may be worked through over years and as budgets allow. Although Arabella Lennox Boyd charges £5,000 a day for her time, most included are within reason (Edlis charges £35, for instance – that's £10 more than some maintenance men).

The crucial bit is to have your garden planned out. (That's the third time I've mentioned planning.)

Choosing a designer
Picking your garden designer is a pretty straightforward procedure:

A – pick the best looking
B – ask to see their portfolio
C – decide whose work and personality you like best

It's probably a match made in heaven. However, there are many species of garden person, all of whom put themselves up for designing gardens. They may be brilliant, but it pays to know what boxes they tick off in terms of skills. Case in point: one well-known, high fee-charging designer planted an entire herb garden which promptly died due to bad positioning – clearly good on design but short on plant knowledge.

Here is a brief Noddy and Big Ears glossary:
Landscape Architect: Highly qualified, five-year degree course and recognized by the Institute of Landscape Architects. Look for letters after their name. Some wear suits and turn up and point; some get their hands dirty. May be planning a town centre at the same time as your terrace. Involved in large-scale public and commercial spaces. Think earth-moving and huge trees.

Garden Designer: Discipline practised on many levels, from large-scale private houses to replanting a single border. Should be a combination of horticulturist and plantsman with a creative side. May have taken a three-month or three-year course. Important to check plant knowledge; some go on to nurseries or further courses to learn more about horticulture.

Plantsman: Kind of does-what-it-says-on-the-tin – puts the design into the ground. Should have good botanical knowledge. Unlikely to have an idea of how to put the plants together in a creative way. More of a collector than a designer.

Horticulturist: Walking encyclopedia. Has vast technical knowledge of plants as well as diseases, soil and pests. Some go on to be designers.

When to start

The planting season runs from October to March. Many designers do not like to plant out of this season, so it pays not to make the mistake of waiting till you've finished hibernating to pick up the phone, hoping to charm your favourite gardener to whip up something wonderful for May. Early autumn is a good time to commission the design; build and plant during the winter months and, hey presto, something wonderful happens in spring. This route saves money by avoiding silly, rushed mistakes.

Don't kid yourself you are going to do your own maintenance – you will never find the time and your garden will die.

Find out if your designer can maintain and if not, make sure he recommends a local maintenance firm. Plan for a weekly/monthly/quarterly routine. Anything less than quarterly and you may as well let Mother Nature take over. Those with acreages will probably have a gardener; if not, rope the designer into the interviewing process and avoid being blinded by green science.

Dos and Don'ts

- Do see plenty of designers, at least three goodies and get recommendations where you can. You must be happy enough to commit to their vision and experience.

- Do try and hire someone who will get on with your architect or vice versa.

- Do collect lots of pictures – not just of gardens but of architecture, style and atmosphere you like. This is great information for the gardener but it also starts you thinking about why certain styles appeal.

- Do allow some freedom and creativity to come from your designer – a too prescriptive approach won't get the best results – remember why you hired a designer in the first place. Expect a certain element of trial and error, and be realistic – this is an organic art form.

- Do have a lengthy discussion about aftercare and maintenance. The more TLC and expert care your garden is given, the greater the garden.

- Do insist on a watering system – plants die, especially in August when you go on holiday – most people don't know how to water anyway.

- Do have a think about how patient you are. Most plants will come in a range of sizes and range of price tags to match. An instant garden will hit the pocket harder and will require more aftercare to get started.

- Do be upfront about money. As with the house, the garden's budget will steer the direction of the designer.

- Do make sure that your partner is fully aware of all that is happening both creatively and financially from the word go. Someone will eventually have to have an answer to 'Darling, why are there two JCBs in the garden?'

- Don't expect this to be like planning a drawing room – you're dealing with nature not swatches and paint.

- Don't underestimate the weather; lots of jobs are just impossible in bad weather, and forcing them ahead can be damaging to the site.

FINALLY…
- Don't buy a puppy a week before the garden is completed.

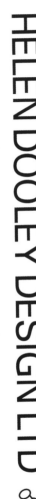

HELEN DOOLEY DESIGN LTD

Helen Dooley Design Ltd
Zion House
Salisbury Road
Shrewton
Wiltshire SP3 4EQ
T: 01980 621 638 M: 07974 219 212
helen@hdgardens.com
www.hdgardens.com

Costs £15–£80K
Travel Happy to
Size Small urban to large country.
Attitude Nature and style colide.

I picked Helen and James Dooley as the pin-ups for this chapter because, quite simply, they would be my choice if I were doing a garden. Their credentials are, of course, great, but it's their thinking and attitude to what they do that got me hooked. Which just goes to show what a personal choice this whole business is and why you need to check out a few designers to find one who will suit you.

Helen and James Dooley have very real talent with no formal training, which somehow feels right in this industry. Originally combining sculpture and plant growing at home in London led to starting a small perennials nursery in Wiltshire. When the owner of Petersham House, Francesco Boglione, bought Petersham Nurseries, he asked the Dooleys to design and oversee the project. This husband and wife team created and, for a while, ran a wonderfully eclectic destination that can see the likes of Mario Testino, Mick Jagger, Alan Yentob and Alan Rickman wandering its avenues on any one day.

The designing evolved from clients loving the planted-up areas that Helen did around the nursery. Initial projects held an element of trust, with Dooley turning up with boxes of plants and bags of ideas.

On the whole Helen designs and James manages the making of the gardens. Both are infatuated with all their projects, and you get the feeling huge amounts of energy – physical and emotional – get poured in. By hiring these two, you also get the benefit of their address book of interesting suppliers and specialist contractors from far and wide, from Wiltshire to Italy.

There is a wildness and size to Helen's planting that holds a natural rhythm. It gives a fluid feel, blurring the boundaries between garden and landscape. She is big on hedgerows for her country landscaping. 'Clients should be able to see the big picture but then be able to focus-in on unusual or rare-coloured plants.' In her London gardens, which she describes as for 'people who want to be in the country', she includes plants and elements that remind them of what nature is about. Paul Smith's garden around his Westbourne Park shop is a good example.

All the press attention and the famous clients are great, but for the Dooleys it's all about the plants and garden. They would really like to live in a wood and make jam, but an appointment with Princess Lowenstein looms and Prada are turning up at 3pm.

What the clients say
'Helen worked on the design and planting of my garden at Westbourne House, the shop I have in a house in Notting Hill Gate. The result was fantastic and continues to look great, very in keeping with the house and the area.'
Paul Smith, designer

A – B

Architectural Plants
Cooks Farm
Nuthurst
Horsham
West Sussex RH13 6LH
T: 01403 891 772
F: 01403 891 056
www.architecturalplants.com

Costs Not cheap but certainly top quality. The average spend with Christine Shaw is £5K – £10K.
Travel Happy to ship abroad and will advise what will survive where.
Size of job Single shrub to entire garden.
Attitude Pioneer.

Angus White was inspired 20 years ago by the National Trust Gardens around Haywards Heath but, unable to find and buy their exotic contents for his garden ('I went around with a pad and pen and wrote down the names of everything I liked'), the self-taught White, previously a furniture designer, set about growing and buying these hard-to-find architectural plants. 'What identifies these plants is their value for shape and texture; they are more architectural and evergreen.' In 1990 Anna Pavord wrote a piece in the *Independent* on this maverick horticulturist, helping to put him on the map as a top ten destination for garden designers and enthusiasts.

This is a two-centre nursery: Nuthurst is worth a day trip; the other, near Chichester, is good for larger plants and trees. At Nuthurst there are architectural plants of vastly varying sculptural shape and proportion – think Jurassic Park jungle or a traditional Chinese garden. You can opt to ignore everyone and just wander around with your trolley. Alternatively, someone will walk around the nursery with you offering advice or you can enlist the help of in-house designer Christine Shaw, who wrote *Architectural Plants* and offers a basic but super-friendly approach to designing. If you are looking for something more high powered, Shaw or White will recommend from a list of tried and tested garden designers up and down the country – this process of matching personalities and requirements has been very successful.

What the clients say
'I credit him with changing the nature of garden design in the South East over the past 25 years.'
James Fraser of Avant Gardener

Avant Gardener
16 Winders Road
London SW11 3HE
T/F: 020 7978 4253
M: 07831 196 416
www.avantgardener.co.uk

Costs From £6K – £60K. Maintenance/design, £25 an hour.
Travel Happy to.
Size of job Balcony to several acres.
Attitude Wild.

'My gardens are in-your-face and not for the faint-hearted,' admits James Fraser, who is currently sporting a Mohican as untamed as his wild jungle-like gardens.

This New Zealander who passed through and decided to stay – 'London is a good habitat for plants' – has raised eyebrows in the industry and made a name for himself with more adventurous (often American and Canadian) clients wanting something big and bold and not at all English. HQ is the side of a railway track in Battersea, where he lovingly grows most of his own plants and trees, with a shed that looks like a den you may have had when you were small.

Stepping into one of his larger gardens gives the feeling you've arrived at a rainforest clearing, random pieces of wood and loose planting make them seem as if they have no real structure, just a flow. Fraser wants his clients (who include the architect Seth Stein) to be spiritually lifted in their gardens every day of the year. He takes a holistic approach to a project, involving himself with the maintenance and evolution of his gardens over the years.

What the clients say
'James is an immensely creative garden designer. He creates unique environments that are utterly different from conventional garden lay-outs, particularly in his use of plants from his native New Zealand. James has a particular strength in his ability to match plants to microclimates in which they will flourish.'
Alex Cohen, client

BBUK
Jonathan Bell
1 Prince of Wales Passage
117 Hampstead Road
London NW1 3EF
T: 020 7387 9214 F: 020 7387 8709
jb@bbukstudio.com
www.bbukstudio.com

Costs Ranges from £500–£500K.
Travel Jobs have taken him all over Europe and as far as Qatar.
Size of job Window boxes to urban redevelopment.
Attitude Boy next door.

Jonathan Bell is laid-back, considered and completely un-grand, despite having worked with the great and good of modern architecture – Silvestrin, Pawson and the like – since starting his practice in 1992. His designs reflect this modernist style but that's not to say he doesn't do romantic. One of his recent commissions feels like a modern take on Pooh's 100-acre wood. Client relationships are strong and long lasting: on one large domestic job he was the only contractor not to get fired. He worked with Ushida Findlay on an award-winning pool house with a garden planted on the roof.

'I like going into great detail and see no reason why a garden should be less considered than a kitchen or bedroom,' is Bell's attitude to his trade. There doesn't seem to be much this 40-something veteran has not done or probably wouldn't do – except perhaps a traditional English Garden. Clients range from the One Hundred Rich list to Cistercian Trappist monks in the Czech Republic. You get the impression he's not particularly taken by current trends and you are unlikely to find him at the Chelsea Flower Show.

What the clients say
'Jonnie and I share a deep aesthetic affinity. It is a huge pleasure working with someone who speaks the same language, someone whose vision for landscape corresponds so closely with what I am looking to achieve with built space.'
John Pawson, architect

Karena Batstone Design
21 Somerset Street
Kingsdown
Bristol BS2 8LZ
T: 0117 944 1004
F: 0117 944 1153
info@karenabatstone.com
www.karenabatstone.com

Costs £75 an hour.
Travel Predominantly West Country, but will travel throughout the UK.
Size of job Budgets from £15K–£200K.
Attitude Innovative.

Karena Batstone is a not just any old landscape designer. Formerly a biologist working at the Natural History Museum, she continually researches new garden technology and concepts. Currently, she's into green walls: 'I've been very interested in the work they have been doing in Germany on green roofs, and I'm trying to put that on the vertical,' she explains. 'The walls are quite difficult to achieve.' Her style is architectural and site specific, which means that you can't really pick up one of her gardens and put it somewhere else. To get the design concept across to her clients (Nigella Lawson and Massive Attack's Robert Del Naja), she uses mood boards and plasticine models. 'When you are doing ground shaping and extensive tree planting, it is quite interesting to see how the light falls… A plasticine model gives you a really good idea of how the atmosphere is going to change through the day.' She believes that a garden designer should bring something unique to the project: 'If the client has thought of it themselves, then you are redundant really.' She loves clients who keep in touch, and doesn't mind re-jigging.

What the clients say
'Karena is like a fresh breeze shaking the established notions of garden layout. She has a passion for strong geometry in both hard landscape and planting. She understands the relationship between buildings and their surroundings – and, equally, architects and garden designers. It's a privilege to work with her.'
Jeremy Dain, Inscape Architects

B – C

Jo Boggon
106 Askew Road
London W12 9BL
T: 020 8749 3399
www.joboggon.co.uk
jboggon@lineone.net

del Buono Gazerwitz
1 Leinster Square
London W2 4PL
T: 020 7243 6006
F: 020 7243 6116
info@delbuono-gazerwitz.co.uk

Costs Hourly fee £50.
Travel Across the country.
Size of job Projects from £5K–£30K.
Attitude High-energy and enthusiastic.

Costs £10K–£1million. Hourly rate of £80 for del Buono and Gazerwitz, £50 for assistants.
Travel Worldwide.
Size of job Balconies to several acres.
Attitude Two men and a dog.

Think cosy, calm, romantic hideaways when it comes to Jo Boggon's garden designs. Man-made structures complement planting 'to give the area more than three dimensions', such as 'a socking great big arbour with roses climbing up…' Meticulous at sourcing materials, Jo will use only the best York stone or the best reclaimed brick. With a hands-on attitude, she is known to build walls herself. Her style is the antithesis of contemporary. She claims that: 'As for painted woodwork and walls, I think that will date. You will look at that colour for six months and then you will hate it; it will start to look really awful.' What she likes to do is to complete a garden with mature plants: 'So that within a year it can look like it has been there for ten years.' Unlike other garden designers, Jo trained as a florist before moving to Atlanta, Georgia, and working for a large garden design firm. There, she worked on Elton John's garden before returning to the UK to establish her own company. She has recently completed an enclosed cobbled garden for Julia Peyton. Other former clients are film producer Daisy Goodwin and Julian Metcalfe, founder of Prêt-à-Manger.

What the clients say
'It is always a pleasure to see Widget, Jo's dog, running around, and know that within a couple of hours Jo will have created another wonderful work of art in the garden.'
Julian Metcalfe, Prêt-à-Manger

This relatively new Italian and American partnership is attracting much attention from the fashion crowd, including Tom Ford, Isabella Blow (this fashion editor/ queen of bizarre hats got a non-statement garden billowing with beautiful grasses and an elegant water feature), as well as high-profile architects such as Jamie Fobert and David Collins.

Working with mainly urban spaces, their chic yet soft gardens work with, rather than compete with, the existing architecture. 'We like simplicity in layout and geometry, with great emphasis on the planting,' explains del Buono. He and Gazerwitz met at Arabella Lennox Boyd, where they left to join forces in 2000. These guys are ultimate professionals with impeccable planting and horticultural skills. Don't call them when the sun starts shining and expect an instant garden: 'Careful planning stops mistakes and saves money – a stone terrace in the wrong place is an expensive mistake.'

This four-strong team, plus Gina the terrier who thinks she's a cuddly toy, have recently spun their talent for the Greenhouse restaurant in Mayfair, an RIBA award house owned by journalist Geraldine Bedell, and a brutalist concrete house in Highbury by architect Azman Owens – the latter so hot that Gazerwitz says their garden will pale by comparison; a humble touch from a couple of rising stars.

What the clients say
'Paul and Tommaso are exceptionally talented designers, approaching each commission with a fresh eye combined with an insightful appreciation of their clients' requirements and lifestyle, as well as an instinctive understanding of the "spirit of the place". As an office we've loved working with them on projects over many years and find their knowledge and experience of plants and horticulture invaluable, especially when combined with their unusually deep understanding of architecture and the relationship between built form and landscape.' Tom Croft, architect

Cedar Landscapes
Springwood Copse
Brighton Road
Godalming
Surrey GU7 1NS
T: 01483 423 941
F: 01483 423 730
www.cedarlandscapes.co.uk

Costs **Gardens from £5K–£60K.**
Travel **Happy to.**
Size of job **Borders to large country gardens.**
Attitude **Dutch.**

This Dutch landscape gardener understands how to work with the usual budget issues, i.e., the dog-eaten ends of the build budget.

Jeroen van Raalte plans many gardens in stages, designing the big picture and prioritizing projects over time. 'I hope to have reasonable results with what money is left and then go back in a couple of years and set about doing what was discussed in the first place.' Most of his work is on post-build sites and the ruined landscapes that usually ensue: 'I do what I am asked
to do but try to utilize what people have rather than flatten and start again.'

Leaning towards modern gardens with straight lines and rows, Raalte creates definition with large planted groups, aiming for tranquillity as the end result. Refreshingly, he does not take up the current trend to diss decking, and thinks his love of water 'might have something to do with coming from Holland'. Has a liking for wild flower meadows where he can mix formal and informal; dislikes colour schemes on garden walls, which he feels don't work with the light in the UK.

Cedar Landscapes has a full-time crew of nine, offering both design and maintenance with a strong reputation for great contractors – electricians, plumbers, irrigation, etc.

What the clients say
'I use only him. Brilliant, has lots of resources. His crew enables him to spruce up a garden in two days, if needs be.'
Simon Brown, architect

Laara Copley-Smith
101 Framfield Road
London W7 1NQ
T/F: 020 8933 1344
M: 07947 070 454
gardenlandscapedesign@yahoo.co.uk

Costs **£30K–£300K.**
Travel **International.**
Size of job **Small town to big country gardens.**
Attitude **Gentle person with a deep sense of integrity and respect for the client.**

In person, she looks like a yoga teacher. In action, she would make those he-men on TV weep. Laara spent ten years in the creative arts and TV before turning to horticulture and garden design. She did a short design course with Robin Williams and, finding his passion for his subject infectious, caught the gardening bug herself. She talks about 'gardens with a certain sense of energy'. She means this both in the holistic sense, where she believes you can feel the energy in the ground, as well as in a design sense, where one component of a garden flows effortlessly into another – a patio area into a more structured lawn area with paths and perennial bedding. She keeps things simple and loves to use box hedging to provide a solid frame, with panic grass to provide a lighter element. Even Laara admits that her designs look almost too simple, but she is 'incredibly analytical about angles'. Sculptures and water features help to juxtapose these angles, to bring a softness to the garden.

What the clients say
'She is amazing. Very creative, very intuitive about what a client really wants – even if the client hardly knows. Knowledgeable about plants, a fine aesthetic sense, determined to get every detail right – from the texture of the stones to the directions the leaves should grow when the plants are put in. She gets out in the mud herself when the time comes, and she handles workmen really well. She can do big projects with running water, or little ones that require delicate balance. She is a delightful, unusual woman.' Kate Bucknell, novelist

C – G

Alice Coptcoat
Flat U
95 Eaton Square
London SW1W 9AQ
M: 07802 320 888
alice@coptcoat.co.uk

Henrietta Courtauld
Milk Studios
13b Hewer Street
London W10 6DU
T: 07711 017 427
gardens@henriettacourtauld.com

Costs **£5K – £300K**
Travel **Within an hour of Blewbury, but worth a try.**
Size of job **Anything from two to ten acres.**
Attitude **Pro.**

We couldn't have had more people recommending Coptcoat, a trained gardener with a maths degree from Oxford. Initially starting in London in 1993, she has since based herself in Blewbury, Oxfordshire, where she built her own show-piece ten-acre garden – a must-see for anyone thinking of using her. Her look is contemporary Mediterranean with soft planting but holding strong outlines and good sense of colour.

A working mother, Coptcoat will only really choose projects within an hour radius of Blewbury and is picky about who she takes on. If you do manage to get the nod, her devotion to your outside space is endless, starting with exact scale sketches of a master plan and ideas that can be done in stages. This is a design and build team, with Coptcoat overseeing up to 12 contractors, as well as offering consultancy days for clients and/or their gardeners.

For those looking for inspiration, Coptcoat's garden is open twice a year for the National Garden Scheme (see under The Manor House, Blewbury).

What the clients say
'Having put many obsessive years into creating our own garden, we were dubious about the value of importing a designer who did not know the place as intimately as we did. Alice removed that doubt; her profound talent, sense of structure, plantsmanship, brought fresh life to the scheme. Her own garden in Oxfordshire is clear testament to her strikingly original designer's mind.'
Piers Gibson, Sussex

Costs **£40 an hour. Projects generally starting around £20K to big bucks.**
Travel **Mostly central London.**
Size of job **Simple roof terrace to complex garden over swimming pool.**
Attitude **Versatility.**

One day Henrietta Courtauld was dreaming about gardens and doodling pretty benches whilst languishing as a barrister in Paris, the next she was potting plants at Angus White's Architectural Plants nursery. With the urge to do something creative, and after reading an article about his other-worldly place, Courtauld approached him for a job. Not shy of knocking on doors, Tom Stuart Smith was her next port of call, just before her Inchbald course. This was followed by time with one of gardening's great innovators, Christopher Bradley-Hole: 'I was blown away by his garden at Chelsea and approached him for a two-week internship.' Clearly the respect was mutual as she ended up staying two years.

Inspired by the modernist structure and principles through her time with Bradley-Hole, Courtauld goes for clean, simple, geometric, asymmetrical lines. This love of strict structure is softened by overlaying with very feminine planting: meadow grasses, climbing roses and wisteria, leaving a sense of wildness. Working mainly in London, lots of thought goes into when we actually spend time in our gardens, with the emphasis that urban gardens 'should work all year round with wonderful surprises'. With many clients away at weekends or working, 'there should be a sense of glamour for drinks or after dinner'.

Courtauld works closely with interior designers such as Veere Grenney and Melissa Wyndham. Rather like her Inchbald classmate Luciano Guibillei, she has limited herself to a handful of jobs a year in order to spend more time on each one.

What the clients say
'We were the first to employ her and thought she was so wonderful she has done six gardens for us.'
Veere Grenney, interior designer

Joan Edlis
26D Redcliffe Square
London SW10 9JY
M: 07813 125 725
F: 020 7373 5944
jedlis@earthlink.net
www.joanedlislandscape.co.uk

Costs **Good value – charges £35 an hour.**
Travel **Very happy to.**
Size of job **Budgets of £6K upwards.**
Attitude **Military organization.**

Joan Edlis left her native Chicago in 2001 with a Fine Arts degree in Industrial Design from the University of Illinois. She then proceeded to study at the Chelsea Physic Garden, so let's just say she knows her stuff.

Her gardens have a strong sense of proportion and colour (she is also an accomplished photographer and artist) combined with abundant planting and archictcural lines.

Her motto is: 'It's *all* in the detail' explaining that 'it makes the difference between going to B&Q and getting a good builder'. She is hot on time line planning with everything calculated and recalculated 'to make sure there are no costly mistakes when the contractors move in'. The industrial designer in Edlis comes into play with all the functional problems such as drainage as well as the ability to design everything from gates to tables.

What the clients say
'She's contemporary yet sensitive, with a strong artistic sensibility. This combined with her efficiency and superb organization makes her an absolute joy to work with!'
Scott Maddux, interior designer

Luciano Giubbilei Garden Design
Studio C10
The Old Imperial Laundry
71 Warriner Gardens
London SW11 4XW
T: 020 7622 2616 F: 020 7498 6767
garden@lucianogiubbilei.com
www.lucianogiubbilei.com

Costs **£60K upwards.**
Travel **All over.**
Size **Doesn't matter.**
Attitude **Tom Ford of garden design.**

Luciano Giubbilei runs around on a Vespa (we suspect the black V-neck and jacket are Gucci). Though still young, he has made a conscious decision to be picky about what projects he takes on. After graduating from Inchbald in 1995 and armed with the right introductions, he started designing gardens for the 'it' interior designers of the moment, Kelly Hoppen, Michael Reeves and Jonathan Reed. Don't expect acres of wild meadows: this is immaculate and highly symmetrical minimalism.

The grass, hedging and trees that tend to make up his gardens have led to accusations that he is anti colour and flowers, something he quietly refutes and may have the opportunity to address with two of his current projects, a vineyard in Italy and a country garden outside Amsterdam.

On Giubbilei's yet-to-do list are a garden in the English countryside – not to be confused with an English country garden, and collaborations on a public spaces with artists – the likes of Stephen Cox and Keiichi Tahara.

What the clients say
'I think he is brilliant! His designs are simple and elegant, and he is passionate about what he does. I always recommend him to my clients.' Avery Agnelli, architect

H–L

Duncan Heather and Associates
Greystone
Colmore Lane
Kingwood Common
Oxfordshire RG9 5NA.
T: 0800 458 2990/020 7690 0774
www.garden-design.org
www.garden-design-courses.co.uk

Costs **£10K–£100K-plus. Half-hourly rate of £30.**
Travel **Yes.**
Size of job **Small town plot to large country one.**
Attitude **Visionary.**

Most garden designers will tell you that each garden reflects the building for which it is meant; a rather bland, catch-all explanation and one that personally I think stretches the imagination somewhat. Duncan Heather on the other hand chooses not to skirt around how he does it, explaining how his diverse portfolio of gardens work to a formula each and every time. Heavily influenced by John Brooks, his mentor, teacher and subsequent employer, the upshot of this formula is that his gardens don't carry a huge exclamation mark, rather blending from house to countryside – taking more geometric and architectural lines the closer to the building and softening out as the land pulls away and blurring into the landscape, acreage providing. Heather is big on maintenance and after-care.

In 1992, at the age of 28, Heather decided to address a growing gap between what was being taught at the time to would-be garden designers and what was needed to be a professional. The answer was to set up what is now one of the country's leading garden design schools, the Oxford College of Garden Design.

Dividing his time between running the college (accredited by Brooks College) and his own practice, Heather likes to keep a pretty low profile for the benefit of his clients (rumoured to include Elton and Tom Jones's son) – consequently, his designs are rarely given for publication. However, good news travels fast and demand from urban dwellers is growing; enter Emily Black, ex-student of Heather's, who has set up a London office. Black, a relaxed, super-friendly Scot, who had a previous incarnation as a theatrical set and costume designer, works to create patches of peace and tranquillity.

What the clients say
'We got exactly what we wanted, low maintenance and the wow factor. Duncan was always on hand to come up with new ideas and change plants whenever we got bored with them.'
Susanna Stanton, client

Martin Kelley
Fairwater Ltd
Lodge Farm, Malthouse Lane
Ashington
West Sussex RH20 3BU
T: 01903 892 228
F: 01903 892 522
www.fairwater.co.uk

Costs **£1K–£750K.**
Travel **Yes, in an advisory capacity.**
Size of job **Gargoyle to four-acre lakes.**
Attitude **Knows a thing or two about water.**

Anything to do with water in the landscape environment is Martin Kelley's bag. He has been called upon to conjure up everything from lakes, streams, fountains and natural swimming pools to a simple gurgling gargoyle. From the age of 16, he worked with Anthony Archer-Wills, the great innovator of water gardens, then he set up Fairwater in 1993. Jobs mainly come through architects, landscape architects and garden designers (many in this book have worked with Kelley and think he is brilliant, using what he, self-deprecatingly, calls his 'fairly mundane, but practical skills' to make their ideas and, more importantly, the resulting water feature work. Or work comes direct: 'Clients sometimes approach us with an idea scratched on the back of a fag packet and we make it happen.' Some of his work is renovating existing water landscaping – natural streams, silted lakes, dams and weirs, as well as planting to re-establishing the eco-system.

Kelley's client list is vast and as far reaching as 10 Downing Street. Working around our prime minister's child-friendly needs, Kelley completed a water feature, designed by Julie Toll, as part of the Royal Parks brief to encourage wildlife.

Kelley counts his dad amongst his employees, an enthusiastic gardener who a few years ago stopped him throwing away the vast amount of plants discarded as rubbish during projects. The result is a water nursery with more than 20,000 varieties of plants and while not open to the public, you can call to make an appointment.

What the clients say
'He inspires me with confidence; he has a good feel for the landscape and for interpreting designs.'
Julia Brett, garden designer

Landscape London
3 Edgerton Terrace
London SW3 2BX
T: 020 7581 4000
F: 020 7838 1030
info@fairwater.co.uk
www.landscape-london.com

Costs **£30 – £35 an hour.**
Travel **Loves working abroad – current projects in Morocco, Jamaica, California and the Netherlands.**
Size of job **£800 – £800K.**
Attitude **Positive and enthusiastic**

Johnny van Hage is on the move between projects – trying hard to sit still in his shiny new office/showroom, the walls of which are covered in water-colour sketches worthy of their elegant frames and wall space. 'Sketches are important, plans can be confusing… I deliver exactly what I draw,' is van Hage's explanation for the attention to detail and colour. The biggie job on as we speak is a 50-acre project for Elton John's neighbour Sheik Wallid – 'a weird and wonderful mesmerizing concoction of funky ideas mixed with the grand the elegant' (a dream combination for van Hage). It sounds fun – especially as Elton has a tendency to pop round to chuck in the odd idea.

From a Dutch family with at least three generations of history in horticulture – from growing bulbs to coming up with the idea for the first garden centre in 1941 – van Hage junior certainly didn't disappoint. After training with John Brooks, followed by working for the family biz, he went on to become the youngest person ever to win a Gold at Chelsea at 25.

Now, 14 years on, van Hage's design-and-build practice has 14 full-time staff and about 40 contractors whose time they pretty much monopolize. Don't be fooled by the owner's charming air of gentle chaos, it's a slick business delivering fine-detailed planning. With this high-powered background it comes as a surprise to learn that the only thing he would bear a grudge working with is a whirly washing line. However, a tip to potential commercial clients: ditch the suit and tie and put some thought into the project – there is no love here for corporate money thrown at a soulless proposal.

What the clients say
'We have an urban garden 20 foot by 40 foot and my wife had been dreaming of a proper garden. She did a sketch and Johnny really delivered. I thought there was no way I could afford him – actually it turned out I could. Johnny has 20–25 years experience and it shows, as well as fantastic resources with a great team. The quality of plants is amazing. I'm thrilled. Listen to him, he has a vision.' Henry Harris, owner and chef of Racine

Nicola Lesbirel
68a Hammersmith Grove
London W6 7HA
T: 020 8563 8483
Nicola@lesbirel.com
www.lesbirel.com

Costs **£30 – £60 an hour.**
Travel **Very happy to.**
Size of job **£7K upwards.**
Attitude **Heart and soul with a roll-up.**

After only five years as a garden designer, Nicola Lesbirel scooped a Gold at the 2004 Chelsea Flower Show for her Conran Kitchen Garden. No one was more shocked than Lesbirel herself. Terence Conran was probably less surprised – he's hardly one to pick a dud. They had been working together on and off since the mid-80s. After studying at the Inchbald, Lesbirel worked with Dan Pearson, recently described as Europe's leading plantsman and designer.

Very keen that a garden should have 'good bones', she does a lot of landscape and soil preparation before setting to work on her abundant planting, combining structure and texture interspersed with spaces to 'be and do, lie about and have dinner'. Her designs can't be described as nostalgic or old-fashioned but more 'softly modern'. Hard materials have to have a 'mellow touchability' to them. Lesbirel has only recently set up her own practice and has already completed work in Tokyo, Italy and the UK. Projects under Pearson included gardens for über-architect Michael Hopkins and Jude Law.

What the clients say
'Nicola Lesbirel is a confident designer who is clear in her intent and execution. She has a great deal of style, and her gardens are calm and sophisticated spaces that are a pleasure to spend time in.' Dan Pearson, garden designer and plantsman

235

Michael Littlewood Consultancies
The Trading Post
Lopen Head
South Petherton
Somerset
TA13 5JH
T: 01460 240 168
www.ecodesignscape.co.uk

Costs £350–£400 per sq metre. Maintenance is lower than that of a chemical pool.
Travel Yes.
Size of job Minimum size is 40–50 sq metres up to 'lakes'.
Attitude Green.

Pools were once bright blue, then they went all angular and black granite. Now they look at one with the landscape, so natural, in fact, that most people would hesitate before so much as inserting a toe.

Littlewood comes with a big digger, digs a big hole and puts in a rubber liner – so far like everyone else's pool, except that his pools do not act or look like everyone else's. Littlewood, an eco landscape architect and environmental planner, introduced natural pools (no scary chemicals and naturally self-cleaning) to this country in 2001, lamenting the fact that our children are absorbing chlorine in public pools and lidos. No surprise that a natural swimming pool is currently being installed on the Duchy estate in Cornwall.

Made from stone, brick, blocks or recycled plastic, the design is totally down to you. Littlewood has done all shapes and sizes, formal and informal, to suit the surrounding buildings or landscape. A wall is built around the liner to hold the plants and their natural habitants that act as the natural cleaning system for the water. You can leave it at that and jump in or, if you feel a bit icky at the thought of being so close to nature, you can add decking, ladders, solar panels, pumps, skimmers and vacuums.

The important thing is you are swimming in totally natural water. The 'technology' is a circle of nature that works all year round, leaving pools completed 15 years ago as crystal-clear as the day they were installed.

What the clients say
'We were looking for ways to use grey water to sustain our farm pond. Together, we developed our original concept into a project to build a natural bathing pool. We all learned on the job but we kept to our budget, the system has worked and our pool has been a constant source of interest and enjoyment over three seasons. Michael has sustained his enthusiasm for the project. He's in regular touch and always ready to give useful advice.'
Mr and Mrs Ricard

Mark Lutyens Associates
Unit 10
81 Southern Row
London W10 5AL
T: 020 8969 4206 F: 020 8969 4184
M: 07768 991 925
mlutyens@dircon.co.uk
www.mark-lutyens.co.uk

Costs Hourly rate, £50 plus V.A.T.
Travel Worldwide.
Size of job £20K–£1million.
Attitude Sensitive, uncluttered, but often with nice touches.

Mark Lutyens is like a modern-day Lancelot 'Capability' Brown. His designs need time to mature. He says: 'I try to create something that is well structured and uncluttered, but with the opportunity for the garden to grow and develop, because the materials are growing materials.' Although he's the favourite landscape architect for those with large country estates and parks, don't write him off for your window boxes. Mark charges by the hour and is as happy doing small jobs, as well as large. Other talents tucked up his sleeve are his one-off furniture and garden accessories. If you want a love seat, a fountain, pergola or a folly, Mark will design and make it for you. His greatest pleasure after designing a garden is when, as he describes it, 'magic occurs'. That is, when 'one's expectations are exceeded'.

What the clients say
'Mark has a great gift for listening to his client, and endeavours to ensure that the final design meets the client's wishes and intentions rather than overriding them… I have been highly impressed by Mark's work. The work he has done for me has been completed in time, within budget, and to my complete satisfaction.' Lord Milford, Q.C.

Practicality Brown Ltd
Iver Stud
Swan Road
Iver
Bucks SL0 9LA
T: 01753 652 022 F: 01753 653 007
abeddall@pracbrown.co.uk
www.pracbrown.co.uk

Costs Hedges start at £150 a metre. A yew hedge at two and a half metres high will set you back £350 a metre. Semi-mature trees range from £300–£19K – the latter for a lime tree that nearly made it into the *Guinness Book of Records*.
Travel Mainly in the UK but are happy to go to Europe – have worked in France.
Size of job Bit of hedge or avenue of trees.
Attitude We understand the concept of time famine.

Who can be bothered to wait 10–30 years for hedges or trees to grow? We want our gardens and we want them now. Horticulturist Alistair Beddall, founder of Practicality Brown, recognized our demanding and impatient ways while running a design-and-build garden company. He sources from around the world and now sells instant hedges, which range from 30-year-old yews to hornbeam and variegated holly. Interest is high and this year was Beddall's first at the Chelsea Flower Show.

Once you've bought ten years of growth, maintenance is pretty key. Beddall offers the whole service, from installation, handover and advice on how not to destroy years of careful nurturing, as well maintenance contracts for larger installations. Other services include moving or clearing trees as well as storing them. For serious design issues they will refer you to a professional.

What the clients say
'Practicality Brown are efficient, keep you well informed and supply good-quality trees. Their instant hedging is second to none. They also clean up after the job and are very good at the maintenance side.'
Jonathan Simpson, grounds manager, Hackwood Park

Rio Pool Construction Company Ltd
Sunday School Rooms, The Chipping,
Kingswood, Wotton Under Edge
Gloucestershire GL12 8RT
T: 01453 521 101
F: 01453 521 044
swim@riopools.co.uk
www.riopools.co.uk

Costs Pools range from £30K–£150K for outdoor; anything up to £350K for an indoor pool and building.
Travel Mainly UK.
Size of job From cedar-lined hot tub to indoor oasis. Hot tub, from £4.5K–£13K. DIY possible, where Rio Pools offers the equipment and advice with the client doing most of the work.
Attitude Service, Service, Service.

Family-run Rio Pools have more than 2,500 pools under their belt. No slouches with technology, they offer every kind of water treatment: that hit of chlorine has long gone – we're talking ozone, UV and active oxygen. Owner Rob Bateman also specializes in narrow-access pools – pools in places you may not have thought possible, such as a basement, garage, etc. One job involved hand-digging a pool and spa at the bottom of a 25-stair basement; another, a baptism pool in a church.

They offer fibre optics, retractable roofs and walls, underground pools with trapeze swings (for the children, of course) and finishes sympathetic to the surroundings – mostly in stone and slate.

The digging of a pool is a big construction job so while you are about it why not throw in a tennis court? Sally Bateman, daughter of the founding father, explains this can make a lot of sense, as all the heavy equipment is there on site. Over the past 15 years they have built simple basic to flood-lit to drop side courts. Clients range from politicians to media types.

What the clients say
'We were so impressed by the job Rio Pools did building our pool that we asked them to build our tennis court as well. When a friend asked if we could recommend someone to put up a conservatory my wife, Anne Robinson, said: "I'd get Rio Pools to do it." Our friend said: "Do they do conservatories as well?" "No," said my wife, "but I reckon they could do a better job than most." Without doubt, Rio Pools are the strongest link.'
John Penrose, Anne Robinson's husband

Joe Swift
The Plant Room and Modular Garden
T: 020 7619 0100
T: 020 7700 6766
F: 020 7700 1083
info@plantroom.co.uk or joe@modulargarden.com
www.plantroom.co.uk

Helen Tindale
32a Chalcot Square
London NW1 8YA
T: 020 7281 4414
M: 07779 026 052

Costs **Hourly design fee £80.**
Travel **London and surrounding counties.**
Size of job **The Plant Room £25K–£300K;**
Modular Garden £6K–£25K.
Attitude **Throw a prawn on the barbie/stop fussing so much.**

Sharp, geometric lines; bright-coloured walls; strong on texture and architectural forms – Joe Swift is at the forefront of functional, contemporary, garden design – anaemic designs make him wince. Inspired during his travels to Australia and Indonesia, where the inhabitants view their garden as another room to their house, Joe knew he could do the same and change the attitude of the urban Brit. 'I want to do for gardens what Conran did for interiors,' he says. To realize his vision, he has divided his company into couture and prêt à porter: The Plant Room focuses on providing a bespoke garden design service; Modular Garden condenses the ideas of the bespoke garden into a pre-made package, for 'high-quality gardens accessible at a reasonable price'. Nothing gets Joe more depressed than to return to a high-maintenance garden to find it neglected. 'If you know you are not going to look after your garden, tell me.' Honesty in his clients is appreciated, only then can he conceive a garden that will suit the client's time commitments. His passion is infectious, though. He does want to get people enthused and involved in their garden. What he doesn't do is work with architects, nor does he hire in contractors: 'I don't trust them.'

What the clients say
'To say we are totally and utterly overwhelmed by the finished results would be an understatement.' Mark Hyman, client

Costs **£10K upwards.**
Travel **Mainly London.**
Size of job **Small London gardens to large country ones.**
Attitude **Quiet pioneer.**

'Nigella got lots of variations on concrete,' says Helen Tindale, referring to the late 1990s and the reputation for wildly experimental gardens. Both she and her partner Karena Batstone took much responsibility for changing the landscaping of urban gardens and the use of new materials.

Tindale is now working in London after a sabbatical tour of Mexico, returning to pick her own projects carefully – still bold and architectural but with a much softer feel. Expect to find lots of grasses and perennials, giving a kind of beautiful bad-hair-day effect.

Much inspiration is taken from her first job with American landscape architects Wolfgang Oehme and James van Sweden (known for revolutionizing meadow planting), and recently put to great effect when asked to define a garden in the open plains of Wyoming. Current projects include a school, a church and private gardens in Holland Park and Primrose Hill.

What the clients say
'I know my clients will like her work and she is so easy to deal with, which, quite frankly, can be half the battle.'
Guy Stansfeld, architect

Julie Toll Limited
Business & Technology Centre
Bessemer Drive,
Stevenage
Hertfordshire SG1 2DX
T: 01438 310 095 F: 01438 310 096
info@julietoll.co.uk
www.julietoll.co.uk

Costs Hourly rate £60.
Travel UK and abroad.
Size of job £8K–£300K.
Attitude Eco-friendly naturalist.

Julie is well known for both her wildflower meadows and gardens. She introduced the wildflower concept at the Chelsea Flower Show and, not surprisingly, won a gold medal. 'I realized then that people did like them,' she says. What may look untouched by human hand has been scrupulously designed: 'I create order through plants and hard landscaping,' says Julie. You will find no unforgiving, minimalist lines here, though she will use man-made structures to provide interest, such as a softly spiralling slate wall or an oak-plank walk-way. Her love for gardens was fostered by her father; later she trained as a horticulturist and now you can find her designing gardens as far away as the Caribbean. She has notched up seven Gold, one Silver-Gilt and two Silver Medals at Chelsea since 1990, as well as the coveted Fiskar's Sword of Excellence, the award for the very best garden at Chelsea. It's enough to make her competitors green with envy. With such a wealth of talent, it is no wonder she was selected to design a water garden at 10 Downing Street for Tony Blair. The only downside is that she's busy.

What the clients say
'We had a boring 40x40 lawn and garden, and Julie created something quite magical. She has a wonderful 3D imagination and understanding of space, combined with a real vision of how to change appearance and atmosphere. Friends' jaws drop when they see it.' Janet Evans, client

Henry Vereker
Capital Garden Products Ltd
Gibbs Reed Barn
Pashley Road
Ticehurst
East Sussex TN5 7HE
T: 01580 201 092 F: 01580 201 093
www.capital-garden.com

Costs Standard £100–£1K. Bespoke £1K–£15K, depending on detail involved (the client keeps the mould).
Travel Will export worldwide.
Size of job Big pot, small pot.
Attitude Can do.

We included Henry Vereker in this section because even the best gardener can be let down by his choice of pots. In fact, that's what inspired the idea for the business in the first place (and takers include anyone from Sheik Al Maktoum to Claridges and the Lanesborough in London).

Henry Vereker's company Capital Garden Products can supply any pot, planter or plant container of any size and finish. He has more than 250 designs on the books, and also offers a bespoke service. Predominantly, most of his pots are fibreglass as they are lightweight and 'last for ever'. In fact, the antique reproductions are so incredibly authentic says Henry that, 'You will find quite a few of our planters in National Trust Gardens.' However, if it is lead that your heart desires, then his firm also does traditional sand-cast lead planters. Henry also produces a modern range, not just antique reproductions, saying: 'There is something for everyone.' Sheik Al Maktoum ordered two-metre high, gold-leaf pots.

They don't do fountains (except those listed in their catalogue), but will supply the bowl if someone else does the hydrodynamics.

Butter Wakefield
2 Ashchurch Park Villas
London W12 9SP
T: 020 8743 2931
F: 020 8932 2462
M: 07973 516 149
butter@wakefield.biz

Costs £7K – £80K. Hourly rate: £45.
Travel Predominantly London and surrounding counties.
Size of job Tiny urban to large industrial estate.
Attitude Big on structure with a lot of floral chaos.

Butter Wakefield (an American with a Hollywood smile) designs gardens that have as much impact in the winter months as they do in the summer. Structure, scented plants and lighting achieve this goal. She says: 'I'm very keen on some form of structure in the garden, whether it is beech columns or yew pyramids, so that in the winter when it is flat and the perennials have died back, you've got some sort of big evergreen structure that your eye can land on when it is bleak.' As to scented plants, she tries to 'incorporate as much as humanly possible… if you have scent, particularly in the winter months, you will get a whiff of it coming up the path and you think "oh, gosh, fantastic". It is really lifting.' And nothing beats sitting outside in summer, with a gin and tonic in one hand, while rubbing the perfumed leaves of a rosemary or lavender bush in the other.

Lighting is Butter's final medium to create a breathtaking garden: 'It looks so pretty if the garden is well lit, winter or summer; it gives it a kind of magic. If a big tree is floodlit, then you see into the canopy and that's gorgeous.' She is also big on maintenance, and has a strong team of professional gardeners to solve problems. 'I say to my clients, if there is a problem, call me, don't leave it,' though she also warns that 'the most effective maintenance programme comes from the owner' – so don't let your plants wilt, turn on the water. Big names under her gardening belt are Johnny Boden, owner of the fashion mail-order catalogue, as well as Mary Moore, daughter of sculptor Henry Moore.

What the clients say
'I couldn't be happier to recommend Butter… she was hugely accommodating of my long list of wants… very good at the after birth bit.' Johnny Boden, Chairman and Founder of Boden

LINDA AGRAN CLOTHES STO
CUSHION THE IMPACT ART
POPPY BUCHER CONCIERGE
LONDON MOTORING CLUB
THE DOG HOUSE IONA GRA
ANIMAL AUNTS BLADES CO
CONCIERGE LONDON HIRE
JEANETTA ROWAN HAMILTO
PICTURE HANGING CHANGIN
COLETTE KASE LINDA AGRA
ART SEARCH LIMITED ANIMA
BURFORD VALET SERVICE H
THE PURE PACKAGE POPPY

AGE BURFORD VALET SERVICE
EARCH **SERVICE PLUS** BINES
ONDON THE PURE PACKAGE
LIFORNIA CLOSETS BUY:TIME
CATERING STELLA CHRISTIE
NUCOPIA FOODS KASIMIRA
TELLIGENCE SCREWDRIVER
CARPET RIGHT SUZI MORRIS
PLACES KATIE SHAPLEY LTD
CLOTHES STORAGE BLADES
AUNTS CUSHION THE IMPACT
LIMA BINES POPPY BUCHER
UCHER CONCIERGE LONDON

I have written quite a bit in my time about 'hurry sickness' and 'time famine'. We're all 'cash rich, time poor'. Being in a hurry has become a kind of recreational sport in Britain. It's a cocaine substitute: what James Gleick, author of *Faster: The Acceleration of Just About Everything* calls manic depression without the depression. 'Those of us in the faster faster cities and faster societies and faster mass culture of the technocratic dawn of the third millennium are manic,' he writes. 'The symptoms are all too familiar: volubility and fast speech, restlessness and a decreased need for sleep with a heightened motor activity.' Laundries that return shirts the same day, plumbers who arrive on scooters in two hours (and charge £80) are responding to this phenomenon. All these personal services company (Hire Intelligence, buy:time) have sprung up because PAs and secretaries are no longer allowed to do chores or personal things in large organizations (and after the whole Goldman Sachs affair, I'm not sure you'd want them to).

Homemaking voyeurs

Being busy is almost a competitive sport. People are even known to suffer from 'stress envy'. My point is that, whether we like it or not, we are now cramming more things into a day than anyone ever thought would be possible. If you can't be a real diva because you run Slaughter and May, you can be what trend guru Faith Popcorn calls a 'home-making voyeur'. These are the ladies who buy Nigella's cookbooks but use the microwave. They own as many designer ironing-board covers as they do Manolos, but still send all the laundry out.

Dog consultants and people to put photos into photo albums for you

Busy has created a thriving new service economy. We spend £4 billion on domestic services alone in the UK. That's a lot of cleaners and dog walkers. But we don't do it because we're lazy; we do it because we're smart. 'The history of economic progress is to command for a fee what was formerly done for free or by oneself,' says Jim Gilmore of the Cleveland-based consultancy, Strategic Horizons LLP. 'Fifty years ago the idea that you would take your car to a garage and someone would change your oil for you or that you took your children to a hair salon rather than stick a bowl over their head and cut around it was unheard of,' he says. The economist David Ricardo's theory of comparative costs was 'outsourcing' before we called it that, the gist of which is: 'Wealth is maximized if you specialize and let someone else do the rest.' CEOs do not type their own letters. They could sit there hacking away with two fingers all day, but then that wouldn't leave much time to focus on your stock portfolio, would it? 'When outsourcing is done better, life is better,' says Gilmore. 'Everyone is gainfully employed.'

Other miscellaneous people like cooks and bill payers

So you moved in and the Boffi kitchen hasn't been connected, or the heating doesn't work or you're so exhausted that you haven't opened a single box, so how could you cook? We've provided a few people who will do it for you.

We thought that you might want to go through your wardrobe and get rid of things or have an image change to match your new house. If you have no time to pay the bills that are mounting, here are some more people who will do it for you. And now that you have a house, you need a dog.

Then you can either wait 16 years (like me) and put the photographs into an album yourself or you can hire someone like Jeanetta Rowan Hamilton. DIY put-togetherers Screwdriver (our pin-up company because it was just such a good idea) spare us all so much grief. If only they would go to Ikea for us as well.

There are no dos and don'ts here. You don't need them. This section is about people who specialize in good service. No concierge service would last ten minutes if they were to say: 'Can't get around to your request today, sorry luv.' They have to do the job better than you do, remember?

SCREWDRIVER

Screwdriver
T: **0800 454 828**
screwdriverltd@hotmail.com
www.screwdriver-homework.com

Costs £42 for the first hour and then £9 for every 15 minutes.
Travel All of the UK.
Attitude Jolly.

A recent survey commissioned by Standard Life Bank found that the British population has given up on DIY. We no longer have the time or the ability. Besides, we (men) often hurt ourselves in the process.

Screwdrivers founded by Jack Bock in 1995 figured this out a long time ago. Not only will they come and put together all those self-assembly bookshelves you bought at Ikea on impulse (which turned out to be more complicated than landing on the moon) but the 140 operatives they send all over the country to do it are mostly retired. 'We supplement their sadly reduced pensions with screwmoney' says the formidable Bock.

Screwdrivers is our Service Plus pin-up for having such a great idea. All you have to do is ring and one of their operatives will arrive on your doorstep within three days and do what they do for Peter Jones, Marks & Spencer and the Habitat Group – put your flat-pack back together for you. They will also do other home-repair jobs such as putting up/fixing roller blinds, curtain poles, mirrors, pictures, shelving and loo roll holders. But, bear in mind that they will not do any plumbing, carpentry, decorating or electrical jobs – however much you plead (because they're not qualified to do so).

Turnover is now £300K and growing. Clients include Nigel Havers and virtually any store in the country that sells self-assembly products.

What the clients say
'Screwdriver's service is excellent. There are people who can do this kind of thing for less but they're not as qualified. Not all self-assembly kits are standard: it can be quite tricky. You are assured with Screwdriver that they will do it properly.'
Karais Kabraji, client

A – B

Animal Aunts
Smugglers Cottage, Green Lane
Rogate
Petersfield
Hampshire GU31 5DA
T: 01730 821529 F: 01730 821057
office@animalaunts.co.uk
www.animalaunts.co.uk

Costs **Minimum fee is £40 a day plus VAT; aunt's food and travel extra.**
Travel **UK-wide.**
Attitude **Everything can be dealt with.**

When you need to leave your beautiful home and have no idea of what to do with the dog or pet elephant, an 'aunt' will pitch up at your house and will keep everything (cleaning, gardening, livestock) ticking over until you return – irrespective of whether that is three days or three months later. No creature is too difficult, from hamsters and horses through to monkeys and mynah birds.

What the clients say
'Extremely reliable and friendly. They seem to cope with anything.' Jane Dawson, client

Art Search Limited
T: 020 8969 9844
info@artsearchlimited.co.uk
www.artsearchlimited.co.uk

Costs **His fee is tied into that of the artist.**
Travel **Based mainly within M25, but will travel across the UK.**
Attitude **Friendly.**

Art Search's owner Philip Herriott ran the Federation of British Artists for several years, which means he knows everyone in the world of art. If you have a home with empty walls, Philip is the best person to help you find something to fill them, irrespective of whether it's for a loo or a drawing room. Approachable and unpretentious, he will guide beginners through the labyrinthine tunnels of the art trade while, at the same time, he can source precisely what the cognoscenti, such as the Sultan of Brunei, Abbey National, GlaxoSmithKline and Shell, want to acquire. He has a particular gift for looking at a space and knowing exactly what will suit it best.

What the clients say
'I was delighted with the help and advice Philip gave me about the art for my apartment. The whole selection process was enjoyable. It was also particularly helpful that he could bring work to me so that we could view it in situ in the apartment, to see if it was suitable – and that he could work around my busy schedule. I use the apartment regularly for entertaining. The quality of the art work is regularly complimented. I would recommend Philip extremely highly.' Jonathan Moulds, banker

Halima Bines
T: 07769 973 598
halimabines@hotmail.com

Blades – The knife duo
James and Shaun Martin
T: 07951 969 603

Costs £60 an hour, plus expenses for travel outside London.
Travel London and home counties.
Attitude Very friendly, stylish and approachable.

It's great that you have a stonking great house with galleries of closet space, but now what? Enter Halima Bines, the friendly version of Trinny and Susannah. Halima will pitch up and go through your wardrobe to work out what the problems are (most people only buy clothes in two colours) and where the gaps are. She'll come shopping with you, whirling from high street to haut couture, depending on your budget, and advise on what suits you best. Her taste is infallible – she regularly sends clients suitcases full of clothes to be tried out and absolutely nothing is sent back.

What the clients say
'Halima is wonderful. She is unbelievably efficient and organized; she'll go through your entire wardrobe examining every article closely. She has an innate sense of what people should wear. She makes you feel great.' Sarah Allen, client

Costs £2 – £2.50 a blade.
Travel Mainly in London with periodic visits to the home counties.
Attitude Cheerful.

Sure, we all have those knife sharpeners at home, but who uses them?

Cockney duo (complete with rhyming slang) James and Shaun Martin go door to door for this reason. The Savile Row company of the blade-sharpening world, their family has been in the knife trade for generations and they used to tout for business by ringing a bell from their horse-drawn cart. Things have changed a bit since then and they travel in a van now, with a mobile grinding unit, and will sharpen anything from knives and scissors through to shears and scythes. They also specialize in mowers and provide a complete overhaul service. All larger work is collected and delivered.

What the clients say
'They are very nice, very friendly and very good. They've just done my lawn mower and done a smashing job of it.'
Ida Moia, client
'They are very efficient, friendly and turn up regularly. It's what London used to be like.' Caroline Tate, client

B–C

Poppy Bucher
42 Northumberland Street
Edinburgh EH3 6JE
T/F: 0131 556 0529

Burford Valet Service
T: 07774 476 327
stephenhaughton@aol.com

Costs From £18 per person for a buffet; from £24 per person for a dinner party.
Travel Scotland.
Attitude Friendly and capable.

One of Edinburgh's best-kept secrets, Poppy is adept at cooking for dinner parties, preparing most of the menu at home and then applying the finishing touches when she gets to the client's house. She covers a wide range of styles, from traditional British and French through to Thai and Chinese. Her clients range from housewives to merchant banks.

What the clients say
'As an MD of a private bank I am used to eating in restaurants fairly regularly, but it is always a huge joy to be entertaining clients at the bank when I know that Poppy is our chef. The presentation of her food is exciting and her cuisine is excellent.'
Ray Entwistle, managing director, Adam & Company

Costs Suits, £13.90 for a sponge and press; £19.90 for a full service; £6.50 for a shoe high shine.
Travel London and some home counties
Attitude Acts like a banker.

Stephen Haughton, the founder of this travelling valet service, has rafts of suave Italian clients (such perfectionists when it comes to clothes that they won't let a housekeeper within 50 yards of their wardrobes). 'Businessmen are passionate about their clothes,' he says. 'They will often spend between £1,000 and £1,500 on their suits. They want them to be looked after.' He will collect suits from clients' houses on a weekly or monthly basis and return them sponged, pressed and repaired. He polishes shoes as well. 'My clients went to Harrow and Eton, and then to the army. They expect their shoes to have a military shine.' He also provides a personal packing and unpacking service.

What the clients say
'Stephen is efficient and he is good at what he does. He provides an extremely convenient service.'
Alireza Ittihadieh, chief executive

buy:time
78 Tremadoc Road
Clapham
London SW4 7LP
T: 020 7498 7934
F: 020 7498 8161
info@buy-time.co.uk
www.buy-time.co.uk

Costs Hourly rate £35; 10 hours for £290; 20 hours for £500.
Travel Based in London but can organize things anywhere.
Attitude Capable.

MD Claire Brynteson came from Goldman Sachs so she knows a thing or two about busy people (her former colleagues are now her clients). Whether it's finding a new house, arranging social events or handling repairs in the home, buy:time is there to let you get on with your life. The company offers a tailored lifestyle management service for businesses and individuals: you simply hand them your 'to-do' list and they will take over, whatever the size or nature of the job. They are happy to work by the hour, by the day or to create a plan to suit you. There are no joining fees or subscriptions – YOU simply buy time when you need it.

What the clients say
'I am a single parent who also works very hard, and buy:time acts as the middle person between me and the electrician, Sky, the garage and all the others I don't have time to see. Buy:time runs my life and is very good at it.' Jeremy Davies, shipbroker

California Closets
Unit 8 Staples Corner Business Park
1000 North Circular Road
London NW2 7JP
T: 020 8208 4544
F: 020 8208 3733
www.calclosets.co.uk

Costs Fitted storage solutions from £550.
Travel Worldwide.
Attitude Pro-active.

For people too busy to bother with bespoke joiners, California Closets make closets at twice the speed of anyone else. This is the world's biggest in-home storage solutions company. Experienced designers will visit your home and provide you with a customized system to bring order to your clutter. Nothing is out of bounds, from bedrooms and utility rooms through to kitchens, garages and offices. If you want a bespoke walk-in closet or a fitted wardrobe with minimum hassle, this is the place to go. Very anal but ultimately you stop buying new clothes because now you can find everything.

What the clients say
'I came across California Closets just before they launched in the UK some four years ago. I wasn't looking for a system at the time, but when I saw the fantastic organization that it would give me, it seemed like a solution that I couldn't live without! The difference it has made has been phenomenal – I have a place for everything, and I can see and find my stuff instantly. California Closets has really simplified my life – my husband was so impressed that we had them back to install a system for him!' Baba Hobart, PR for California Closets

Carpet Right
Amberley House
New Road
Rainham
Essex RM13 8QN
T: 0845 600 4123
enquiries@carpetright.co.uk
www.carpetright.co.uk

Costs **Dependent on area required and carpet chosen, but a small two-bedroom flat can be fitted from approximately £500.**
Travel **Nationwide.**
Attitude **Convenience and cost-cutting.**

This is a great idea: bring the world's supply of carpet samples to you (rather than you schlep to Chelsea Harbour). This is a huge, no-frills organization that offers great discounts on leading brands, with the added advantage that its customer services department is second to none. A local consultant will be found in your area who will arrange an appointment to come to your home at a time that suits you (within a three-hour slot), seven days a week. After having pitched up with more than 2,000 carpet, vinyl and laminate flooring samples, he will then measure the designated area, recommend a brand within your budget and draw up a quotation using a computerized system – all free of charge. If you order then and there, the carpet and carpet fitter should be with you in the next 10–14 days. There is only one down-side – you have to do all the furniture clearing.

What the clients say
'An excellent service. Very quick and good value.'
Matthew Thornton, client

Changing Places
Susan Cable Alexander
Shepherds
Golden Square
Petworth
West Sussex GU28 OAP
T: 01798 343 258 or 07802 682 275

Costs **£25 an hour.**
Travel **All over the UK.**
Attitude **Elegant, stylish and efficient.**

Changing Places aims to remove the 'chaos, confusion and stress' from moving house. Its founder, Susan Cable-Alexander, will organize your home's contents from the attic to the basement before the removal men arrive and then help you reposition everything in your new home. Even if you are not moving, she will come and reorganize your house and free it of clutter. Having worked in a homemade-furniture shop, she has a great eye for sourcing bits and bobs should you need any. Likewise, thanks to her extensive raft of contacts, she can have objects priced and sold if you want to get rid of anything.

What the clients say
'We've used Sue recently on a job where she had to unpack about 40 boxes in a client's house. She unpacked them, put everything neatly away into cupboards or on display, brought laundry, helped with cleaning and much more! She has exceptional taste, works quickly, efficiently and is a pleasure to work with.' Lavinia Dargie, interior designer

Concierge London
Studio D3 The Depot
2 Michael Road
London SW6 2AD
T: 020 7736 2244
F: 020 7736 2255
info@conciergelondon.co.uk
www.conciergelondon.co.uk

Costs From £2K to join; thereafter hourly fees from £30.
Travel All over the world.
Attitude Can recommend the best of everything.

Lady Annabel Goldsmith, Jemima Khan and Tara Palmer-Tomkinson are all fans of Cosima Somerset's company. Unlike some concierge services who pretend to have great contacts but actually get them from the *Yellow Pages* ('tis true), this one's for real. The (let's admit it) very upmarket and posh Cosima knows everyone anyway, so she just has to open up her address book.

If the kids need picking up from school, you meant to call a plumber but haven't had time, the car needs an MOT, the TV licence hasn't been paid, you just call them. 'We do absolutely everything,' says Somerset, who particularly appeals to fat-cat American bankers. 'We can organize doctors' and dentists' appointments, recruit staff, find tradesmen, manage relocation, sort out Christmas shopping – the list is infinite.'

What the clients say
'I moved over from New York two years ago. Concierge London fixed me up with doctors and paediatricians. They do all my travel arrangements. The people they've sent me (such as yoga teachers) are better, I would say, than any I had in New York. I don't have to deal with any repairmen!'
Nathalie Samale, client

Cornucopia Foods
Unit 22H
Wincombe Business Park
Shaftesbury
Dorset SP7 9QJ
T: 08450 633 699 F: 01747 858 590
sales@cornucopiafoods.co.uk
www.cornucopiafoods.co.uk

Costs From £3 for a single *sous vide* main course; home-made Parisian desserts for 12 people from £12.
Travel UK and Europe.
Attitude Will bend over backwards to make sure you are happy.

When the Italian kitchen never arrived… Cornucopia will send you everything from fruit preserves through to *pata negra* (a rare Spanish ham made from pigs raised on acorns). This company specializes in mouth-watering ready-made frozen meals using a unique French method called *sous vide*, which results in intense flavours and very, very tender meat. Recipes span from simple stews through to lamb shanks in a wine jus, with spinach fondue and aubergine cake. It's the equivalent of having a full-on French restaurant in your deep freeze. All orders of frozen, chilled and ambient food are guaranteed next day delivery.

What the clients say
'Cornucopia Foods are superb – it's a delight dealing with them. The food is delicious and always arrives on time.'
Bas Stewart, software developer

Cushion the Impact
68 St Peter's Street
London N1 8JS
T: 020 7704 6922
info@cushiontheimpact.co.uk
www.cushiontheimpact.co.uk

Costs An adhoc single hour is £25; £120 for five hours; £22.50
an hour for ten hours or more.
Travel Mainly based in London, but with clients in Edinburgh,
New York and Cambodia.
Attitude Incredibly helpful.

One of the more reasonable personal services
companies. This small company offers a non-corporate,
personal service aimed at helping you manage the
routine but time-consuming parts of everyday life,
from buying a new vacuum cleaner to organizing
a cocktail party or finding and overseeing a last-minute
plumber. Cushion the Impact works like gift tokens –
you can buy time in bulk and then dip into your hours
as and when you like within the year.

What the clients say
'Cushion the Impact do all sorts of jobs for me, from finding
a reliable window cleaner who actually arrives, to sorting out
insurance issues. I just give them the problem, no matter how
small or big it is, and they deal with it properly, exactly how
I would have done it myself.' Allison Elliott, investment banker

The Dog House
Dinas Fram
Talog
Carmarthenshire SA33 6PD
T: 07000 364 364
F: 01994 484 474
www.thedoghouseonline.co.uk

Costs From £22 plus VAT a day; individual consultation £80
plus VAT.
Travel Weekly bus picks up and deposits canine clients in
London and along the M4.
Attitude Caring.

No time to find someone with whom to park the
pooch? Your PA says: 'You've got to be kidding?'
    The Dog House is the canine version of a health
farm: your pride and joy disappears off to the depths
of Carmarthenshire in Wales for a week or two and
comes back fit, healthy and better behaved. Set up by
Mark and Gillian Thompson in 1994, the Dog House
is the first company in the UK to take care of dogs with
a strong emphasis on health, exercise, games and
education. Courses include gun-dog training, puppy
socialization and general companionship. Once 'bitten'
by the Dog House you are invariably smitten and,
unsurprisingly, it has a very loyal client base, including
actress Felicity Kendal, MP Robin Cook, singer Seal
and footballer Frank Lampard.

What the clients say
'Mark truly is a dog whisperer – dogs absolutely adore him.
Unlike normal kennels, your dog comes back from The Dog
House healthy and really happy.' Victoria Sharp, client

Hire Intelligence
78A Leathwaite Road
London SW11 6RT
T: 020 7350 0664
F: 020 7350 2010
info@hireintelligence.co.uk
www.hireintelligence.co.uk

Costs Free initial consultation, thereafter £50 plus VAT.
Travel Predominantly London.
Attitude As much or as little as you want.

'We've had clients who haven't looked at their post for a year and who have still been paying out pet insurance for a dead cat,' says Heather Johnston of Hire Intelligence. 'It happens remarkably frequently.' Employing Hire Intelligence (which recently merged with Urban PA, but still operates under its own name) is the equivalent of having your own personal assistant to take the sting out of admin. You can have a one-off blitz to set up filing systems and archive old material, or you can have a weekly/daily fix to keep everything in order, from post opening through to having your car serviced. For those who only need flights booked or a Sainsbury's shop, Urban PA (www.urbanpa.com; 020 8487 9400) is the affordable alternative.

What the clients say
'I originally worked with Hire Intelligence's founder, Emma Chapman, and didn't think anyone could be as good, but I have to say that Heather has never looked perplexed or bemused at my inability to manage my personal affairs, in particular my paperwork. Although my husband baulked at the expense in the beginning, what he didn't realize was that she was going to save us hundreds and hundreds of pounds.'
Helen Kirwan-Taylor, author, *Home UK*

Iona Grant Catering
203 Hammersmith Grove
London W6 0NP
T: 07720 443 132
iona@macunlimited.net

Costs From £4 a head for a school picnic; buffets from £15 a head; dinner parties from £25 a head.
Travel Mainly within M25 but will travel across the country for larger events.
Attitude Nothing is too difficult.

Hey, want to pretend you're a domestic diva? Iona Grant will cook a dinner party for you and deliver it to your door, so by the time your guests arrive you can gingerly pretend to be putting on the last-minute garnish. Alternatively, she can set everything up at your home, including laying the table, organizing flowers and sourcing waiting staff so that you can stagger back from work and not have to worry about a thing. Iona caters for all occasions, from small dinner parties (she will even teach you how to cook the food yourself) and school picnics, through to large buffets and canapés for 300.

What the clients say
'She's fabulous – she can cook up a storm.' Kym Edwards, former vice president (Europe) of Ever Ready Batteries

Colette Kase
124 Bramley Close
London E17 6EG
T: 020 8527 0349
pet.sense@btinternet.com
www.petsense.net

Kasimira
29 South Terrace
London SW7 2TB
T: 020 7581 8313
F: 020 7581 5383
enquiries@kasimira.com
www.kasimira.com

Costs **Consultation (1–2 hours), £110; group puppy classes, £100 for eight sessions.**
Travel **Mainly within M25, but will go further on occasion.**
Attitude **Big sense of humour.**

Your admin is up to date, your house is finally perfect, your children are presentable – the only thing letting the side down is the dog, which has no concept of house training and invariably deserts you in the park in order to disrupt someone else's picnic. Before you throttle it, do what artist Sam Taylor-Wood, journalist Rachel Johnson and author Sebastian Faulks have all done, and give Colette Kase a call. She has the magic touch – with both dogs and their owners. A couple of sessions with her and you will have a pooch so well trained that even Barbara Woodhouse would be proud of it. If you are thinking of acquiring a puppy, talk to Collette first – she will be able to advise you as to what breed will fit into your life best and will also be able to help you find a suitable breeder.

What the clients say
'She's a great personality – very disciplined, patient and reliable. She has remarkable techniques for getting dogs to behave.' Peter Shalson, businessman

Costs **Minimum fee of £100 for a party; baby sitting £7 an hour plus £5 admin fee.**
Travel **Predominantly London.**
Attitude **Professional and fun.**

Children's entertainment is one area of life that we would all love to outsource. Whether you need a babysitter, a child minder, a tutor (up to A-level) or a clown, Kasimira will find someone for you. Children's yoga and Pilates classes are firm favourites, with mothers actually joining in because they are such fun. Kasimira has also built up a strong reputation for organizing superb children's parties, catering from small private dos through to Deutsche Bank's annual children's Christmas party.

What the clients say
'They really are terrific.' Cynthia Oakes, former banker

Linda Agran Clothes Storage
Unit 5 The Links
Popham Close
Hanworth
Middlesex TW13 6JE
T: 0845 083 0111 F: 020 8894 0522
lagran@lindaagran.co.uk
www.lindaagran.co.uk

Costs **Suits, from £22; ball gowns, from £100.**
Travel **Across the UK by post; pick-ups in London.**
Attitude **Makes good garments look great.**

Launched in 2004, Linda Agran offers a personal
valeting and storage service. Clothes can be stored for
as long as required, and when requested, the garments
are personally delivered to your door. The dry-cleaning
service is the best in the country – chief operator Tony
Luke used to dry-clean all of the Princess of Wales' ball
gowns. Clothes take seven days to be processed.

What the clients say
'Linda Agran's Clothes Storage is a fantastic concept. It enables
us to have a service at our fingertips, whether it's for storing our
couture garments or dry-cleaning them. Once stored, the clothes
are available at the drop of a hat – you just call up and they are
delivered to you, in lovely prestigious packaging and in
immaculate condition.' Lindka Cierach, couturier

London Motoring Club
PO Box 619
Keston
Kent BR2 6BR
T: 0845 601 8843
info@londonmotoringclub.com
www.londonmotoringclub.com

Costs **Subscription prices start at £100 per annum for one
or two cars; £200 per annum for six or more cars.**
Travel **Central London, but will deliver cars across the UK.**
Attitude **Capable.**

What with clamping, congestion charging and over-
zealous parking attendants, having a car in London
is enough to drive you completely round the bend
with frustration and rage. London Motoring Club,
started by Constantine Tsoflias, were quick to jump
in. This unique service neutralizes all car catastrophes
– if you get clamped, a member of the team will sort
everything out and deliver your car back to you; if you
need a new resident's parking permit, they'll pick it up
for you; if you are going away and are worried that
you might get zapped by a parking suspension in the
meantime, they'll keep an eye on your car and move
it if necessary; if you can't get online to pay your
congestion charge, they'll take care of that for you as
well. Like the author Rita Konig and actor Stephen Fry,
you'll suddenly find it's worth having a car in London
after all.

What the clients say
'An efficient service, very friendly.' Liz Brewer, author

The Organiser
133 Elmbridge Avenue
Surbiton
Surrey KT5 9HE
T: 0845 226 6046
info@theorganiseruk.com
www.theorganiseruk.com

Costs £40–60 an hour, depending on the project.
Attitude Organized, lateral thinking.
Travel Based in London with clients around the world.

Need a wife? Don't laugh: this is a booming business, particularly in LA, where celebrities are often in between 'wives'.

Being a surrogate wife is how Katie Shapley sees her role: she and her team are the ultimate fixers. They will organize anything from opening post and setting up direct debits, through to completing tax returns and overseeing building projects and renovations. They find the right school, organize birthday presents and work out travel arrangements. She will also trouble-shoot for families that have a backlog of administration to clear up. Her clients are usually high-net-worth individuals who just don't have the time to cope with day-to-day household management.

What the clients say
'Superb – she can do things that no one else appears to be able to, from organizing a party in the space of 24 hours to overseeing error-free paper work.' Mary Ravenshire, businesswoman

Picture Hanging
Peak Rock, Unit 30, DRCA Business Centre
Charlotte Despard Avenue, Battersea Park, SW11 5HD
T: 020 7498 8444
F: 020 7498 8333
habib@picturehanging.com
www.picturehanging.com

Costs £45 for a 20ft rail and all attachments.
Travel Anywhere, although the majority of their clients live within the M25.
Attitude Will talk your head off because so enthusiastic.

Don't think you can hang pictures yourself – you can, of course, but it will look awful. Follow the example of Rolling Stone Ronnie Wood and Sarah, Duchess of York, and call in the experts at the start of the job, and you'll save yourself considerable quantities of blood, sweat and tears. Nigel Hunt's company, Picture Hanging, takes the sting out of the process by installing a very simple rail around the top of your wall. A transparent cord with adjustable hooks attached to it hangs down from the rail so paintings can be positioned and repositioned easily. Installation for a big room doesn't take more than a day.

What the clients say
'Very good. They came, they worked, they were efficient. No problems at all.' Edna Brim, client

The Pure Package
Arch 39–40
New Covent Garden Market
London SW8 5PP
T: 0845 6123 888
F: 020 7720 8583
info@purepackage.com
www.purepackage.com

Costs From £26.99 a day.
Travel Within the M25.
Attitude Attentive.

This idea comes from America where no one eats normal food anymore.

The worst part of being a fashion victim is having to prepare all those healthy meals that you need to eat in order to look like Jennifer Aniston. The Pure Package is the perfect answer for anyone who needs a specialist diet or who simply doesn't have the time to think about food. A temperature-controlled designer package containing an entire day's meals, including snacks, arrives on your doorstep each morning. The menus are put together by a nutritionist and prepared by an award-winning chef. An initial consultation ensures you get exactly what you need, from low carb to allergy-specific foods. The recipes are exotic (such as fresh crab, avocado and plum tomato tian) and healthy.

What the clients say
'This is hassle-free food at its very best – ideal if you are working to deadlines and don't want to live off junk food.'
Eloise Napier, writer

Jeanetta Rowan Hamilton
51 Gloucester Road
London SW7 4QN
T: 020 7584 3030

Costs £40 per hour.
Travel London, most people bring photos to her.
Attitude Extreme patience mixed with artistic flair.

Everybody has one – a draw or a cupboard stuffed full of photographs. You keep meaning to stick them into a photo album, but it's 15 years since you first thought about it and you still haven't managed to do anything yet. Jeanetta Rowan-Hamilton, a former cashmere designer, can do it for you. She has been known to collect dustbins' worth of photographs from clients, which, like magic, she returns neatly cut to size and glued into albums, complete with dates and art work. Buying her time as a present for someone is always a hugely popular gift.

What the clients say
'What Jeanetta did was total perfection. She is so creative. Everyone was bowled over by what she did for me.'
Linda Cooper, IMG

S

Space Healing: for your home and office
31 Ifield Road
London SW10 9AZ
T: 020 7351 1788
info@suzimorris.co.uk
www.suzimorris.co.uk

Costs **From £250, depending on building size; Alexander Technique lessons £45.**
Travel **Across UK.**
Attitude **Otherworldly.**

Suzi Morris has been a healer for 23 years and is one of the UK's top Alexander Technique teachers. For the past six years, she has also turned her attention to buildings and clearing the negativity from them. It may sound a little esoteric, but the results are astonishing – houses often sell quicker and have a noticeably peaceful and harmonious atmosphere. Even the professionals, including property developers Tyler London and TV production company Tiger Aspect swear by her.

What the clients say
'She is a really lovely, genuine and very delicate woman.'
Katia Hadidian, writer

Stella Christie Lighting
9 New Trinity Road
East Finchley
London N2 8EE
T: 07967 603548

35 Regent Place
Abbey Hill
Edinburgh EH7 5BG
T: 0131 466 4641
stella@stellachristielighting.co.uk
www.stellachristielighting.co.uk

Costs **Lights vary in price from £50 to £595. Stella's fee depends on the time and effort needed to source a light.**
Travel **Although based part-time in Edinburgh and part-time in London, she will travel all over the UK.**
Attitude **Very approachable.**

We're all a bit crazy when it comes to lighting today. Stella Christie specializes in indulging fetishes for period lamps. A specialist in sourcing and restoring original lighting from the 1930s to 1960s, she is particularly knowledgeable on German designers and manufacturers, from Christian Dell and Marianne Brandt through to Kaiser & Co and Helo. A Fulbright scholar who went on to run an antique furniture business, Stella knows the antiques world inside out and can usually find even the most obscure objects. She only deals in articles of the best quality and has recently finished work on the Zetter Hotel in Clerkenwell.

What the clients say
'We chose Stella Christie to source vintage desk lamps for the Zetter Hotel interior. She was able to supply 60 fully reconditioned Bauhaus era lights within our required budget and timescale. We would certainly recommend her services to both domestic and trade clients alike.'
Meriel Scott, design consultant, Precious McBane

✛

ROBERT AAGAARD & CO AB
SPOTLESS AD MAIOREM DI
COLLINGWOOD ARCHITECT
CLOTHES STORAGE YOON H
LTD ALL CARE ANIMAL AUN
COMPUTERS ARCHITECTU
RW ARMSTRONG & SONS
LTD RICHARD ASHBY ASSOC
AVALON RESTORATION LTD
HOME AND GARDEN EDW
KARENA BATSTONE DESIGN
W&A BAXTER BBUK SUSIE
JONATHAN BELL BELLHOUS

INDEX

A

Aagaard & Co, Robert 162
Abberley Design 22
Absolutely Spotless 202
Ad Maiorem Dei Gloriam 32
Adams + Collingwood Architects Ltd 23
Aga Clean 203
Agran Clothes Storage, Linda 259
Ahn, Yoon Hee 162
Alexander Maltby Limited 88
All Care 203
Animal Aunts 250
Anta Scotland 60
Antiques & Interiors Limited 60
Apollo Computers Limited 144
Architectural Plants 228
Arikoglu, Alp 23
Armstrong & Sons, RW 89
Arnold, Gail 163
Art Search Limited 250
Ashby Associates Ltd, Richard 24
ATD (UK) Ltd 88
Atelier One 89
Avalon Restoration Ltd 204
Avant Gardener 228

B

Baileys Home and Garden 200
Barnsley Workshop, The Edward 163
Batstone Design, Karena 229
Baxall Construction Ltd 90
Baxter, W&A 90
BBUK 229
Beart, Susie 61
Becher Joinery Ltd 164
Jonathan Bell 229
Bellhouse & Company 61
Bell House Restoration Ltd 204
Belvoir, Paul, at
  Gordon Watson Ltd 164
Berger, Harry 165
Berning, Dominic 165
Berry and Vincent Limited 91
Bevan, Rupert 166
Bines, Halima 251
Blades – The knife duo 251
Boggon, Jo 230
Boontje, Tord 166
Boyd Design, Ann 62
Broom, Cameron, at
  The Curtain Clinic 126
Brown, Simon 91
Brownstone 92

Brudnizki Design Studio Limited,
  Martin 62
Buildec Ltd, J&P 92
Building Services Ltd, JND 93
Building Works Ltd, The 93
Buono Gazerwitz, del 230
Bucher, Poppy 252
Burford Valet Service 252
Butler, Patrice 167
buy:time 253
Buzz Build Ltd 94

C

CA1 167
Caldrea 200
California Closets 253
Calmels Design Ltd 168
Carden Cunietti 63
Carpet Right 254
Carter McArthur 168
Carter Shopfitting Specialists Ltd,
  S&P 94
CC Construction Ltd 86-87
Cedar Landscapes 231
Centre for Advanced Textiles (CAT) 169
Changing Places 254
Chelsea Construction 95
Chester Row Project Management 95
Christie Lighting, Stella 262
Clark Architects, Jonathan 24
Clark Furniture, Colin 169
Clarkson Builders Ltd 96
Clifford, Paul 170
Cocksedge, Paul 170
Colefax & Fowler, Sibyl & John 64
Collett-Zarzycki Architects
  and Designers 50
Concierge London 255
Construction Resources 96
Connolly, Catherine,
  at Northwick Design 72
Copley-Smith, Laara 231
Coptcoat, Alice 232
Cornflake.co.uk 144
Cornucopia Foods 255
Cornwall, Nicky 171
Courtauld, Henrietta 232
Crawford, Ilse 64
Croft Architect, Thomas 25
Crosland Interiors, Charlotte 63
Crossman Architects, Louise 25
Crudge, Paul 171
Cullinan Joinery, Richard 172
Cushion the Impact 256
Czainski, Paul 172

ACKNOWLEDGEMENTS

Three degrees of separation

I didn't set out to write Hello magazine: even the youngest, just-got-out-of-school architect turns out to have a celebrity client (Gwyneth no less). The humble, well not so humble upholsterers (Tim Powell in particular) read like a who's who in Hollywood. Even the marble cleaning man I accosted in a neighbour's house works for Simon Cowell. Our paint specialists practically need bodyguards. As for the Consultants section? There were so many famous names that we started to think that we had stumbled onto some celebrity cult.

We couldn't get away from celebrities but to be clear: we are journalists. We found out who the clients were because a designer who recommended a builder who recommended an IT consultant who's best friends with an actor who is presently coaching my son in maths, told us. Or we happen to have used them ourselves and already know. Robbie Williams used to live four doors down from me. Of course I know who works for him because I say hello to them on the street. There is no crime in being a celebrity or being employed by one.

But just because an upholsterer happens to have Madonna as a client does not mean he doesn't want your business. Hopefully there is someone here for everybody and every budget.

Authors acknowledgement

To everyone who opened their address books and shared the numbers that frankly they would rather have kept to themselves.

To the many researchers and journalists who worked on this book: Carolyn Innes, Natalie Johnson, Henry Coram James, Liz Bailey, Katia Hadidian, Eloise Napier and Rachel Boser in particular.

To Lorraine Dickey, the Publishing Director at Conran Octopus.

To Maria Aguiar for making us great lunches.

To my husband Charles who put up with it.